THE ORNITHOLOGIST'S DICTIONARY

OR ORNITHOLOGICAL AND RELATED TECHNICAL TERMS FOR LAYMAN AND EXPERT

Johannes Erritzoe, Kaj Kampp, Kevin Winker & Clifford B. Frith

THE ORNITHOLOGIST'S DICTIONARY

OR ORNITHOLOGICAL AND RELATED TECHNICAL TERMS FOR LAYMAN AND EXPERT

Cover: Jackass Penguin (*Spheniscus demersus*) taken at the wild colony at The Boulders, near Cape Town, Republic of South Africa, December 2006 © Clifford B. Frith.

Recommended bibliographical reference:

Johannes Erritzoe, Kaj Kampp, Kevin Winker & Clifford B. Frith (2007). *The Ornithologist's Dictionary*. Lynx Edicions, Barcelona.

First edition: November 2007

© **Lynx Edicions** – Montseny 8, 08193 Bellaterra, Barcelona (Spain)
© Texts: authors
© Illustrations: Johannes Erritzoe

Printed by Ingoprint, S.A., Barcelona

Dipòsit Legal: B-43614-2007
ISBN: 978-84-96553-43-9

CONTENTS

ACKNOWLEDGEMENTS

We express our thanks and debt of gratitude to the following persons who have contributed to this work:

Prof. Dr. Anders Pape Møller kindly checked a number of rare and mysterious terms, some of them proposed by authors long ago but never accepted by later researchers and therefore omitted herein.

Dr. Lorenz Bergmann provided much inspiration, especially in relation to medicine.

Physician Ellen Merethe Moesgaard has helped with many morphological questions and terms related to diseases, and her husband Dr. Peder Moesgaard with unravelling Latin and Greek words.

Bent Sunesen has corrected and adjusted the English language of some latter additions. Clifford Frith thanks Dr. Dawn Frith for helpful discussions and support.

INTRODUCTION

The aim of this dictionary is to provide the non-specialist ornithologist with a convenient tool to facilitate the study of ornithological text in English, whether of the strictly scientific or the more popular kind. It is, however, intended to meet the needs of novices as well as more experienced students of the fascinating world of birds. Moreover, it is meant to cater not only to English speaking users but also to those of other nationalities, seeing that it is evident that ornithological literature is increasingly being written and published in English. In this field as elsewhere, the prevalent internationalization and the concurrent growth of the importance of English as a means of worldwide communication has made it nearly imperative to be able to cope with specific English professional terminology.

To that end, we attempt to make each entry as succinct as possible to enable the user to obtain clear information on the immediately relevant point without being bogged down by lengthy and distracting disquisitions. Technical terms for specialists are explained scientifically, but all other words are to a great extent explained first in common English words followed by the technical term within parenthesis. Rare and abstruse technical terms (e.g. as used in anatomy) are not exhaustively covered because they are usually explained in texts where they appear, even in scientific journals. Besides, for the specialist there are books dealing precisely with such items, e.g. for anatomical terms, Baumel (1979) or a later edition of the *Nomina Anatomica Avium*, within which some 5,300 terms are explained. Conversely, ordinary English words of the kind found in every English dictionary are normally not included, except when they have a special meaning in ornithology or in American usage. However, especially as a help for users who are not native English speakers, some non-ornithological terms that are very often found in ornithological contexts are included, e.g. common food items, weather conditions, botanical terms, habitats, genetics, etc. Terms that essentially explain themselves, such as 'bathing behaviour', 'sun bathing', or 'food selection' are not treated. Information on these terms can be found in other sources. To facilitate readers of older literature, outdated terms and nomenclature are included to some extent. Where a term has more than a single spelling all are listed after the preferred one. As an aid to understanding the many words of Greek or Latin origin, prefixes and suffixes are included where examples of their use are listed, and many Latin words and abbreviations in common use are also included.

The taxonomic Orders and Families of birds are listed by both their scientific and English names together with an indication of the number of described species to give the reader an impression of the size of the group in question; the number is often approximate because sources differ in this respect. In general, we follow E. C. Dickinson (2003) *The Howard and Moore Complete Checklist of the Birds of the World*, Christopher Helm, London. The interesting checklist by C.G. Sibley and B. L. Monroe Jr. (1990) *Distribution and Taxonomy of Birds of the World*, Yale University Press, New Haven and London, the first based largely upon DNA analysis, produced many newly-proposed relationships. Because many of these represent untested hypotheses, we have not incorporated all of their proposed groups, nor used their figures for diversity in these groups. In a few cases where one or more groups suggested by these molecular studies might have relationships to quite another family than stated to be the case by Dickinson (2003), this is mentioned. All bird families are listed as an Appendix.

The authors would be most eager and grateful to hear from any reader about comments on and, in particular, corrections or additions to, this work as it is our firm hope that the book will be constantly updated via future editions in one form or another. Please do mail direct to erritzoe@birdresearch.dk.

We might add that we hope that this dictionary will be some small help towards bringing ornithologists all over the world together. Surely, being able to learn and communicate in the same language about our shared topic of interest is bound to contribute to the enhancement of our knowledge of the birds we all love and admire.

ABBREVIATIONS

Am. = American usage
abbr.= abbreviation, abbreviated
adj. = adjective
approx.= approximately
BP = before present
c. = circa, approximate
cf. = compare (or consult)
d. = day(s)
e.g. = for example
etc. = and so on
Eur. = European usage (i.e. British usage)

hr. = hour
hrs. = hours
i.e. = that is
Is. = island(s)
kcal. = kilocalories
mya = million years ago
n. = noun
(pl.) = plural
s. lat. = in the broad sense
sp. = species (singular)
spp. = species (plural)
syn. = synonym

DICTIONARY

A

a.: from Latin = *anno* = in the year.

ab.: from Latin *aberratio* = aberrant.

ABA: abbr. for the American Birding Association, publishing the journal *Birding*.

abdomen: ventral part of the body between the breast and the base of the legs, adj. **abdominal**; also called belly.

abdominal air sacs: paired thin-walled sacs at the caudal end of the body, part of the avian respiratory system; *cf.* air sacs.

abductor muscle: a muscle that draws a bone away from the body; as opposed to an adductor muscle.

aberrant: abnormal, not typical in some way; atypical. Often in connection with the plumage, e.g. distribution of pigments or an unusual feather shape.

aberrant return: a spring migrant that has arrived outside of its range.

abiotic: lifeless; e.g. the physical and chemical components of the environment like fire, local climate, hurricanes, ocean currents, etc.; *cf.* biotic, habitat.

abmigration: migratory system in which birds of one sex may end up far from their natal area, because pair formation takes place in winter quarters shared by birds from different breeding areas. Commonly found in waterfowl (Anatidae), in which males follow females to their chosen breeding grounds.

abort: to arrest or terminate development; **abortion**.

abrasion: wearing down, for example of the feathers due to environmental conditions.

abrasive moult: abrasion of the tips of the feathers, by which many passerines acquire their summer plumage without a second moult; e.g. the Starling (*Sturnus vulgaris*), and the male House Sparrow (*Passer domesticus*).

abscissa: pl. abscissae, the horizontal axis of a coordinate system, often called the x-axis.

Acanthocephala: a group of thorny-headed endoparasitic worms.

acacia: thorny evergreen tree or shrub with narrow leaves. Genus *Acacia*.

Acari: syn. ***Acarina, Acarida***, mites and ticks, an order of invertebrates within in the class Arachnida; some of the 20,000 species are ectoparasites on various hosts, often birds.

acceptor species: a bird species that accepts parasitic eggs in its nest, in contrast to a rejecter (or rejector) species that removes foreign eggs or reacts by deserting the clutch.

accessory sex organs: in males the *ductus deferens*, and in some birds a cloacal penis; in females the oviduct, and in some birds a cloacal clitoris. Also termed secondary sex organs; *cf.* secondary sexual characters.

accidental: only seen a few times at a place outside the normal range of the species, sometimes called vagrant; *cf.* casual.

accident: a bird killed by a bird strike, collision accident, casualty traffic accident, etc.

Accipitriformes: order of birds comprising the families Accipitridae (hawks, c. 226 species), Pandionidae (one member, the Osprey), and Sagittariidae (also only one species, the Secretary-Bird). Found worldwide. Most authors now include the falcons (Falconidae) in the order, in which case the order is usually called Falconiformes.

acclimatisation: the process by which an individual adapts to a new environment; *cf.* allochthonous, naturalisation.

accommodation range: the range or distance over which the lens of the eye can maintain a focus at the retina by changes in the curvature of the lens and cornea.

acetabulum: the socket of the pelvis in which the head of the femur fits.

achromatic plumage: plumage with predominantly white, grey and black colours.

acid rain: rain, snow, or fog with a low pH, usually due to the presence of sulphuric or nitric acid.

acid habitat: an aqueous habitat having a pH less than 7 and usually poor in nutrients, commonly found in cold climates.

acoustics: the study of sound.

acoustic orientation: orientation by use of acoustic clues; *cf.* echolocation.

acquired character: a character acquired as a result of environmental influence rather than inheritance; *ct.* neo Lamarckism.

acre: = 0.405 hectares, abbr. ha.

acromion: anterior projection of the scapula united to the 'wishbone' (clavicle).

acronym: a name made up from the first letters of the name of something,

often an organization, e.g. 'AMNH' for the American Museum of Natural History.

acrotarsium: the horny anterior sheath of the tarsus (tarsometatarsus); *cf.* planta.

actinic action: photochemical change of feather colour by ultraviolet radiation from the sun.

aculeate: pointed.

acuminate: tapering to a sharp point.

acute: 1) sharp, pointed, also used of an angle less than 90°. 2) figuratively of rapidly developing and often serious disease.

acutely toxic: strongly poisonous.

acutiplantar: term for a tarsus that is angled on the hind side; the opposite of latiplantar.

A.D.: abbr. Latin = *Anno Domini*, in the year of the Lord.

Adansonian taxonomy: syn. ***Adansonism***, a numerical taxonomy based on many equally weighted characters.

adaptation: any change in an organism that improves survival or reproduction; if genetic, generally arising through mutation and increasing in frequency in a lineage through natural selection; *cf.* adaptive characters, mutations, adaptive radiation, preadaptation.

adaptive character: any phenotypic modification improving fitness, i.e. enhancing survival or reproduction.

adaptive divergence: evolutionary divergence between two populations or lineages due to adaptive selection.

adaptive landscape: a conceptualization of fitness space in relation to organismal genotypes, figuratively portrayed as a topographic landscape upon which the most fit genotypes occur on adaptive peaks and less fit genotypes occupy slopes or valleys. Also called adaptive topography.

adaptive radiation: the evolutionary process of speciation in one lineage to produce a multitude of new forms, usually in a rather short evolutionary time, e.g. after colonisation of a new geographic area, e.g. the Galapagos finches (*Geospizinae*); *cf.* divergence.

adaptive topography: a conceptualization of fitness space in relation to organismal genotypes, figuratively portrayed as a topographic landscape upon which the most fit genotypes occur on adaptive peaks and less fit genotypes occupy slopes or valleys. Also called **adaptive landscape**.

addled: of eggs, being dead, having a dead embryo inside; *cf.* infertile egg.

adductor: a muscle that brings one part of the body together with another part, e.g. the lower jaw with the upper.

adeno-hypophysis: the part of the hypophysis producing gonadotrophic hormones (luteinizing hormone and follicle stimulating hormone). Also spelled without a hyphen. Syn. anterior lobe of hypophysis.

adherent nest: a cup nest built of mud or saliva and plastered to a vertical surface, like a swallow (Hirundinidae) or swift (Apodidae) nest; *cf.* burrow nest, cup nest, domed nest, globular nest, hole nest, platform nest, pensile cup nest, pendulous nest, retort nest, statant cup nest.

ad hoc: Latin = to this, for a particular purpose only and without justification.

ad int.: from Latin: *ad interim* = for the present, provisionally, for the meantime.

ad infinitum: Latin = without limit, for ever.

adipose tissue: fat tissue.

ad libitum: without restraint or limit, from Latin = according to pleasure.

A-DNA: a right handed helix; variant of the dominant B-form of DNA in solution, in which the base pairs are tilted out of the perpendicular orientation to the axis of the helix; *cf.* B-DNA, E-DNA, Z-DNA, deoxyribonucleic acid.

adrenal glands: paired glands located at the anterior ends of the kidneys; produce hormones, e.g. corticosterone, androgen, testosterone, and oestrogen (Am. estrogen).

adrenalin: hormone from the adrenal medulla, produced especially under stress.

adult: abbr. ad., sexually mature and/or in final plumage.

adult non-nuptial: older Am. for the plumage termed adult winter or adult non-breeding in Europe.

adult nuptial: older Am. for the plumage termed adult summer or adult breeding in Europe.

adventitious coloration: feathers stained from the environment, e.g. the rusty colour on the neck and head of swans (*Cygnus*) and on the breast and belly of the Bearded Vulture (*Gypaetus barbatus*).

adventitious moult: feather replacement for reasons of loss between normally scheduled moults.

adv: Latin *adventicius*, alien, introduced.

advertising display: a type of display usually performed by males to attract females or deter rivals; often accompanied by song, also called **advertising behaviour**.

advertising song: song that advertises the singer's presence.

aegithognathous: the structure of the palate as found in passerine birds, with large prevomers fused and truncated in front. From Greek *aigeithalos*, a name used for some small birds.

Aegypiidae: a synonym for Accipitridae.

aegyptianellosis: a viral infection found only in geese and domestic fowl.

Aepyornithidae: elephant birds, an extinct family of large, flightless birds from Madagascar.

aeria: the nest of a large bird of prey (Accipitridae) Am. **aerie, aiery**, or **ayre**. Most common name eyrie.

aerial: of the air; in birds, e.g. a swift (Apodidae) or tern (Sternidae) that spends most of its life in the air.

aerial feeder: a bird that catches its food in flight, e.g. swallows (Hirundinidae) or swifts (Apodidae).

aerial flycatching: 1) the capture of flying insect prey on the wing, common, e.g. in swallows (Hirundinidae), swifts (Apodidae), and tyrant flycatchers (Tyrannidae). 2) uncommonly, a term used for the seizure of flying small birds in the bill of larger, not normally predatory birds, e.g. storks (Ciconidae) and crows (Corvidae).

aerial-piracy: food-stealing by one bird from another in flight, as in e.g. skuas (Stercorariidae); *cf.* kleptoparasitism.

aerial-skimming: a foraging technique by which a bird flies close to the water surface with its lower mandible submerged and closing its bill when prey is struck; used by skimmers (Rynchopidae).

aerobic: pertaining to, involving, containing or requiring oxygen.

Aerocharidae: a synonym for Vangidae.

aerodynamics: the branch of physics that deals with the motion of gaseous fluids – air – and with the forces acting on bodies moving in such fluids; adj. **aerodynamically**.

af.: from Latin *affinis* = related, akin to.

affinity: the relationship between a bird or a group of birds to another bird or group.

afforestation: the establishing of a forest; *cf.* reforestation.

Afrotropical Region: the biogeographical region of sub-Saharan Africa including southern Arabia and Madagascar, more often called the Ethiopian Region. Some authors treat Madagascar and the Mascarene Islands as a separate region, the Malagasy faunal region; see zoogeographical regions.

aftershaft: a smaller, often downy or vestigial feather growing from the underside of the base of the main feather shaft. Considered a primitive trait, aftershafts occur on the contour feathers in many bird families, e.g. emus (Dromaiidae), cassowaries (Casuariidae), waterfowl (Anatidae), pheasants and partridges (Phasianidae), grouse (Tetraonidae), and trogons (Trogonidae), but are absent or greatly reduced in passerines (with the exception of Acanthisittidae). Also called **afterfeather** or hyporachis, Am. **after-feather** or hypoptile.

aftertuft: an afterfeather lacking its shaft.

agamete: a young gamete that develops directly into an adult without fusing with another gamete.

age dimorphism: the presence of differences in appearance between young and adult birds.

age ratio: the proportion of birds of different age-classes.

age-specific fecundity: the average birth rate for females of different ages.

age structure: syn. for age ratio.

age terms: see pullus, juvenile, immature, subadult, adult, 1st calendar year, 2nd calendar year, etc.

agglutination: sticking together, e.g. of blood cells in a (positive) test of the blood for antibodies.

aggregation: a gathering of birds of one or more species (i.e. to feed, drink, bathe, etc.) as distinct from a flock or flocking.

aggression: a behaviour involving threatening display or attack against other animals, whether of the same or other species.

agonistic behaviour: behaviour involved in conflict, including direct attack or ritualised displays (postures, movements, sounds, etc.) as well as submissive, appeasement, and retreat behaviour; *cf.* antagonism.

AIC: Akaike Information Criterion (AIC) is a criterion for the selection of a model from among a series of nested or related models in which selection is based on the trade-off between the fit of a model and its complexity.

aigrette: loose, long, and fine ornamental feathers (plumes) with free barbs, found in scapular and breast regions of some egrets and herons (Ardeidae); only present in breeding plumage.

ailment: disease or illness, often not life-threatening.

air chamber: an air-filled cavity in bird eggs.

airfoil: an asymmetric object on which an air flow creates lift.

air sacculitis: an inflammation of the airsacs.

air sacs: components of a bird's respiratory system, in the body cavity and also entering some of the bones. The air sacs have walls of very thin, transparent tissue. The system is comprised of the clavicular, abdominal, cervical, and thoracic (anterior and posterior) sacs. Members of some families, e.g. grouse (Tetraonidae), have inflatable air sacs used for display.

airspeed: speed relative to the air (as opposed to the ground).

akinesis: static or motionless behaviour in response to acute danger; e.g. seen in the Eurasian Bittern (*Botauris stallaris*), also called catalepsy.

al.: from Latin *alii* = others.

alar: pertaining to the wing.

alar bar: wing-bar.

alar tract: the *pteryla alaris* feather tract, which involves the wing feathers (remiges) and associated coverts; *cf.* humeral tract.

alary: 1) pertaining to wings. 2) wing-shaped.

alate: having wings.

Alauda: The title of the ornithological periodical for the Société d'Etudes Ornithologiques in Paris. Published since 1929. Also a genus of larks (Alaudidae).

albino: an aberrant animal lacking colour pigment, either partially or totally; in birds full albinos have white feathers and red eyes. Birds normally white, like swans (*Cygnus*), are not albinos; adj. **albinistic**; *cf.* partial albinism, depigmentation, leucism.

albumen: egg-white, composed primarily of the water-soluble protein albumin.

alcid: a bird belonging to the auk family (Alcidae).

aldosterone: a hormone from the adrenal glands important in the control of kidney function.

aldrin: an organochlorine pesticide.

algal bloom: an overproduction of algae in water resulting from the enhancement of plant nutrients such as nitrates and phosphates; *cf.* eutrophication.

alien: a species occurring in an area to which it is not native. Also used for the egg or chick of a brood parasite in a host's nest.

alimentary system: the food canal from the mouth to the cloaca, also called **alimentary canal** or digestive tract; *cf.* esophagus, crop, proventriculus, gizzard, intestine, pancreas.

alkali flat: mud with a high alkali content (pH above 7) and seasonally dried-up, most often found in steppe habitats.

allantois: a membranous bag lining the inner surface of the membranes surrounding the embryo, receives waste products from the embryo.

Allee effect: when the population of a species falls below a certain threshold level necessary for successful reproduction, the species goes extinct.

The classic example is the Passenger Pigeon (*Ectopistes migratorius*).

Alleghanian Zone: part of one of the six life zones in North America, the transcontinental eastern humid division.

allele: version of a gene; each individual of a species has two copies, which may either be the same (homozygous) or different (heterozygous), **allelic, allelism.**

allelomimetic behaviour: mutual stimulating imitative behaviour.

allelomorph: syn. for allele.

Allen's Rule: a biogeographic rule, according to which warm-blooded animals living in colder climates tend to have shorter extremities (bills, legs, and wings) than populations of the same or related species in warmer regions; *cf.* ecogeographical rules.

Allee's principle: each species has an upper limit of density in a habitat where its survival and reproduction can be maintained.

allochronic: not living in the same geological time, the opposite to synchronic.

allochthon: alien, extralimital, pertaining to a species in an area in which it has not originated but has recently become established either naturally or by human assistance, e.g. the Collared Dove (*Streptopelia decaocto*), adj. **allochthonous**; *cf.* autochthonous.

allochthonous activities: a behaviour completely irrelevant to the situation and current activity of an animal, e.g. when two fighting birds suddenly start to preen; also called displacement behaviour or activity, disinhibition, vacuum activity.

allofeeding: the passing of food by one bird to another that is not its offspring; *cf.* courtship-feeding.

allohiemic: different populations of the same species are allohiemic when

they have separate winter distributions.

allometry: the study of the effect of size on, e.g. physiology and metabolism or the different growth rates of different body parts of an organism; *cf.* allometry, static allometry, evolutionary allometry, metabolism, ontogeny

alloparent: an individual who provides care to offspring of another individual; mostly used when alloparent and parent are of the same species. Alloparental care by males is **alloparental** by females **allomaternal**; for more on this subject, see altruism, helpers.

allopatry: spatial separation of populations or species, i.e. living in different geographical areas; adj. **allopatric**; *cf.* sympatric, dichopatric, parapatric.

allopatric speciation: the formation of new species through differentiation achieved by geographic isolation of initially conspecific populations. Also known as geographic speciation.

allopreening: the preening of one bird by another, usually of the same species, and usually on the head and neck. Also called mutual preening.

allospecies: the species comprising superspecies; allopatric populations that differ enough to perhaps be full species, but which are so similar that they might integrate if they came into contact; *cf.* semispecies, paraspecies, superspecies, sympatric species.

allotype: any specimen in a type series (paratype) of the opposite sex to the holotype, referred to when a new species is described; *cf.* paratype, type specimen.

alloxenia: conspecific brood parasite with different host species, e.g. various subpopulations of the Cuckoo (*Cuculus canorus*), each specialized on their own host species; **alloxenia** more commonly called gens; *cf.* homoxenia.

llozyme: variant of an enzyme, having the same activity but a slightly different amino acid sequence.

llozyme electrophoresis: the process of running allozymes (proteins) through a gel matrix in an electric current to separate those with slightly different amino acid sequences, which, upon staining, enables allele scoring for genetics studies; used historically in systematics and as a method of estimating paternity.

lluvial forest: a flat, wooded, non-inundated area close to rivers.

lluvium: the deposits of sea or river organic or mineral sediments (i.e. mud, sand, or silt) that form estuaries, river banks, flood plains, etc.

lopecia: baldness, patchy or general loss of feathers without immediate replacement.

pha diversity: species diversity within a particular habitat; *cf.* beta diversity, gamma diversity.

pha male: the top male in a dominance hierarchy.

pine: pertaining to habitats at high elevations.

pine tundra: one of the main biomes, found in high mountains, e.g. in the Andes and Himalayas; *cf.* tundra-, boreal-, desert-, savanna-, and rainforest biome.

ternate plumage: Am. for breeding or summer plumage, nuptial plumage; found in birds having two moults per year; *cf.* plumage sequence, moult.

titudinal distribution: distribution (in mountainous regions) relating to elevation.

titudinal migration: migrating between higher and lower elevations in mountainous regions, usually by birds having high-altitude breeding areas and low-altitude non-breeding areas, also referred to as elevational migration; *cf.* latitudinal migration.

altricial: syn. nidicolous, term characterizing chicks that are born naked, blind, and helpless, and usually with closed eyes (e.g. all perching birds). The opposite of precocial or nidifugous; *cf.* semi-altricial.

altruism: behaviour of one individual acting in such a way as to benefit or increase the fitness of an unrelated or related individual; unselfish behaviour.

Aluconidae: synonym for Strigidae.

alula: pl. alulae, syn. bastard wing, false wing; a group of small, stiffened wing feathers on the thumb (first digit) or the wrist (carpal joint); it serves as an aerodynamic slot in slow flight. Hummingbirds (Trochilidae) have no alula.

alula coverts: small coverts covering the base of the (normally three) alula quills.

alular digit: the thumb, or first digit. Also called the pollex; *cf.* major digit, minor digit.

ambiens: a muscle of the leg that closes the claws.

ambient temperature: the temperature of the surroundings, the external temperature.

Ambiortus: an ornithurine bird from the Cretaceous, found in Mongolia, about the size of a pigeon and with a well-developed sternal keel.

ambivalent behaviour: syn. compromise behaviour, a behaviour that is the outcome of two incompatible motivations, e.g. the impulse to flee or to attack; *cf.* displacement behaviour.

amelioration: improvement.

American Birds: periodical published by the National Audubon Society (U.S.A.), formerly called *Audubon Field Notes*. Publishes the Christmas Bird Count.

American Ornithologists' Union: abbr. AOU, the leading scientific society for ornithologists in the Americas.

Publishes *The Auk*, since 1884, and *The Check-list of North American Birds.*

amino acid: a unit molecular building block of proteins. There are 20 different sorts of amino acids.

AMNH: acronym for the American Museum of Natural History, New York.

amniotes: common name for the truly land-living vertebrates (but not the amphibians), whose embryos develop in an amnion, a liquid-filled sac enclosed by membranes.

amnion: syn. amniotic sac; see amniotes.

amorphous layer: a chalky covering of an eggshell, that may conceal the egg colour.

amorphous urates: seen in urine and are usually the result of refrigeration. A pink pellet after centrifugation is characteristic of amorphous urates. Under the microscope, it appears as a yellow-brown mass of small rounded particles. Used, e.g. to diagnose Pacheco's parrot disease.

Ampelidae: bird family containing a single species, *Hypocolius ampelinus*, which is now usually placed in Bombycillidae (waxwings).

amphibolic: a limb that can move both forward and backward, e.g. the outer toe of an owl (Strigidae).

amphigamy: the fusion of male and female gametes, adj. **amphigamic.**

amphigenesis: the fusion of egg and sperm resulting in a fertilized egg (zygote).

amphirhinal: having two bony nostril openings on each side, one anterior to the other. Found in many passerines.

amphitropical species: animals with two disjunct distributions on each side of the equator.

amplitude: extent of a periodic variation, e.g. a movement in a ritualised behaviour or the pressure variation in a sound wave.

amylase: an enzyme that aids the digestion of starch and found in the salvia of grain-eating species.

anabolism: synthetic reactions in the body, i.e. the metabolic processes by which complex molecules and living tissue are created; opposite katabolism.

anabolites: the chemical raw material brought by the lymphatic- and blood- circulating system for anabolic processes.

anaerobic: a process that does not involve oxygen, e.g. the energy-yielding pathway of metabolism without oxygen, in which, basically, food molecules are oxidized incompletely to lactic acid; *cf.* aerobic.

anaerobic metabolism: cellular creation of energy without molecular oxygen in vertebrate muscle, for example through breakdown of glycogen to lactic acid and carbon dioxide; diving birds use this process to reduce oxygen consumption during prolonged diving so that only the most important organs are supported through aerobic metabolism.

anagenesis: evolutionary specialization over time; *cf.* cladogenesis.

anagenetic: evolution within a lineage, i.e. evolutionary change not involving speciation (see, however, chronospecies); *cf.* phyletic evolution.

anal: pertaining to the anus.

Analgesidae: feather mites; *cf.* ectoparasites.

anal glands: outdated and inappropriate term (Am.) for the oil glands (uropygial glands) found in most birds on the lower rump.

analogous: similar in form and/or function despite having separate evolutionary origins, *cf.* homologous.

analysis of variance: abbr. ANOVA, statistical method used to examine potential differences between two or more sample groups, through part tioning the total variability between considered causes of this variance. Particularly useful in experimental design.

anatid: member of the family Anatidae.

anatine: member(s) of subfamily Anatinae, comprising most of the world´s ducks.

anatomy: the study of the structure of the body, adj. **anatomical**.

ancestor: any preceding member of a lineage.

ANCOVA: analysis of variance, a statistical procedure combining linear regression and analysis of variance (ANOVA) to determine whether relationships describes by two or more regression equations might have come from population having the same slope; used when sampling conditions (sets of observation or measurements) have accompanyig variables that cannot be eliminated or controlled.

androgen: any of the male steroid sex hormones, e.g. testosterone, secreted mainly by the male gonads (testes) and regulating the development of secondary sexual characters in males.

androgyny: the occurrence in an organism of both male and female sexual organs, adj. **androgynous**; *cf.* hermaphrodite.

anemia: Am. for anaemia, shortage of blood.

anemotaxis: movements in response to air currents, either towards (positive) or away from (negative) the air flow.

angiosperm: a flowering plant; *cf.* gymnosperm.

anhedral: of wings being held downward, below the level of the back.

anisodactylous: of a bird having three toes facing forward and one backward, as in passerines and many other birds; *cf.* zygodactylous, heterodactylous, syndactylous, pamprodactylous.

anisogamy: the fusion of gametes that are different in shape, size, and/or motility, as found in all sexually reproducing animals; any one of the gametes is an anisogamete, the larger and less motile is an ovum (egg), the smaller a spermatozoan (sperm).

anisotrophy: having different physical properties.

ankle joint: the joint between the tarsometatarsus and tibiotarsus.

Annelida: phylum of invertebrates comprising the polychaetes, oligochaetes (e.g. earthworms), and leeches; **annelid worms**.

annual rhythm: syn. circannual rhythm or cycle, endogenous rhythm with a period of approx. one year; controls breeding, moult, and migration.

anorexia: lack of appetite.

anosmic: having no sense of smell.

ANOVA: abbr. **analysis of variance**, a general statistical method used in hypothesis testing to examine potential differences between two or more sample groups, usually through partitioning the total variability among a set of observations between possible and statistically independent causes of this variance. Particularly useful in experimental design.

Anseriformes: order of birds comprising three species of screamers, family (Anhimidae), one Magpie-Goose (*Anseranas semipalmate*), and 158 species of ducks, geese, and swans, family (Anatidae).

Anserinae: the subfamily within Anatidae that comprises the true geese and the whistling ducks.

antagonism: hostile or aggressive behaviour; *cf.* agonistic behaviour; **antagonistic display**.

Antarctic: the continent of Antarctica and surrounding seas south of the Antarctic Convergence.

Antarctic Convergence: the coming together of Antarctic and sub-Antarctic waters, where cold north-flowing surface water meets south-flowing sub-Antarctic water at approx. 50°S in the Atlantic and Indian oceans, and between 55-62°S in the Pacific Ocean, resulting in the upwelling of nutrient-rich water and a concomitant bloom in marine productivity.

antcatcher: an old name for antbird.

antebrachium: a term for the forearm, supported by the ulna and radius; *cf.* brachium.

antepisematic: of behaviour or features of threatening character, especially plumage coloration.

anterior: foremost (e.g. part of the body); the opposite of posterior. Also called cranial.

anterior lobe of hypophysis: the part of the hypophysis producing gonadotrophic hormones (luteinizing hormone and follicle stimulating hormone). Also called adeno-hypophysis.

ant follower: common name usually applied to about 50 species of antbirds (Thamnophilidae), and woodcreepers (Dendrocolaptidae), that follow army ants and eat insects flushed by the ants.

anthesis: the flowering period in plants.

anthophilous: an animal feeding on flowers, e.g. hummingbirds (Trochilidae).

anthropogenic: caused or influenced by man.

anthropomorphism: any case where human qualities, motivations, or behaviours are ascribed to animals, adj. anthropomorphic.

anti-: prefix from Greek *anti* meaning against or Latin *ante* before.

antiae: a term for the feathers at the base of the bill in some birds.

anticipatory food bringing: bringing food to a clutch of still-not-hatched eggs; an example of a vacuum activity.

anticryptic: used of a coloration of an animal facilitating the capture of prey; *cf.* cryptic, procryptic.

antigeny: sexual dimorphism, **antigenic**

anting: behaviour where ants are allowed to enter the plumage and reach the skin or are actively crushed and applied to the plumage during preening; may help to control ectoparasites. A behaviour found in many passerine birds.

antioxidant: an agent that inhibits oxidation.

anti-peristalsis: the act of the upper food canal (esophagus) pushing pellets or food 'backwards' towards the mouth.

antiphonal singing: duetting between the members of a mated pair.

anti-predator behaviour: defensive behaviour that serves to protect a bird from predation, e.g. by foraging near cover.

antrorse: bent forwards, used of nasal tufts and rictal bristles, *cf.* retrorse.

anurans: a term for frogs and toads.

anvil: a stone or other hard object against which some birds break shells of snails and other difficult food items; well-known in the Song Thrush (*Turdus philomelos*) and in many pitta species (Pittidae). Anvils may be recognised by the many shell fragments around them.

aorta: the main artery from the heart transporting oxygenated blood to the body; *cf.* caval vein.

AOU: abb. for American Ornithologists' Union, publishing *The Auk* and *The Check-list of North American Birds.*

ap.: from Latin *apud* = with, in the publication of.

Apatornis: a genus of fossil toothed birds from the Late Cretaceous of North America.

apical: from Latin *apex*, tip; terminal at the outer (distal) end, as opposed to proximate.

Apodiformes: order of birds comprising 94 species of swifts (Apodidae), 4 species of treeswifts (Hemiprocnidae), and 331 species of hummingbirds (Trochilidae).

apomorphy: an advanced character derived from an ancestral condition, **apomorph**; *cf.* plesiomorphy.

aponeuroses: white, fibrous membranes separating muscles; may serve as muscle sheaths and will sometimes connect muscles and tendons.

aposematic: colouration that protects an organism, often used exclusively for warning coloration of unpalatable or poisonous potential prey animals, also called proaposematic colouration.

appeasement behaviour: pacifying behaviour.

appendage: an adjunct, such as the comb of a cock; or, simply, a limb.

appendicular skeleton: the part of the skeleton that is composed of paired limb bones and the pectoral and pelvic girdles; *cf.* axial skeleton.

appetitive behaviour: early phase of an instinctive behaviour or behavioural sequence; a behaviour for which there is no releaser, typically searching behaviour. Also termed exploratory behaviour.

applied ornithology: the study of birds for practical purposes, e.g. in connection with conservation, animal welfare, domestication, falconry, management, guano utilization, or other human exploitation of birds.

a priori: from Latin *a priori* = from what is before. 1) of reasoning proceeding from causes to effects; deductive. 2) of hypotheses developed prior to an experiment or study, as opposed to *a posteriori*. 3) loosely, as far as one knows.

apterium: (pl.) apteria, area of the skin of a bird outside the feather tracts (pterylae), i.e. an area carrying no contour feathers. Penguins (Spheniscidae), kiwis (Apterygidae), screamers (Anhimidae), and mousebirds (Coliidae) have their feathers evenly distributed over the entire body surface and therefore lack apteria; *cf.* pterylosis.

apterous: without wings; *cf.* apterygie, asinistrimus.

apterygie: a bird born with only one wing, left or right, *cf.* asinistrimus.

Apterygiformes: order of birds comprising the kiwis (Apterygidae) with three species; today often included in Struthioniformes.

aptosochromatosis: change of feather colour without moulting, as seen in, e.g. Starling (*Sturnus vulgaris*) and House Sparrow (*Passer domesticus*).

apud: abbr. ap., Latin meaning in the work of.

aquatic: living in water.

Aquila: 1) an ornithological periodical published by the Instituti Ornithologici Hungarici since 1894. 2) a genus of eagles in the family Accipitridae.

aquiline: of eagles, or eagle-like.

aquintocubital: an older name for eutaxic = having secondaries forming an unbroken series, as opposed to diastataxic.

arable land: cultivated land or land available for ploughing or tillage. Grassland and pasture are excluded.

arachnids: spiders and their relatives.

Araneae: spiders.

arboreal: relating to or living in trees.

arbovirus: virus transferred from one host to another by blood-sucking arthropods.

Archaeopteryx lithographica: a famous fossil bird from the Jurassic, found in lithographic limestone near Solnhofen in Bavaria and showing many 'reptilian' features such as teeth and no sternal keel, but with asymmetrical flight feathers. The first of the seven known specimens was found in 1861, only three years after the theory of Darwin and Wallace was made public, and it contributed greatly to the acceptance of the theory of evolution.

Archaeornithes: subclass of fossil birds, comprising *Archaeopteryx* and its relatives.

archetype: the hypothetical ancestral type of a group.

archipelago: group of islands.

Archosauria: a major group of amniotes, comprising the dinosaurs (including birds), pterosaurs, crocodiles, and a number of less well known extinct groups.

Arctic: pertaining to high latitudes of the northern hemisphere. The Arctic is a collective term for northern seas and landmasses having an arctic climate (it is not restricted to regions north of the Arctic Circle), and so includes the northern parts of both the Palearctic and the Nearctic zoogeographical regions; *cf.* Holarctic.

Arctic tundra: habitat type of low-growing vegetation that occurs north of the limit of trees; *cf.* **alpine tundra**.

ardeid: member of the heron family (Ardeidae).

Ardea: periodical published by the Nederlandse Ornithologische Unie (abbr. NOU) since 1912. Also a genus of herons (Ardeidae).

Ardeola: periodical published by the Sociedad Española de Ornitologia (abbr. SEO) since 1954. Also a genus of herons (Ardeidae).

area centralis: the area of the retina with the sharpest visual acuity; *cf.* fovea.

area cladogram: a branching diagram for species with a common ancestor showing their range; *cf.* cladistic methods, cladogram.

arena: a place where males gather to perform communal displays, as in the

Ruff (*Philomachus pugnax*) and many other birds with promiscuous mating systems; *cf.* lek.

arid: dry; arid climates are characterized by an annual precipitation of less than 250 mm and therefore generally supporting a sparse vegetation.

aril: the spongy, fleshy, and often edible covering of some seeds; adj. **arillate**.

Arizona infection: an acute or chronic egg-transmitted infection, primarily of turkeys, caused by *Salmonella arizonae*. Also called paracolon infection.

arm: the section of the wing between the body and the carpal joint.

arms race: a sequence of mutual counter-adaptations in two coevolving organisms, e.g. a parasitic cuckoo (Culidae) and its host, or a predator and its prey; *cf.* red queen effect.

arrested moult: moult that is started before, but interrupted during, migration as found in, e.g. the Common Tern (*Sterna hirundo*) and among some individuals of other migratory species; also called suspended moult.

artenkreis: largely a syn. for superspecies; a group of closely related species that replace each other geographically.

arterioles: tiny blood vessels branching from arteries.

arteriosclerosis: a term for the thickening and calcification of the arteries, most often seen in old parrots.

arteriovenous shunt: a vascular system in birds' legs that serves to reduce heat loss in cold weather by reducing blood flow to the feet.

artery: blood vessel that carries blood away from the heart. Arteries have thicker walls and are more elastic than veins; *cf.* aorta, capillary, vein, arterioles.

arthritis: a term for inflammation of skeletal joints.

arthropod: a member of the phylum Arthropoda, which includes joint-limbed animals with a chitinous outer skeleton. Arthropoda is the largest phylum in the animal kingdom and totals several million species (many still undescribed), including insects, centipedes and millipedes, crustaceans, and arachnids.

articular: a paired bone of the lower jaw that connects with the quadrate bone.

articulation: the way in which joined bones are connected.

artificial: in ecology meaning a habitat or community that has been changed drastically from its original condition by human activity; sometimes referring to attempted restoration or surrogate habitats.

artificial selection: selection by humans of a lineage or breed for certain characteristics, e.g. egg or meat production in chickens, or for certain plumage traits by an aviculturist. Only those individuals exhibiting the best of the traits selected for are chosen to reproduce.

Ascaroidea: an endoparasitic group of roundworms (nematodes); some live in the caecum and can transfer the blackhead disease.

ascendent: pertaining to the numbering of flight feathers, or their sequence of moult, and meaning from the outermost feather towards the body. Was until recently the preferred numbering method for primaries in Europe, but has now been replaced by the descendent method (from the innermost and outwards); secondaries are always counted ascendently, i.e. from the carpal joint inwards; *cf.* transilient.

ascorbic acid: syn. with vitamin C.

ascr.: from Latin *ascriptum* = ascribed to.

aseasonal: without or uncorrelated with season.

asexual reproduction: reproduction with no sexual interchange of genes among individuals (e.g. most protozoan animals and corals).

asinistrimus: an older, misleading name for apterygie (a bird without a wing); translates to 'something missing its left wing', but birds may just as well be born with a missing right wing as a missing left wing.

aspect: a position facing a particular direction (e.g. of a nest or nest hole).

aspect ratio: a measure of the shape of the wing: the ratio of wing span to the mean chord, usually calculated as the square of the wing span divided by the wing area; long and narrow wings have high aspect ratios. Of interest as a measure of flight ability.

aspergillosis: a fungal disease in the respiratory system caused by the genus *Aspergillus*, usually fatal; particularly common in penguins (Spheniscidae), waterfowl, and gallinaceous birds, including domestic fowl, in which it is most often found in debilitated birds kept in unhygienic and overcrowded conditions.

asphyxia: the lack of oxygen.

assemblage (assembly): an intra- or inter-specific gathering of birds (e.g. at a food source). Not synonymous with 'flock', which implies social interaction. Also a portion of a community, e.g. the birds in an ecosystem; *cf.* association.

assimilation efficiency: the effectiveness with which the energy in the diet is utilized.

association: an interspecific grouping of animals (i.e. a mixed species flock of birds); also used to describe a relationship between individuals of two species (i.e. the association between honey badgers and honeyguides, family Indicatoridae); *cf.* assemblage.

assortative mating: non-random pairing with respect to age, size, or – in polymorphic species –appearance.

astaxanthin: a carotenoid found in the feathers of bush-shrikes of the genus *Laniarius.*

astringer: a falconer with hawks. Also spelled **austringer.**

asymptotic: describes a curve or function approaching but never quite attaining (in finite space) a certain terminal value.

asynchronous hatching: occurs when the eggs of a clutch hatch over several days, resulting in young of markedly different age and size, so the youngest may starve if the food supply is insufficient; common, e.g. among raptors (Falconiformes) and owls (Strigiformes); *cf.* synchronous hatching, brood reduction strategy, brood survival strategy.

atavism: ancestral character reappearing after several generations during which it has not been evident; throwback; adj. **atavistic.**

ataxia: a weakness resulting in less coordination of locomotion.

atlas: 1) anatomy: the first cervical vertebra with the odontoid process attached to the skull. 2) mapping the geographic area of the occurrence of species; *cf.* axis.

atlas project: maps produced on a grid basis with dots for each record and from a short period of years.

atlassing: to compile an atlas of bird distributions of a certain area.

atoll: coral reef that develops as a ring around a central lagoon and eventually may form an island.

Atrichiidae: syn. for the two species of scrubbirds (Atrichornithidae).

atrioventricular valves: valves between each atrium and the corresponding ventricle in the left and right sides of the heart that prevent backflow; *cf.* semilunar valves.

atrium: any of the two heart chambers to which the blood flows from the body or lungs, and from which it flows to the ventricle. Also called auricle.

atrophy: evolutionary reduction of an organ because of an insignificant function, e.g. the second toe in the Ostrich (*Struthio camelus*), or partial reduction of the digestive system before migration, e.g. in some shorebirds; as opposed to hypertrophy.

attentive period: the time spent in the nest during incubation, as opposed to inattentive period.

attenuate: to taper to a narrow tip; or to decrease in strength or intensity.

attenuated primary: a primary feather that tapers, or narrows, toward its distal tip.

attrap: a model of, e.g. an egg, also called a 'dummy'.

auditory capsule: the part of the skull that encloses the ear (auditory organ).

auditory communication: communication by use of acoustic signals (sound); also called acustic communication.

auditory meatus: the external ear.

auditory tube: the canal connecting the middle ear with the pharynx. Also termed Eustachian tube or pharyngotympanic tube.

Audubon, John James: (1785-1851): naturalist, hunter, artist, and early American ornithologist.

Audubon: quarterly publication of the National Audubon Society; originally called *Bird-Lore* and later *Audubon Magazine.*

Audubon Christmas Bird Count: bird census taking place every Christmas in USA, conducted since 1900 by the National Audubon Society and published in *American Birds*, which was the Christmas Count edition of Audubon *Field Notes*. Since 1999 published separately from Field Notes, and from 2004 only available as an online publication.

Audubon Field Notes: a supplement to the periodical *American Birds*, published by the National Audubon Society of the USA, since 1999 produced by the American Birding Association.

Audubon Society: the National Audubon Society, founded in 1905 in New York, is one of the largest non-profit conservation organisations in the world. Until 1941 called the National Association of Audubon Societies for the Preservation of Birds.

Auk, The: quarterly scientific journal published by the American Ornithologists' Union since its founding in 1884; actually a continuation of the former *Bulletin of the Nuttall Ornithological Club* (1876-1883). Also the name of an extinct member of the family Alcidae.

auricle: 1) a chamber of the heart, syn. for atrium. 2) the external ear.

auriculars: ear coverts, the loose feathers covering the external ear opening.

auris media: the air-filled cavity; the middle ear.

austral: pertaining to the southern hemisphere; see also life zones.

Australasian (region): the biogeographical region of Australia, Tasmania, New Guinea, New Zealand and its dependencies, some islands of the SW Pacific, and the Moluccas; some authors include Hawaii; *cf.* zoogeographical regions.

Australo-Papuan: Australia and New Guinea.

austringer: a falconer with hawks. Also spelled astringer.

autapomorphy: a derived (advanced) character unique to the species or group considered; *cf.* apomorphy.

autecology: the ecology of a single species; *cf.* synecology, ecology.

auto-: prefix from Greek *autos*, meaning self.

autochthon: of a species (group): native to, i.e. originated in the area in which it now occurs, adj. **autochthonous**; *cf.* allochthonous, endemic, indigenous.

autochthony: indigenous, native.

autocoprophagous: of an animal that consumes its own faeces. Also called coprophagy.

autolycism: taking advantage of other animals' activities without being a parasite, for example when a Peregrine Falcon (*Falco peregrinus*) breeds on a building.

autonomic nervous system: a scattered web of nerve fibres not consciously controllable by the bird and controlling processes such as the blood flow, endrocine glands, heartbeat, gut movements, etc.; *cf.* central nervous system, peripheral nervous system.

autopsy: a post-mortem examination. Also called necropsy.

autosome: any chromosome apart from the sex chromosomes.

autotrophy: the means by which bacteria or most plants live from inorganic materials (i.e. autotrophic).

autumn: the season after summer and before winter in temperate regions; Am. fall.

auxiliary (bird): syn. helper, a non-breeding bird assisting in a cooperative breeding association; *cf.* co-operative breeding.

auxiliary feeding: nestlings or fledglings being fed by individuals other than their parents or foster parents.

avenue bower: two parallel vertical walls, constructed of sticks or grasses on the ground and used by male bowerbirds (Ptilonorhynchidae) for aiding courtship and mating; *cf.* maypole bower.

average: mathematical mean, although often used more loosely.

Aves: the scientific name for the class of both fossil and recent birds.

avian: pertaining to birds, Aves.

avian cholera: a bacterial disease caused by *Pasteurella multocida*; among the symptoms are small blood spots on the skin and necrosis of the liver. Found in many bird families but most often in waterbirds. Syn. fowl cholera, **avian pasteurellosis**.

avian diphtheria: an outdated term for the form of fowl pox, that affects the mucous membranes of the mouth and upper respiratory tract.

avian influenza: an RNA influenza A virus causing disease in birds and mammals; waterbirds (e.g., ducks, geese, and shorebirds) are typical hosts, but the virus can emerge into atypical hosts such as landbirds (e.g. chickens) and mammals (e.g. pigs, seals, mink) and become more virulent. Pathogenicity is defined based on an influenza strain's effects in poultry (chickens), and highly pathogenic (HP) strains can cause severe economic damage in the poultry industry. Strains are named based on their hemagglutinin (H) and neuraminidase (N) subtypes. Epidemic and pandemic human influenza episodes have frequently stemmed from avian influenzas that have apparently undergone subsequent mutations in another mammalian host; *cf.* H5N1.

avian malaria: a protozoan infection that destroys red blood cells. The intermediate hosts are mosquitoes. Several species of malaria parasites (*Plasmodium*) exist, and most only produce a mild illness, different from malaria in humans.

avian monocytosis: a viral infection in domestic fowl.

avian pox: a viral disease causing vesicles and swelling of the skin and later scab formation, especially on the head and feet; most often seen in pigeons.

avian tuberculosis: disease caused by the bacterium *Mycobacterium tuberculosis* that often enters the body through the alimentary tract; different from tuberculosis in humans.

aviary: a large outdoor cage for birds.

Avicultural Magazine: periodical published by the Avicultural Society of the UK since 1894.

aviculture: the keeping and breeding of birds in captivity. An older name for aviculturists is bird fanciers.

avifauna: the birds of a certain geographical area.

Avocetta: periodical published by the Centro Italiano Studi Ornitologici since 1978.

axial skeleton: the part of the skeleton of vertebrates that includes the skull, vertebrae, sternum, ribs, and pelvis but not the limbs; *cf.* appendicular skeleton.

axillary: syn. subhumeral, any of the (usually elongate) feathers of the armpit (the **axilla**).

axis: the second vertebra, articulating with the atlas.

axon: a cable-like extension of a neuron that makes contact with other nerve cells; *cf.* sensory neurons, motor neurons.

azimuthal projection: in geography, a map projection onto a tangent plane to the globe. In normal (or polar) aspect, the point of tangency is one of the poles, and meridians are shown as radial straight lines through the pole, while parallels appear as concentric circles. Distortion in the map increases with distance from the point of tangency. Because distortion is minimal near the point of tangency, azimuthal projections are useful for representing areas having approximately equal extents in the north-south and east-west directions.

azimuth: the arc of a celestial great circle extending from the zenith to the horizon.

azimuth compass: the ability of diurnal migratory birds to use the sun as compass and compensate for the sun's movements using their internal clock; *cf.* magnetic, olfactory, sun, and star compasses.

B

bacillary white diarrhoea: a disease caused by bacteria of the genus *Salmonella*, giving diarrhoea. Liver and spleen become white or grey spotted. The bacteria are excreted in bird droppings. Also called salmonellosis, infectious enteritis, paratyphoid infection, and fowl typhoid.

back: term loosely applied to the mantle, scapulars, and back down to the rump. Some authors, however, use 'mantle' for the whole upperparts except the rump, others distinguish between mantle, upper back mantle, the rest of the back, and the rump, but most will differentiate between mantle, scapulars, upper back, lower back, and rump.

back vertebrae: the vertebrae between the neck and the three lowest lumbar vertebrae. The ribs are connected to the dorsal vertebrae. Also called dorsal vertebral column; *cf.* os dorsale.

backcross: the mating of an F1 hybrid individual to one of the two parental forms, types, or genotypes.

badge: a chin, throat, or upper breast patch of contrasting colour that serves as a visual signal, e.g. the black badge of the male House Sparrow (*Passer domesticus*), also called a bib.

band: 1) a horizontal marking, broader than a bar. 2) in Am., a ring placed on a bird's leg to mark it.

banding: Am. for ringing birds with metal or plastic rings on the legs,

making them identifiable when recaptured; *cf.* marking.

bandsharing coefficient: an index of similarity between two DNA fingerprint patterns, based on the proportion of shared bands.

Bank Swallow: Am. name for Sand Martin (*Riparia riparia*).

baobab: a general term for eight species of trees in the genus *Adansonia* growing in Africa, Madagascar, and Australia; famous for their hugely swollen trunks; also called monkey bread tree.

bar: a fine, transverse mark; *cf.* band.

barb: a narrow individual part of the feather that branches off the shaft (rachis), it is composed of a main central axis called the ramus and two rows of barbules extending off the ramus, both proximally and distally to the feather. A flexible plane (the vane of contour feathers) is formed by interlocking barbs when the barbules on the distal side possess barbicels, or small hooks, that interlock with the proximal barbules on the neighbouring, distal barb. An absence of barbicels on the barbules causes barbs not to interlock, resulting in a downy feather; *cf.* rachis, barbules, barbicels.

barbicels: tiny projections from the barbules on the barbs of contour feathers. Barbicels on distal barbules (those on the side of the barb towards the tip of the feather, as opposed to proximal) are shaped like hooks (called hamuli) that attach to ridge-shaped barbicels on the proximal barbules of the neighbouring barb. Barbicels are responsible for the cohesion and flexibility of the feather. About one million barbicels are found in a single flight feather from a crow (*Corvus* sp.); *cf.* barb, barbules.

barbule: lateral branch from the ramus of both sides of a barb. Barbules of contour feathers are provided with projections (barbicels) that interlock where barbules of adjacent barbs cross each other, thereby forming the closed vane of the feather; *cf.* barb, barbicels.

bare parts: exposed areas without feathers, i.e. bill, feet, and naked areas as found in many bird species, e.g. on head or neck; sometimes referred to as soft parts. Note, this term does not refer to apteria.

barial: a mud flat.

bark-gleaning: feeding on prey taken from the bark of trees; *cf.* foliage-gleaning.

baroreception: the detection of change in barometric pressure. Pigeons have this ability.

barrier: physical obstruction that may prevent the dispersal of a species or of individuals between populations, for example mountains, oceans, deserts, or even forests or grassland. Term used by ecologists and biogeographers, and evolutionary biologists when considering gene flow.

Bartlett's test of homogeneity of variances: statistical procedure for testing whether three or more samples are equally variable (see *F*-test for two-sample case).

basal: pertaining to the base (of a structure, a lineage, etc.); *cf.* distal, proximal.

basal metabolic rate: abbr. BMR, the minimum energy requirement per time period of an organism, measured (in units such as calories or kilojoules per unit time) when the organism is inactive and the ambient temperature is optimal; *cf.* metabolic rate, standard metabolic rate.

base substitution: a nucleotide difference between homologous strands of DNA or RNA (whether comparing individuals, species, or lineages), in which one nucleotide (adenine, guanine, cytosine, or thymine/uracil) has been substituted for another through mutation. Synonymous substitutions are changes that do not alter the amino acid being coded (by coding DNA) and are therefore invisible to selection; non-synonymous substitutions result in protein coding differences.

basibranchial: a tongue bone posterior to the basihyal bone between the two long and slender united bones. Also called urohyal; *cf.* hyoid apparatus, basihyal, ceratonranchial, epibranchial.

basic plumage: Am. syn. for non-nuptial plumage, the non-breeding plumage (most often the winter plumage) in species having more than one plumage each year, and also the plumage of birds having only one plumage; the majority of birds moult only once a year; *cf.* alternate plumage.

basihyal: the posterior end of the visible tongue; *cf.* hyoid apparatus, basibranchial, ceratonranchial, epibranchial.

basilar membrane: a thin structure of the inner ear.

basilar papilla: a membrane inside the cochlea in the inner ear upon which sensory hair cells are arrayed.

Bassian Fauna: the fauna occupying the moist, sclerophyllous eucalypt forests and woodlands of south-western and south-eastern temperate Australia, *cf.* Eyrean Fauna, Torresian Fauna.

bastard wing: a group of small, stiffened feathers associated with the thumb (first digit) or the wrist (carpal joint) of the wing; also called *alula* or false wing. It serves as an aerodynamic slot in slow flight.

Batesian mimicry: a sort of mimicry in which a harmless species (insect) gains protection from predators by its resemblance to an inedible or poisonous species. Not known in birds.

batrachian: an amphibian, e.g. frog or toad, **batrachia**.

bauplan: from the German for 'structural type', used in zoology to refer to a generalized body plan.

Bayesian (coalescent) analysis: any analytical method using Bayes' theorem, a statistical procedure that estimates parameters of an underlying distribution based on the observed distribution.

BC: abbr. (of the date) before Christ.

B cell: a type of lymphocyte producing antibodies; *cf.* bursa of Fabricius, T cell, memory cell.

B-DNA: a right-handed helix, the dominant conformational variant of DNA in solution, in which the base pairs are stacked nearly perpendicular to the axis of the helix; *cf.* A-DNA, E-DNA, Z-DNA, deoxyribonucleic acid.

Beached Bird Survey: a survey organised by the Royal Society for the Protection of Birds and the Seabird Group to monitor the mortality of birds at sea in the North Sea, the Irish Sea, and the English Channel.

beaconing: in bird navigation, a goal-directed orientation based on a stimulus gradient emanating from the bird's goal.

beak: another term for bill used especially for birds of prey (Falconiformes) and other birds having strong and hooked bills.

beak-wiping: a behaviour shown by many species of birds, to keep the bill clean but also in response to the eating of noxious or toxic insects; also termed bill-wiping.

beard: the bristly-feathered appendage on the front of the lower neck of a Turkey (*Meleagris gallopavo*).

beater-effect: prey flushed by one bird in a flock can be caught by another member of it.

behaviour: Am. spelled behavior. Includes all processes by which an animal senses and responds to the external world and the internal state of its body. Behaviour is always the outcome of a highly complex integration of muscle contractions. Also termed habits.

belly: the part of the underparts between breast and undertail coverts, also called abdomen.

belly-soaking: sandgrouse (Pteroclididae) carry water for their chicks in soaked belly-feathers often over long distances, and some tropical plovers (Charadriidae) so bring water over short distances to cool their eggs.

belt: a band of contrasting colour across the breast or belly, e.g. Belted Kingfisher (*Megaceryle alcyon*).

belt transect: a strip across a habitat (the area on either side of the line is also covered) within observational range and used when counting birds to determine their status in the habitat; *cf.* line transect and transect.

bend of the wing: the wrist or carpal joint.

benign tumour: a not life-threatening tumour, in contrast to a malignant tumour or cancer.

Benu: a mythical bird of Egypt that recreated itself daily in the rays of the rising sun, another version of the Phoenix; *cf.* Feng-Huang.

Bergmann's Rule: a zoogeographic generalisation expressing the observation that populations of birds and other endothermal vertebrates tend to be larger in body size in cooler climates than in warmer ones; *cf.* Allen's Rule, Gause's Rule, Gloger's Rule.

Beringia: western Alaska, NE Russia, and the shallow parts of the Bering and Chukchi seas, where a land-bridge existed during the last ice age.

Bering land bridge: the land bridge connecting Russia and Alaska during the last ice age, also known as the North Pacific bridge.

Berne Convention: a convention on the conservation of wild plants and animals as well as natural habitats in Europe. Founded 1982.

BfV: now called NABU, Society for the Protection of Birds in Germany.

biandry: a specific case of polyandry in which one female mates with two males; *cf.* bigyny.

bi-: prefix from Latin *bis*, meaning twice.

bias: (in statistics) a systematic error or latent influence in sampling inherent in the sampling technique that causes the distribution of the sample to deviate from that of the population.

bib: a chin, throat, or upper breast patch of contrasting colour that serves as a visual signal, e.g. the black marking of the male House Sparrow (*Passer domesticus*), also called badge.

bibliographic reference: a list of books and papers on a specific subject. The most important ornithological source has been the annually published *Zoological Record*, section Aves, but the American weekly *Biological Abstracts* has also many useful references. *Recent Ornithological Literature* was published from 1983 to 1997 as a collaboration among the journals *Auk, Ibis*, and *Emu*, and is now continued on the internet: www.birdlit.org. The annotated German *Ornithologische Schriftenschau* has both German and English references.

bicentric: having two centres (e.g. the distribution of a species).

biceps brachii: a muscle on the forearm (humerus); *cf.* triceps brachii.

biceps femoris: a muscle posterior to the thigh (femur); *cf.* sartorius, iliotibialis, aponeurosis.

biconical: an oblong oval egg shape, also called ellipsoidal; *cf.* ovate, pyriform, spherical.

bifocal vision: a type of vision occurring when the position of the eyes enables an overlapping of the independent fields of vision of each eye, the overlap is most extensive when the eyes face forward as in owls; also called binocular vision.

bifurcate: forked, with two branches.

bigamy: a specific case of polygamy when either the male or female pairs with two partners; *cf.* biandry, bigyny, polygyny, polyandry.

big bang: the prevailing scientific theory for the origin of the universe 13.7 billion years ago in a massive explosion; since then space itself and all in it has been expanding.

bigyny: a specific case of polygyny in which a male mates with two females; *cf.* biandry, polyandry.

bilateral asymmetry: asymmetry between right and left body parts.

bilateral gynandrism: an animal having both ovary and testis, and characterised by having one side of the plumage female and the other male, changing abruptly along the mid-line; *cf.* hermaphroditic, **gynandromorph.**

bilateral morphological variables: asymmetry between right and left body parts.

bilateral symmetry: symmetry between left and right sides of the body so that they are mirror images of each other.

bile: a greenish fluid secreted by the liver and stored in the gall bladder, apparently aiding digestion.

bile ducts: two canals running from each lobe of the liver to the duodenum.

bill: the upper and lower mandibles of the skull covered with a horny sheath (the ramphotheca) rather than skin and/or feathers; also called beak or jaw; *cf.* culmen, cutting edges, dertrum, gnathotheca, maxilla, rhinotheca.

bill-clappering: a sound made by the bill, e.g. the Stork (*Ciconia ciconia*), when clacking the upper and lower mandibles of the bill together; also spelled **bill-klappering** or called **bill-rattling, bill-fencing**, or **bill-clacking**.

bill-drumming: a loud sound produced by a sequence of blows of the tip of the bill against wood, characteristic of many woodpeckers (Picidae). Sequences can be slow or fast, depending on species; simply termed 'drumming' in most contexts.

bill flange: more correctly gape flange. The soft, fleshy, often colourful area on each side of a nestling bird's mouth.

billing: a form of 'kissing' or greeting ceremony between the members of a mated pair, in which they touch or clasp bills; also called nebbing.

bill-snap: a mechanical sound made by the bill.

bill-wiping: a behaviour shown by many species of birds, to keep the bill clean but also in response to the eating of noxious or toxic insects; also termed beak-wiping.

bimaculate: marked with two spots, **bimaculation**.

bimodal: any frequency distribution having two peaks or modes, e.g. of breeding.

binary character: a character having two states, usually either present or absent.

binary name: a name having two parts (a binomen), such as the scientific name of a species.

binoculars: an optical instrument for use with both eyes, consisting of prisms, mirrors, and lenses that enable one to see objects such as birds greatly magnified. Also called field glasses.

binocular vision: a type of vision that occurs when both eyes have broadly overlapping fields, enabling a three-dimensional perspective on an object's position in space, maximised in groups such as owls with both eyes pointed forward; opposite monocular vision, also called bifocal vision.

binomen: pl. binominal, the principle that the scientific name of a species is a combination of two names (genus and species), together called a binomen. **binomial**; *cf.* trinomial, nomenclature.

binomial classification: the describing of a species using two Latin or Greek names, the first with a capital initial naming the genus, the second with a small initial naming the species. First introduced by Carolus Linnaeus. For naming subspecies, trinomial nomenclature is used; *cf.* International Code of Zoological Nomenclature.

binomial test: a statistical procedure based on the binomial distribution, testing whether the distribution of two possible states (e.g. female/male, successful/unsuccessful) is random.

bio-: a prefix derived from Greek *bios* = life.

bioaccumulation: the accumulation and magnification of concentration of some substance up through the food chain, especially of organochlorine pesticides and heavy metal pollutants. Also called biological magnification.

bioacoustics: the study of vocalization in animals, e.g. bird song.

biochemistry: the chemistry of the processes of life.

biochromes: the pigment colours of feathers, or the 'true' colours caused by pigments such as melanin, carotenoids, porphyrins, and turacoverdin; in contrast to structural colours caused by the way proteins such as melanin are deposited within the feather so that light is scattered (and absorbed) differentially depending on direction and wavelength; *cf.* structural colours.

biocoenosis: all living organisms in an area; *cf.* avicoenosis, synecology, alpha, beta, and gamma diversity.

biocoenotic nexus: the functional interconnections of all or parts of an organismal community.

biodiversity: biological diversity, i.e. the variety (species number) of animals and plants in an area.

Biodiversity Convention: a convention on the biodiversity of birds. Agreed to in 1992 in Rio de Janeiro.

biodiversity hotspot: a small geographic region containing a relatively high proportion of the world's species, usually identified by using one or a few indicator taxa.

biogenesis: the hypothesis that all plants and animals have evolved from previously existing ancestors.

biogeographical rules: patterns associated with differences in climate resulting in adaptation to local conditions. Allen's Rule (proportion rule), Bergmann's Rule (size rule), Gloger's Rule (colour rule), and Rensch's Rule (form of the wings); *cf.* ecological rules.

biogeography: the science of studying the geographical distributions of plants and animals, both past and present; called zoogeography when applied only to animals.

bioindicator: using living organisms and the way they react to ecological conditions to indicate organismal stress or change in the environment, often in the context of pollutants or contaminants; also called biological monitoring.

biological clock: endogenous temporal periodicity; innate time measuring system; *cf.* circadian and circannual rhythms.

biological control: control of pest species by biological means, e.g. by the introduction of natural predators or parasites or by sterilization of a large number of males.

biological diversity: synonym for biodiversity or the diversity of animals and plants, in local, regional, political, or global contexts.

biological equilibrium: stability in any biological system.

biological indicator: a species that, by its presence, absence, or by its abundance, tells something important about the quality of the habitat and thus serves as a tool in monitoring the state of the environment in an area. Also called indicator species.

biological magnification: the accumulation and magnification of concentration of some substance up through the food chain, especially of organochlorine pesticides and heavy metal pollutants. Also called bioaccumulation.

biological monitoring: the use of plants and animals as indicators of environmental conditions.

biological parents: the male and female sources of the gametes producing the zygote; usually parents that tend their own offspring.

biological species concept: abbr. BSC, 'groups of interbreeding natural populations that are reproductively isolated from other such groups' (Mayr 1969), *cf.* ecological species concept recognition species concept, cohesion species concept, phylogenetic species concept.

biology: an all-embracing term that may best be summarised as the study of life.

biomarker: an indicator of a biological state, e.g. pentosidine is an indicator of biological age.

biomass: the total mass (often in units of energy) of a living system (an organism, a population, a species, or a group of species within a given area, etc.).

biome: a major ecological community of often distinctive organisms, e.g. the tundra, desert, rainforest, or savannah biomes. Rarely also termed ecome.

biometry: measurement of morphological and anatomical features, **biometrics.**

bionics: a discipline of applied biology with the aim of using the findings for technological development.

bionomics: an uncommon term for ecology.

bionomic strategy: characters of a bird or a population of birds such as size, colour, migratory habit, fecundity, longevity, etc. that bring the bird(s) increased fitness.

biorhythmicity: the daily, monthly, and annual life cycles and their underlying physiologies.

biospecies: a group of interbreeding individuals that is reproductively isolated from all other groups and therefore represents an evolutionarily independent unit.

biosphere: the part of the world containing life, i.e. the global ecosystem; *cf.* ecosphere.

biota: the total fauna and flora of an area; *cf.* fauna, flora.

biotelemetry: the monitoring of an animal's movements (and/or physiological characteristics) by tracking the signals from a radio transmitter attached to or implanted within the animal.

biotic: pertaining to the components of an environment that is living or came from once-living forms; *cf.* abiotic.

biotic communities: an ecological division, e.g. North America has been considered to have nine major biomes: Tundra, Coniferous Forest, Deciduous Forest, Grassland, Southwestern Oak Woodland, Pinyon-Juniper, Chaparral, Sagebrush, and Scrub Desert. Now rarely used in science; *cf.* life zones.

biotic factors: environmental influences arising from activities of organisms rather than, for example, climate, etc.

biotic index: certain key species or pollution-sensitive species whose abundance gives an indication of the quality of the biotope, more commonly called indicator species; *cf.* diversity index.

biotope: locality of a community of all living substances; a term that means an area with a large extent of a rather uniform flora and fauna. Formerly encompassed only non-living things such as soil, water, and air. Also termed ecosystem and biocenosis; *cf.* habitat.

biparental care: participation of both parents in care of the offspring; *cf.* uniparental care.

bipedal: being two-footed, of (the locomotion of) vertebrates that walk/run on the hind legs only.

bipolar: having two poles; e.g. animals distributed both at high northern and high southern latitudes.

bird: animal belonging to the class Aves. The etymology is unknown.

bird census: the counting of one, some, or all bird populations in a certain area, often involving many people.

bird community: the totality of all birds in an area.

birder: birdwatcher, an amateur interested in birds.

bird fancier: a person who keeps birds in captivity; today usually called an aviculturist, although that term implies that birds are bred in captivity, not merely kept.

bird-fly: a member of the family Hippoboscidae, blood-sucking ectoparasites with a flattish body, tough leathery skin, and well developed claws; some are able to fly, others are not. Also called feather-fly, flat-fly, hippoboscid-fly, ked-fly, louse-fly, spider-fly, and tick-fly.

bird-hipped dinosaurs: one of the two major groups of dinosaurs. Their hips resembled those of modern birds. Also called Ornithischian dinosaurs; *cf.* reptile-hipped dinosaurs.

Birding World: a British journal for birdwatchers, published since 1987.

BirdLife International: formerly International Council for Bird Preservation, abbr. ICBP. A global alliance of conservation organisations working together for the world's birds and people.

bird lime: a sticky substance formerly often used to catch parrots and passerines.

Bird-Lore: a quarterly publication published by the National Audubon Society from 1898; since 1941 called *Audubon Magazine* and later only *Audubon*.

bird louse: pl. lice, belonging to the family Mallophagidae, flattened and wingless ectoparasites that suck blood from feathers and skin. Some species live within the feather shaft. Vectors of a number of avian diseases. Feather damage caused by them may reduce winter survival because it causes metabolic heat loss to increase. Also called chewing louse, feather louse, and body louse.

bird mite: a parasite *Liponyssus sylviarum*.

bird of prey: commonly used term for any member of the orders Falconiformes and formerly Strigiformes as well. In older literature the name diurnal birds of prey was used, the nocturnal birds of prey being the owls (Strigiformes).

bird skin: a bird stuffed for scientific use in a stereotypic posture nearly like a dead bird (without glass eyes) and with an attached label containing data such as sex, age, date, locality, and mass; often supplemented in modern collections with skeletal material, tissues for DNA studies, etc. Birds for display are not called 'skins', and instead are prepared ('stuffed') in life-like postures using different taxidermic methods coupled with accurate and artistic reconstructions meant to display the bird in life.

bird strike: bird collision with aircraft.

Bird Study: the journal of the British Trust for Ornithology. Published since 1954.

bird tick: ectoparasite of the family Ixodidae (Acarida). May transfer pathogenetic organisms such as Lyme disease when sucking the host's blood.

bird-watching: studying or looking at birds in the field.

birth rate: the reproductive success or the number of chicks successfully raised or fledged per year. Also called fecundity.

bisexual: of an individual having both male and female organs; *cf.* hermaphrodite, gynandromorph.

bivalent: applied to homologous chromosomes when they associate during cell division (mitosis).

bivalve: molluscs having a shell made up of two hinged parts.

blackhead disease: disease caused by a protozoon (*Histomonas meleagridis*) that attacks the liver and caeca of many birds, e.g. Turkeys (*Meleagris gallopavo*) and other gallinaceous birds, with a high mortality rate. This protozoon causes gastric disturbance anorexia, and diarrhoea. Also called histomoniasis, heterakiasis, or enterohepatitis.

bladder: a urinary sac, that among all birds occurs only in the Ostrich (*Struthio camelus*) and rheas (Rheidae). Not to be confused with gall bladder. Also called urinary bladder.

blade: the vane of the feather, both the outer (narrow) and the inner (wide) portions of the vane, more often called web or vane.

blastoderm: a germinal spot in an egg (ovum) that becomes the embryo once fertilized.

blastula: a small white circle in the yolk sac of an egg; also called the germinal spot.

bleating: a sound made by the vibration of the outer tail feathers (rectrices) during aerial displays among many species of snipes (*Gallinago*). Also called winnowing, drumming, or instrumental sound.

blending inheritance: of traits that are inherited in offspring as an apparently blended admixture of the parental types, with no apparent segregation in subsequent generations.

blepharitis: an inflammation of the eyelids with watery discharges from nostrils and eyes.

blind: Am. for a hiding place for bird watching; the English term is hide.

blind spot: a small area on the retina without rods and cones and therefore with no optic vision.

blocking: a method of estimating a large congregation of birds by counting the birds in a block and then estimating how many blocks occur in the whole flock.

blood quill: the sheath of a growing feather.

blood-vascular system: the circulatory system, consisting of the heart and blood vessels (arteries, veins, capillaries); the arteries convey oxygen-rich blood from the lungs and from there to and through the tiny capillaries to the cells, where it delivers oxygen and picks up waste products, then to and through the kidneys and back via the veins to the lungs.

blotched: an egg with large amoeba-shaped markings.

blowfly: *Protocalliphora* spp. belonging the family Calliphoridae, medium sized flies; the larvae live in the nest and feed on blood from the nestlings, often with a fatal result.

bluebottle fly: a medium-sized fly laying its eggs in the nest of birds; the larvae ('screwworms') suck blood from nestling birds.

Blue Jay, The: the Canadian ornithological periodical published by the Saskatchewan Natural History Society. Also the English common name of *Cyanocitta cristata.*

BMNH: acronym for the British Museum of Natural History, in London. The scientific bird skin collection has been moved to Tring (although the same acronym is used for this collection/location).

BMR: abbr. for basal metabolic rate, the rate of energy consumption measured in a bird at rest in an environment at normal temperature; see basal metabolic rate.

BOC: abbr. for the British Ornithologists' Club.

body down: the downy feathers that many adult birds have under their contour feathers.

body feathers: all feathers, including wing and tail feathers but not usually the downy feathers; more often called contour feathers.

body louse: pl. lice. An ectoparasite living among feathers and sucking blood and fluids from feathers and skin. Vectors for a number of avian diseases and often causing feather loss. Also called feather louse or chewing louse.

body mass: a more precise term for body weight.

bog: a waterlogged area with alkaline water; *cf.* marsh, fen, wetland.

Bokmakierie: Afrikaans name for the Bush-Shrike (*Telephorus zeylonus*).

bolus: a piece of food carried in the throat for the nestlings or about to be swallowed.

Bombay Natural History Society: Indian society publishing the *Journal of the Bombay Natural History Society* in English, covering all animals of India and with many important bird papers.

Bonn Convention: an international Convention on the Conservation of Migratory Species of Wild Animals. Came into force in 1983. Also called the Convention on the Conservation of Migratory Species of Wild Animals, abbr. CMS.

bony bumps: points of attachment for the secondaries to the ulna.

booming: at a lek, males of the Kakapo (*Strigops habroptilus*) utter a low, resonant, booming call that sounds like distant thunder up to 5 km away. Other species, such as Greater Prairie Chicken (*Tympanuchus cupido*) and Blue Grouse (*Dendragapus obscurus*) and bitterns (*Botaurus*) also produce far-carrying, booming sounds as part of a male's display.

booming sac: a naked, brightly coloured, expansive sac on the throat of some grouse that assists the production of loud hooting or booming sounds during a male's displays.

booming ground: Am., term for the vocal display ground of Greater Prairie Chickens (*Tympanuchus cupido*), and also applied to several other vocally displaying birds.

boot: used to describe boot-shaped nesting cavities excavated in Saguaro Cactus by Gila Woodpeckers (*Melanerpes uropygialis*).

booted tarsus: the tarsus of an adult bird of certain species, e.g. a thrush (*Turdus*), in which the usual scales are fused into one smooth sheath or boot; in juveniles the tarsus is first scutellate but the scales soon fuse.

The condition is also called holothecal and ocreate; *cf.* laminiplantar, scutellate, reticulate, scutellate-reticulate, scutellate-booted.

bootstrapping: a statistical technique by which a distribution is estimated through repeated sampling of a dataset (random resampling with replacement), used to obtain standard errors and confidence limits for a particular statistic.

bootstrap value: in phylogenetic systematics an indicator of the strength of a node on a phylogenetic tree, representing the percentage of occurrences of a particular topology that occurred in a bootstrapped resembling of the dataset (generally over thousands of resembled replicates).

boreal: conifer or needle-leaf forest zone between the Arctic and temperate zones, often called taiga.

Boreal Owl: Am. for Tengmalm's Owl (*Aegolius funereus*).

Borrelia: a genus of bacteria transmittable by avian ticks and lice.

bottleneck: 1) a period when resources are in short supply. 2) when a population or species is reduced to a very few individuals, often considered in genetic terms as when a significant loss in genetic diversity occurs through small population size.

botulism: a severe food poisoning caused by a bacterium, *Clostridium botulinum*, that lives in soil and is able to exist only in the absence of oxygen (an anaerobe). Ducks (Anatidae) and pheasants (Phasianidae) are most often affected and show high mortality.

BOU: acronym of the British Ornithologists' Union. Publishes the ornithological journal *Ibis*.

bounding flight: a flight style in which brief periods of wing flapping alternate with ballistic phases during which the wings are folded; used by smaller birds, including most passerines.

bower: a construction built by male bowerbirds (Ptilonorhynchidae) from sticks and other vegetable matter, typically of maypole or avenue shape, for the purpose of mate attraction, courtship, and mating.

BP: abbr. for before present.

brachial: pertaining to the arm.

brachial plexus: nerve fibres running from the cervical enlargement to the wing muscles; *cf.* lumbosacral plexus.

brachioradialis: a muscle anterior to the radius in the wing.

brachium: the part of the wing between body and the elbow; *cf.* antebrachium.

Brachypteraciidae: the formerly recognized family of ground-roller, now included in the roller family (Coraciidae).

bradytely: a relatively slow rate of evolution.

brailing: cutting the primaries of captive birds to prevent them from flying. Also called clipping; *cf.* pinioning.

brain: the enlarged anterior portion of the central nervous system housed within the skull and comprised of, by size, the cerebral hemispheres, the cerebellum, the optic lobe, the medulla, the olfactory bulb, the pituitary gland, and the optic nerve.

brainstem: the brain of a vertebrate exclusive of the cerebral hemispheres and cerebellum.

breast: the area of the underparts between throat and belly, often further subdivided into upper breast, lower breast, and the sides of the breast; rarely called chest.

breast-band: a band of contrasting colour that runs across the breast.

breastbone: skeletal element forming the ventral part of the rib cage; in flying birds it carries a prominent keel (carina) to which the pectoral muscles are fastened; also called sternum; *cf.* fenestra, rostrum, metasternum,

costal facets, coracoid facets, sternal notch, coracoid facets, lateral caudal process.

breeding bird census: a count of a breeding population of a certain area, often involving many people.

Breeding Bird Survey: abbr. BBS, an annual count of birds from roadsides in USA and Canada conducted by volunteers and coordinated by the U.S. Geological Survey and the Canadian Wildlife Service since 1966 to monitor trends in populations; *cf.* Christmas Bird Count.

breeding dispersal: the movement of an adult bird from the breeding area in one season to the breeding area of the next season, i.e. the change from season to season of breeding area; *cf.* natal dispersal.

breeding plumage: the plumage of an adult bird during the breeding season, also called nuptial or alternate plumage.

breeding potential: the theoretical rate at which a species could reproduce if all eggs hatched and all chicks survived to maturity.

breeding season: the period when an individual, population, or species breeds.

breeding site fidelity: the return of breeding birds to the breeding area of the previous year; *cf.* natal philopatry.

breeding system: the pattern of pair formation found in a population or species, such as monogamy, polygamy, polyandry, polygyny, etc.

breeding success: a measure of reproductive 'efficiency', for example the number of fledged young divided by the number of eggs laid, in a population or a single pair.

Brewster's Warbler: an informal common name for individuals resulting from hybridisation between a Blue-winged Warbler (*Vermivora pinus*) and a Golden-winged Warbler (*Vermivora chrysoptera*). See also Lawrence's Warbler.

bridled: having a head marking patterned like the shape of a bridle, e.g. as in Bridled Terns (*Sterna anaethetus*) and the bridled morph of Common Guillemots (*Uria aalge*).

bridling: a display behaviour seen in the Black Noddy (*Anous tenuirostris*) and the Mallard (*Anas platyrhynchos*), a post-copulatory display in which the male suddenly flings his head upward and backwards.

brigalow: a distinctive Australian sub-humid habitat dominated by the brigalow (*Acacia harpophylla*).

bristle: a stiff, hair-like contour feather, often with a few basal barbs on the shaft but with a largely barbless rachis; a specialized feather for sensory purposes found, e.g. around the mouths of birds that catch flying insects, over the nostrils, or as eyelashes in many birds, on the toes of some barn owls (Tytonidae), and on the legs of the Bristle-thighed Curlew (*Numenius tahitiensis*); *cf.* rictal bristles, semibristle.

British Birds: English periodical for birdwatchers, published since 1907.

British Columbia Beached Bird Survey: a survey that takes place across the entire coast of British Columbia (Canada). Publishes a magazine *Bird Studies Canada* and a newsletter for volunteers.

British Library of Wildlife Sounds: a collection of sound recordings from all over the world at the British Institute of Recorded Sound in London.

British Ornithologists' Club: society founded in 1880, publishing the *Bulletin of the British Ornithologists' Club* and holding six dinners each year for members.

British Ornithologists' Union: abbr. BOU, the oldest British ornithological society, founded in 1858 and publishing the quarterly journal *Ibis*.

British Trust for Ornithology: abbr BTO, founded in 1933, published *Bulletin of the British Trust for Ornithology* 1934-1954, and still publishes *Bird Study* (from 1954) and *Ringing and Migration* (from 1975); *cf* narrow-front migration.

broad-front migration: migration pattern in which the birds move over wide areas, as opposed to narrow corridors.

broad-leaved: trees with broad leaves e.g. oak and beech, as opposed to the needle-like leaves of coniferous trees

broken-wing display: a form of distraction behaviour found in many species, especially ground-nesting birds in which the bird appears to be sick and unable to fly until the predator is diverted away from the nest o chicks; also called deflecting display diversionary display, broken-wing trick, crippled-bird act, or injury feigning.

bronchus: pl. bronchi, the paired air ducts leading from the caudal end o the air pipe (trachea) and the 'music box' (syrinx) to the lungs; *cf.* mesc bronchus, parabronchi, secondar bronchi.

bronchial syrinx: a type of syrinx whit the membranes and intrinsic muscle located posterior to the tracheo-bron chial junction. Found in nightjar (Caprimulgidae), some cuckoos (Cu culidae), and owls (Strigidae); *cf.* tra cheal syrinx, tracheobronchial syrinx

Bronx County Bird Club: Founded i 1924 as an offshoot of the Linnaea Society of New York. The club ha included participants such as Roge Tory Peterson and Ernst Mayr.

brood: the chicks hatched from a clutc of eggs.

brood amalgamation: in waterfowl is common to see an adult (or pair o adults) with more young than they could have hatched themselves, e.g. often seen in Canada Goose (*Branta canadensis*); *cf.* crèche.

brood-desertion: when one of the parents deserts his/her brood by ceasing parental care; also termed offspring desertion or mate-desertion; *cf.* nest desertion.

brood division: division of the young in a brood between the parents, so that each parent takes care of only some of the young.

brooding: the act by a parent bird of sheltering its young beneath itself, protecting and keeping them warm (or cool by providing shade).

brooding rhythm: the interrupted periods of attentiveness to nestlings alternating with periods of inattentiveness.

brood parasite: a bird that lays its eggs in nests of other species (interspecific) or other individuals of the same species (intraspecific), leaving the host to care for and raise the young; *cf.* obligate brood parasite, nonobligate brood parasite, dump nesting, nest parasite, food parasite, facultative parasite, temporary parasite.

brood patch: patch or patches on the lower breast and/or belly from which the feathers are shed prior to incubation, and that, once naked, becomes vascularized and oedematous for the purpose of transferring more heat to the eggs; more correctly termed incubation patch or incubation spot. Pelicans (Pelecanidae), boobies (Sulidae), and some penguins (Spheniscidae) lack a brood patch. New feathers grow over the incubation patch(es) during the first moult following breeding, and in many species only one sex (the sex that incubates) has incubation patches.

brood reduction strategy: a strategy found in many bird families, e.g. gulls (Laridae), herons (Ardeidae), birds of prey (Falconiformes), and owls (Strigiformes). The last egg laid, the 'insurance egg', is typically smaller, which means that if food is scarce the last chick to hatch will die from starvation or be killed by its parents or siblings, and thus preventing the loss of the whole brood; *cf.* brood survival strategy, siblicide.

brood survival strategy: as food resources for egg production tend to be lower at the beginning of egg-laying, there may be a gradual increase in egg size through the clutch, such that the last egg is the largest and has a better energetic start. This strategy is often found among passerines; *cf.* brood reduction strategy.

Brownian movement: movement of small particles such as pollen grains or bacteria when suspended in a colloidal solution, due to their bombardment by molecules of the solution.

Brucke's muscle: a muscle that can change the shape of the soft and flexible lens in an avian eye; *cf.* Crampton's muscle.

BTO: abbr. for British Trust for Ornithology.

Bubalornithidae: a formerly recognized family comprising the buffalo weavers, which are now usually treated as the subfamily Bubalornithinae within the family Ploceidae.

bucca: fleshy portion of the cheek.

buccal cavity: mouth cavity.

buffer zone: an area adjacent to a preserved area and subject to less severe restrictions on human use than the preserve itself.

bug: 1) ectoparasites of the insect order Hemiptera, flattened with two pairs of wings and no true pupal stage, found on swallows (Hirundinidae) and swifts (Apodidae). 2) a word also loosely applied to a wide range of insects.

bulla: or bulla ossea, a bubble-like, asymmetrical, bony part of the syrinx, e.g. found in some ducks (Anatidae).

Bulletin of the British Ornithological Club: periodical containing short scientific papers, formerly often descriptions of new bird taxa. First published in 1892.

Bulletin of the Cooper Club: journal of the Cooper Ornithological Society, only published in 1899; the society then began publication of *The Condor*.

Bulletin of the Nuttall Ornithological Club: Published by the Nuttall Ornithological Club from 1876 to 1883, and continued thereafter as *The Auk* published by the American Ornithologists' Union.

Bulletin of the Ornithological Society of New Zealand: periodical of the Ornithological Society of New Zealand since 1943. Name changed to *Notornis* in 1950.

Bulletin of Zoological Nomenclature: the official organ of the International Commission on Zoological Nomenclature. Founded in 1943; volume 1 was published in 12 parts between 1943 and 1951.

bumble foot: swelling or arthritis of the food pad.

burrow: an elongate, typically excavated, hole in soil leading to or constituting a nest chamber, also called nest-burrow.

bursa: a sac or saclike cavity.

bursa Fabricii: a gland on the dorsal wall of the cloaca, at its junction with the vent, present in young birds only and the secretions of which stimulate the immune system. Also called **bursa of Fabricius** or cloacal bursa.

bush: a more or less dense shrub (includes bushes and small trees) normally not exceeding 1-3m in height.

busking: an aggressive male Mute Swan (*Cygnus olor*) display directed at intruders.

bustard-quail: a synonym for buttonquail.

bustle: the long wing feathers that lay over the tail of cranes (Gruidae) with closed wings.

butcherbird: 1) applied to shrikes (Laniidae) because of their habit of storing food prey by impaling them on thorns, wires, etc. 2) also applied to members of the Australian Cracticidae.

butterball: Am. vernacular name both for the Bufflehead (*Bucephala albeola*) and the Ruddy Duck (*Oxyura jamaicensis*).

butterfly flight: an aerial display with slow wing beats found in, e.g. the Ringed Plover (*Charadrius hiaticula*).

C

c.: abbr. Latin *circa* = approximately, or about, also abbreviated *ca*.

cabinet skin: a bird or mammal prepared in a position as if dead without glass eyes but with a data label attached. Also called museum skin or study skin.

cache: food stored for later use.

Cactaceae: the cactus family, with more than 2,000 species occurring in the deserts and semi-deserts of the New World.

caecum: (pl.) caeca, tubular, dead-end appendage stemming from the lower intestine in birds, especially in terrestrial species. Usually paired, with one on each side of the lower intestine near the cloaca and varying in form from buds to long tubes. The function is still not fully understood, but in grouse it seems that the well-developed caeca enable bacterially aided digestion of plant material. Am.: cecum, pl. ceca or colic ceca.

caenogenesis: the development of organs, structures, and behaviour exclusive to embryos or juveniles/immatures that are adaptive to life, e.g. when a chick in danger flattens itself against the ground, immobile.

cainism: brood reduction by siblicide, i.e. the killing of siblings; the term is generally applied, but especially to species hatching two chicks but rarely or never raising more than one, i.e. where siblicide is the rule, the sec- ond can only be raised in exceptionally good food years; also called **Cain and Abel**; *cf.* cronistic behaviour, fratricide, siblicide.

calamus: the hollow and transparent base of the feather shaft without barbs, also sometimes inappropriately called umbilicus, a term restricted to the two holes in the calamus through which nutrients pass during feather growth (lower umbilicus) and living cells are withdrawn (upper, or inferior umbilicus) once the feather is grown; *cf.* rachis, internal pulp caps.

calcaneus: the heel bone, in birds fused with the tibia (and astragalus).

calcar: the spur of a fowl, adj. calcarate.

calcification: a thickening and sclerotization of the arteries, most often seen in old parrots.

calcitonin: a hormone secreted by the ultimobranchial bodies, a pair of small glands situated below the thyroid glands and supposed to be involved in the regulation of calcium metabolism.

calendar bird: a bird migrating every year at precise times, e.g. the Spotted Redshank (*Tringa erythropus*) and Garden Warbler (*Sylvia borin*), or the European Cuckoo (*Cuculus canorus*), arriving on its northern breeding grounds on the same day, give or take three or four days, year after year; opposite of 'weather bird'. Also called instinct bird; *cf.* vagabond or facultative partial migrant.

calendar year: commonly used unit for the age of a bird, based on the human, 12-month calendar year: 'in 1st calendar year' relates to a bird born in the same year, '2nd calendar year' to a bird born in the previous year, etc.

calies: pl. calies, in the ovary, an empty egg sac or follicle; unlike corpora lutea in mammals, calies in birds are resorbed, leaving no trace after several months, and one cannot determine how many eggs a bird has laid. Also called postovulatory follicle.

call: a short, simple note or notes given in specific contexts such as warning, flight, contact, feeding, distress, or flock calls, and given by both sexes. As opposed to song.

callus: hard skin, term used, e.g. for the resting pad on the breast of an Ostrich (*Struthio camelus*) and Hoatzin (*Opisthocomus hoatzin*).

calorie: one calorie is the amount of heat required to raise one gram of water one degree. Unit of energy formerly widely used in studies of metabolism but now less frequently used as with most other units outside the international system (SI). The SI-unit of energy is the joule (J); 1 cal = 4.186 J, but note that the unit most commonly used is (was) the kilocalorie, and that Cal (with capital C) is standard for kcal: 1 Cal = 4186 J.

calorimetry: a measurement of heat.

CAM: abbr. of chorioallantoic membrane. A membrane complex inside a developing egg that combines the chorion (a protective membrane) and the allantoic sac (involved in respiration and waste retention), having the main function of respiration; *cf.* cuticle, testa, amniotic sac.

camber: the curvature of the wing or of a feather shaft.

Cambrian: the geological period approx. 545-490 million years BP in the Paleozoic era.

camouflage: protective colouring that conceals the bird in its habitat, also called cryptic coloration. The opposite of phaneric coloration; *cf.* countershading, procryptic coloration, anticryptic coloration, deflective coloration, epigamic coloration.

campinarana: low forest on sandy soil

campo: grassy lowland in South America with scattered low trees and bushes, now rare and fragmented. **Campo cerrado** = tree-covered savannah, **campo sujo** = savannah with sparse trees and shrubs.

Campophagidae: synonym for a genus of cuckoo shrikes (*Campephaga*).

Canadian Life Zone: one of six life zones of North America; *cf.* biotic communities.

canary-xanthophyll: a carotenoid found in the feathers of some carduelines (*Serinus, Carduelis,* and *Spinus*).

cancellate: different coloured cross lines on webs between the toes of some water birds.

cancer: a life-threatening tumour developing metastases, also called malignant tumour; *cf.* benign tumour.

Cancromidae: a formerly recognized monotypic family for the Boat-billed Heron (*Cochlearius cochlearius*), now included in the heron family (Ardeidae).

candling eggs: holding eggs up to bright light to see through them and determine whether they are fertile and their stage of incubation; *c.* floatation method.

candidiasis: a fungus disease of the digestive tract, found in geese, pheasants, pigeons, and parrots. Also called moniliasis, oidiomycosis, sour crop or thrush infection.

canebrakes: thickets of robust bamboo-like grass.

canker: 1) a pigeon fancier term for dove disease. 2) a protozoan infection that produces creamy white necrotic material in the mouth, parynx, inner nares, and oesophagus. More often called trichomoniasis, frounce, or diphtheria.

cannonball effect: when juveniles during dispersal spread out considerably; *cf.* intermittent migration.

cannon bone: the three fused bones (metatarsals) comprising the tarsus.

cannon net: a net fired from a 'cannon' to catch birds, especially geese.

canopy: the crown layer of a forest, sometimes subdivided into two or three canopy levels, especially in connection with tropical rain forests.

canopy feeding: 1) feeding in the canopy of the forest. 2) the specialised hunting method of the African Black Heron (*Egretta ardesiaca*), which holds its wings over its head like an umbrella to attract fish into the resulting shade.

canthaxanthin: a synthetic substance added to the food of some captive birds, e.g. flamingos (Phoenicopteridae) as a replacement for carotenoids in the natural diets, from which their plumage gets its pink colour.

cap: plumage on the top of the head, usually covering a greater area than the 'crown' and sharply demarcated in colour from the sides of the head; *cf.* hood.

capillariasis: disease caused by threadworms (*Capillaria*), 10-80 mm long, hair-like nematods endoparasitic in the alimentary canal.

capillary: pl. capillaries; (one of) the narrowest blood vessels; *cf.* artery, vein, venulus.

capital breeder: a migratory bird bringing along stores (body fat) in order to survive adverse condition on breeding ground and to initiate reproduction; *cf.* income breeder.

capital tract: the feather tract on the upper half of the head; *cf.* pterylography.

capon: a domestic cock castrated.

capped: an egg having most of its spotting on the large end.

caprimulgid: belonging to the nightjar family (Caprimulgidae).

Caprimulgiformes: order comprised of 12 species of frogmouths (Podargidae), the Oilbird (*Steatornis caripensis*), 7 species of potoos (Nyctibiidae), 89 species of nightjars (Caprimulgidae), and 9 species of owlet-nightjars (Aegothelidae).

capsizing: the enhancement of water in, e.g. a lake with nutrients such as nitrates, phosphates, and fertilizers resulting in an overproduction of algae that use so much oxygen that aerobic life dies out; also called eutrophication, overthrow, or tipping of balance.

capsule: a dry (capsular) fruit that releases its seeds along more than one suture when ripe.

caput humeri: apex of the upper arm bone, the proximal condyle of the humerus.

carapace: hard external chitinous covering, e.g. of beetles.

carbohydrates: one of the major classes of biochemical compounds, the others being proteins, fat, and nucleic acids. Carbohydrates are simple sugars such as glucose, or polymers such as starch and cellulose; *cf.* protein, vitamins.

Carboniferous: geological period approx. 360-290 million years BP in the Paleozoic era.

cardiac: relating to the heart.

cardiac muscle: a smooth muscle only found only in, and forming most of, the heart; *cf.* skeletal muscle, smooth muscle.

cardiac output: the amount of blood ejected from the ventricles during a given period, a measure of the performance of the heart.

cardiomyopathy: any disease occurring in or involving the heart muscle.

cardiovascular system: the heart and blood vessels.

caress feeding: courtship feeding.

carina: the keel of the breastbone. From Latin *carina*, meaning a keel of a ship.

carinate: having a keel on the breastbone, as almost all birds do except, e.g. ratites and kiwis.

carneus: Latin = fleshy.

carnivore: flesh-eater, e.g. falcons (Falconidae), adj. **canivorous**; *cf.* zoophagy.

Carnosaurs: a group of larger carnivorous, reptile-hipped theropods.

carotenoids: 1) a family of fat-soluble reddish or yellow pigments widely distributed in animals and plants, but exclusively of plant origin. Birds obtain carotenoids from their diets. Responsible for the red and orange colours of many feathers and bare parts, e.g. the wattles of some pheasants, and may give other colours when combined with other pigments such as melanin (bright green) or various other proteins (deep purple). Carotenoids may play an important role in immuno-regulation and detoxification, and evidence of their intensities may provide a signal used in mate selection. 2) each cone in a bird's retina contains a coloured oil droplet containing high concentrations of molecules called carotenoids, increasing the number of colours (e.g. ultraviolet) that a bird can see; *cf.* melanin, porphyrin, cones.

carotid artery: the chief artery serving the neck and head region; *cf.* jugular vein.

carpals: the bones of the wrist proximal to the fingers; in birds there are two proximal carpals, called ulnare and radiale, whereas the remaining metacarpals and distal carpals are fused into one bony element; *cf.* carpometacarpus.

carpal bar: a contrasting area just behind the leading edge of the wing.

carpal joint: the joint between the arm and the hand, also called **carpal wrist.**

carpal remex: in some birds, e.g. gulls (Laridae) and pheasants (Phasianidae), an extra, vestigial remex is found between primaries and secondaries with or without an attached covert.

carpal spur: a sharp, horn-covered bone on the carpal joint of screamers (Anhimidae), sheathbills (Chionidae), jacanas (Jacanidae), some ducks (Anatidae), and plovers (Charadriidae).

carpometacarpus: a large composite bone that supports the first (innermost) primaries; formed by the fusion of the first three metacarpals (the fourth and fifth being lost). Formerly thought to be metacarpals 2-3-4.

carposis: commensal relationship in which only one participant benefits, e.g. Tree Sparrows (*Passer montanus*) breeding in the nest of a Stork (*Ciconia ciconia*); *cf.* commensalism.

carpus: Latin = wrist.

carrier: a bird that has survived a disease but still carries the causal organism.

carrying capacity: the maximum number of an organism that can live in a given area on a sustained basis; may be used loosely or as a parameter in simple population models, usually denoted as K; *cf.* density dependence.

cartilage: skeletal connective tissue and the skeleton of an embryo before calcium is added, largely converted in adults to bone. A 'cartilage bone' can refer to any bone formed from cartilage but tends to be used in ornithology to denote an ossified tendon or the kneecap or patella; also called sesamoid bone.

caruncle: 1) comb, wattle, or lappet, i.e. a fleshy, naked, and often brightly coloured appendage on the head or neck of, e.g. Domestic Fowl (*Gallus domesticus*) and pheasants, turkeys, and vultures; Latin *caruncula*; *cf.* comb, dewlap, lappet, wattle. 2) caruncle is also sometimes used for the egg-tooth, which the chick uses to break through the shell at hatching.

casque: an enlargement on top of the upper mandible of certain hornbills (Bucerotidae), or on top of the head in cassowaries (Casuariidae) and some guineafowl (Numididae); *cf.* shield, frontal.

cast: pellet; a compact mass of regurgitated, indigestible, parts of the food; also called **casting** or pellet.

castanetting: an alarm behaviour involving the rapidly-repeated snapping of the mandibles together, to produce a sound similar to that made by castanets.

casual: a distributional qualifier indicating that a bird species occurs in an area more frequently than would an accidental or vagrant.

Casuariiformes: the order comprising three species of cassowaries, family (Casuariidae) and three species of Emus (Dromaiidae). Some authors include this in the Struthioniformes.

catabolites: waste products of metabolism, carried away by the circulatory system; **catabolism** (or katabolism) is the breaking down of chemical compounds in organisms, generally for release of energy; *cf.* anabolites.

catalepsy: the adoption of a motionless posture to avoid detection by predators, as seen, e.g. in bitterns (*Botaurus* spp.); also called akinesis.

Catamblyrhynchidae: a formerly recognized family for only the Plush-capped Finch (*Catamblyrhynchus diadema*), a species now included as *incertae sedis* in Thraupidae.

caterpillar: larval stage of a butterfly or moth (order Lepidoptera). The term is also sometimes used for larvae of other insects.

Cathartiformes: a sometimes recognized order comprising the New World vultures (Cathartidae), by some recognised as a family (Cathartidae) in the order of storks (Ciconiiformes).

caudal: pertaining to, or toward, the tail, Latin: *cauda* = tail. Also termed posterior.

caudal tract: the feather tract around the tail.

caudal vertebrae: the six tail vertebrae; *cf.* pygostyle.

Caudipteryx: a 120 mya old fossil enantiornithine or 'opposite' bird from China, possibly herbivorous because it carried grit in the gizzard.

caudo femoralis: 1) caudofemoralis: a muscle on the thigh. 2) the muscles on the tail vertebrae.

caval vein: a vein that carries blood from the posterior regions of the body to the right atrium of the heart. Also called vena cava.

cavity adopter: a bird breeding in a cavity that it has not created itself or that was created by natural circumstances such as decay. Also called secondary cavity nester.

cc: cubic centimetres, a volumetric measure at times used in connection with air movement within the bird.

CCAMLR: abbr.: Commission for the Conservation of Antarctic Marine Living Resources.

cecum: (pl.) ceca, Am. tubular, dead end appendage stemming from the lower intestine in birds, especially in terrestrial species. Usually paired, with one on each side of the lower intestine near the cloaca and varying in form from buds to long tubes. The function is still not fully understood, but in grouse it seems that the well-developed ceca enable bacterially-aided digestion of plant material. Also called colic ceca. In Europe called caecum (pl.) caeca.

celiac: the abdominal cavity; also spelled coeliac.

cell: the basic unit of all living organisms; each organism is comprised of one or more cells, each cell usually has a nucleus with chromosomes that carry the DNA (heritable genetic material). Latin *cella*.

Celsius: a thermometer measurement in common use. The Celsius scale has 0 degree Celsius as freezing point of water and boiling point at 100 degree Celsius. Conversion from Celsius (C) to Fahrenheit (F) is: F = 9C/5 + 32.

Cenozoic: the last era in the history of Earth, comprising two periods, the Tertiary beginning 65 million (M) years ago, and the Quaternary, covering the last c. two million years; *cf.* Mesozoic, Paleozoic.

census: a count of individuals of one or more species occurring over a specific time and space or place; e.g. counting individuals using one or several possible methods (mapping census, point count, line transect) to quantify the number of birds in an area or a colony; *cf.* Christmas Bird Count.

centipedes: Chilopoda, carnivorous arthropods with 15 to 190 body segments, each segment with a pair of legs; *cf.* millipedes.

central flyway: a term used among waterfowl biologists. In North America there are four general migration routes or corridors that waterfowl

follow; *cf.* Atlantic-, Misissippi-, and Pacific flyway.

central focusing: binoculars with a central wheel that focuses both sets of optics simultaneously.

central nervous system: abbr. CNS, the brain and spinal cord; *cf.* nervous system, peripheral nervous system, autonomic nervous system.

centrifugal: moving away from a central point or axis; used in biology to describe, e.g. the moult of the tail when it proceeds from the central rectrices outwards. Latin *centrifugus*. Opposite of centripetal.

centripetal: moving towards a centre; used in biology to describe, e.g. a moult sequence proceeding from two centres towards a central point, as occurring in the wings of many birds. Latin *centripetus*.

Centro Italiano Studi Ornitologici: The Italian ornithological society. Publishing: *Avocetta* since 1978.

centrum: the part of an avian vertebra that is connected to the next vertebra, the anterior end saddle-shaped, the posterior end rounded.

cephalic: pertaining to the head; also called **cephalon**.

ceratobranchial: the longest of the paired tongue bones; *cf.* basihyal, basibranchial, epibranchial.

cere: the naked, often brightly coloured and wax-like area around the nostrils at the base of the upper mandible of some birds, e.g. raptors (Falconiformes), pigeons (Columbiformes), and some parrots (Psittaciformes).

cerebellum: a deeply folded part of the hind-brain, important for balance and coordination of movements, but having many other functions as well. Also called metencephalon.

cerebral hemisphere: part of the forebrain and largest part of the bird brain. Its left side controls learning processes, the right side monitors the environment.

cerebrum: a collective term for the two cerebral hemispheres.

cerophagous: eating wax as part of the diet, occurring in, e.g. honeyguides (Indicatoridae), many storm-petrels (Hydrobatidae), and African bulbuls (Pycnonotidae); n. **cerophagy**.

cerrado: semi-xeric grassland, savanna, or woodland of interior southeastern South America.

cervical: referring to the neck. Cervical vertebrae in birds vary from 14 to 25.

cervical rib: referring to the pin-like rib on the posterior neck vertebra. Also called cervicodorsal vertebrae.

cervical sacs: a pair of air sacs lying between the neck and the anterior end of the lungs.

cervical vertebra: any of the vertebrae between the skull and the thorax, recognizable by not being connected to the breastbone by ribs.

cervicodorsal vertebrae: the paired moveable cervical ribs not articulated with the sternum. Also called cervical rib.

cervix: Latin = neck.

cestode: a parasitic flatworm of the class Cestoda, which includes the tapeworms. All are endoparasitic.

cet.: abbr. of the Latin *cetera* = the reminder or the rest.

cf.: abbr. of the Latin *confer* = compare. Also seen abbreviated *cfr.*

chain migration: migrating like links in a chain, one behind the other.

chalaza: pl. chalazae, two strings of albumen that anchor the yolk of an egg; *cf.* vitelline membrane.

Chalcopariidae: old name for Nectariniidae, the family of sunbirds.

Chamaeidae: the formerly recognized monotypic family for the Wren Tit (*Chamaea fasciata*), now placed in Timaliidae, the babblers.

chaparral: a woody shrub found along the California coast. One of the nine major communities (biomes) in North America, characterized by a Mediterranean climate and a vegetation of woody shrubs with evergreen leaves. Also called Mediterranean shrub.

character displacement: the enhancement of differences in, e.g. plumage, size, feeding behaviour, or song, of closely related species where they occur sympatrically, as compared to areas where only one of them occurs; assumed to result from the selective effects of interspecific competition. Bill size and shape in Darwin's finches is a classic example, but clear cases are few and the concept is in need of more research.

character divergence: divergence in a character between two closely related sympatric species due to the selective effects of competition.

Charadriiformes: order of shorebirds comprising 17 families: 9 species of thick-knees (Burhinidae), 3 species of sheathbills and allies (Chionidae), 11 species of oystercatchers (Haematopodidae), the Crab Plover (*Dromas ardeola*; Dromaiidae), the Ibisbill (*Ibidorhyncha struthersii;* Ibidorhynchidae), 7 species of stilts and avocets (Recurvirostridae), 66 species of plovers (Charadriidae), 2 species of painted-snipes (Rostratulidae), 8 species of jacanas (Jacanidae), the Plains Wanderer (*Pedionomus torquatus*; Pedionomidae), 4 species of seed-snipes (Thinocoridae), 92 species of sandpipers and snipes (Scolopacidae), 18 species of coursers and pratincoles (Glareolidae), 97 species of gulls and terns (Laridae), 7 species of skuas and jaegers (Stercorariidae), 24 species of auks (Alcidae), and 16 species of sandgrouse (Pteroclididae).

Chardonneret trap: a trap in which the entering bird triggers a trap-door release, often used on nest-boxes.

charging display: a type of display used in courtship, more generally termed epigamic display.

checkerboard distribution: zoogeography, where each of a group of islands is occupied by only one species of the various members of a polytypic genus.

checklist: a systematic and complete list of all birds found in a certain area or the whole world, usually with information on range. The checklist behind the present work is the third edition of the Howard & Moore checklist of the birds of the world, edited by E. C. Dickinson.

cheek: the lower side of the face, also called the malar region.

cheironym: an unpublished scientific name, also spelt chironym.

chemoreceptor: 1) a receptor cell that responds to chemical substances associated with smell, taste, and touch. 2) a cell that controls breathing by monitoring the levels of oxygen and carbon dioxide in the blood.

chest: another term for breast but not as commonly used in birds.

chevron: V-shaped contrasting mark.

chewing louse: pl. lice, also called feather or body louse of the family Mallophagidae, that live upon or within feathers and suck fluids from them and from skin. Feather damage by them may reduce winter survival in some birds because it increases heat loss. The lice act as a vector to a number of avian diseases.

chick: a rather vague term for a young bird, pullus, or nestling, sometimes applied only to young that leave the nest soon after hatching (precocial young); cf. chicken, cygnet, duckling, eyass, gosling, owlet, squab.

chigger: the larval form of a blood-sucking mite of the family Trombiculidae.

chilling: common term for a suite of undiagnosed ailments in birds, caused by stress, injury, exhaustion, starvation, cold, or other factors that may weaken a bird's resistance.

Chilopoda: the class of centipedes in the phylum Arthropoda.

chin: the area immediately below the base of the lower mandible.

Chionididae: synonym for Chionidae, the family of sheathbills.

chip-counting: an unreliable method of estimating numbers of nocturnally migrating birds by counting the calls given as birds fly overhead.

chipping: 1) a fine chirp or twitter; cf. clicking. 2) the start of the hatching of an egg when it gets its first cracks; cf. pipping.

chironym: an unpublished scientific name, also spelled cheironym.

Chi-squared test: any statistical test that involves the chi-squared probability distribution; typically comparing observed versus expected frequencies.

chitinous: made of or containing chitin, e.g. the external carapace of beetles is made of chitin.

chlamydiosis: a fatal world-wide bacterial disease among birds and mammals. Especially aviculturists who keep parrots (Psittacidae) are prone to this disease. It is an infection caused by *Chlamydia psittaci* transmitted through the air. The lungs are chiefly affected by pneumonia, but the liver and central nervous system can also be attacked. Also called psittacosis, parrot fever, or ornithosis.

chloroplast: the green organelle found in plants and algae in which the reactions of photosynthesis take place.

choana: the two internal nares that open inside the roof of the mouth (palate) with a single slit.

choosy sex: the sex that chooses a partner, usually the female, cf. chosen sex.

chord: the straight-line distance between the ends of an arc, commonly used as a wing length measure ('wing chord') taken on the partially folded wing from the carpal joint to the tip of the longest primary with the primaries in their naturally, curved shape; a variant term for this measure is 'minimum chord'. Rarer variants not technically accurate (because a true chord is no longer involved) are occasionally used: 1) the 'flattened chord', in which the wing is pressed flat against the ruler to flatten the natural arc in the primaries. 2) the 'maximum chord' or 'maximum wing length', in which the wing is pressed flat and the primaries straightened along the ruler, converting the arc of the primaries to the longest possible straight line.

Chordata: a phylum comprising all animals with a chorda and so including the vertebrates.

chorioallantois: a membrane complex inside a developing egg that combines the **chorion** (a protective membrane) and the allantoic sac (involved in respiration and waste retention), having the main function of respiration. The abbreviation has been in two ways: the choriallantoic membrane is often just chorioallantois or CAM; *cf.* cuticle, testa, amniotic sac.

chorion: an outer membrane in eggs surrounding the embryo, fused with an inner membrane allantois (allantoic), together called the **chorioallantoic membrane**.

choroid: the dark middle layer of the wall of the eye, between the sclera and retina; one of three parts of the vascular layer called the tunica vasculosa bulbi. Also called **choroidea**.

chorusing: a group of individuals singing together.

chosen sex: among birds usually the male; *cf.* choosy sex.

Christmas Bird Count: an annual bird count in USA made in late December – early January and conducted each year since 1900. It is organized by the National Audubon Society under strict rules, wherein special reporting forms are mandatory and participants must pay a fee for later analysis and publication; *cf.* Breeding Bird Survey.

chromatic aberration: optical deficiency of some binoculars or telescopes that causes a 'rainbow effect' around back-lit dark objects.

chromatid: one of the two genetically identical chromosome strands.

chromatin: the nucleoproteins of chromosomes.

chromatography: a technique to separate the molecules or ions in a mixture.

chromatophore: a pigment-bearing cell.

chromomeres: chromatin granules arranged linearly along a chromosome, which, when stained, give the chromosome a banded appearance.

chromosomes: small bodies of protein and DNA that carry the genes arranged linearly; a full set of chromosomes are contained in the nucleus of each organismal cell. Each species can have different numbers of chromosomes, e.g. humans 46.

chronic: of long or permanent duration, for example of disease, in contrast to acute.

chronism: the behaviour of parents that, when food is short, kill (and sometimes eat) one or more of their own offspring, found, e.g. in the Stork (*Ciconia ciconia*).

chronocline: a gradual change in characters over time.

chronospecies: a species that is represented in more than one geological age.

churring: a deep and continuous sound given by, e.g. a Nightjar (*Caprimulgus europaeus*); *cf.* reeling.

chyme: the partly digested food leaving the gizzard.

Ciconiiformes: order with three families: 19 species of storks (Ciconiidae),

32 species of ibises and spoonbills (Threskiornithidae), and 65 species of herons, bitterns, and egrets (Ardeidae). Molecular studies place the Hammerkop (*Scopus umbretta*) and Shoebill (*Balaeniceps rex*) in the Pelecaniformes.

ciliary body: muscles around the lens in the eye of a bird that hold the lens in place. Also called **ciliary processes**.

cilium: pl. cilia, 1) 'eyelashes' of tiny bristles. 2) hair-like outgrowth on the dorsal surface of the inner vane of flight feathers that reduce flight noise, found, e.g. in owls (Strigidae). 3) rarely used as syn. for barbicels.

cimicid bug: an ectoparasite of the family Cimicidae, order Hemiptera, belonging to a large insect group related to the bedbug. Sucks blood from birds.

Cinclus: periodical published by Norsk Ornitologisk Forening: abbr. NOF. Published only for 1978; thereafter called *Fauna Norvegica, Ser. C. Cinclus*. Also a genus of dippers.

circadian rhythm: from Latin: *circa* = about, and *dies* = day; a biological clock following a cycle of about 24 hrs. in the absence of external stimuli; also called diurnal rhythm or daily periodicity; *cf.* Zeitgeber, circannual rhythms, biological clock.

circannual: around the year.

circannual rhythm: endogenous rhythm of approx. one year's duration, controlling breeding, moult, and migration. Also called **circannual cycle**; *cf.* circadian rhythm.

circle soaring: soaring in circles to gain height in thermals.

circulatory system: syn. for the blood-vascular system, transporting food and oxygen to the cells and removing waste products; another circulatory system is the lymphatic system. Also called vascular system. See: aorta, artery, caval vein, heart, pulmonary circulation, systemic circulation, vein, ventricle, capillary atrium.

circumorbital: around the eye.

circumpolar: distributed around the pole of either hemisphere.

cit: abbr. of Latin *citatus*, meaning to cite or cited.

CITES: abbr. Convention on International Trade in Endangered Species, an international convention regulating the import and export of rare and endangered animals and plants. Came into force in 1975. Also known as the Washington Convention.

clade: a group of species including all descendants from a common ancestor and therefore constituting a monophyletic group.

cladism: the philosophy and methods applied by many scientists studying phylogenetic relationships, characterized by working with monophyletic groups and by focusing on branching patterns, elucidated from distributions of shared derived characters; *cf.* cladistic method.

cladistic biogeography: phylogenetic method of reconstructing the evolutionary history of lineages to understand the distribution of taxa.

cladistic method: a method in systematics of grouping organisms using phylogenetic hypotheses and recency of common ancestry to reconstruct relationships and based on carefully determined states of homologous characters; results usually depicted by branching diagrams (trees or cladograms); *cf.* clade, derived character, homologous characters, phenetic taxonomy.

cladogenesis: generation of new lineages through divergence.

cladogram: a branching diagram or an evolutionary tree, depicting relationships among lineages, obtained through cladistic or other systematic analysis; *cf.* rooted cladogram.

clap net: a small net that can be propelled over a bird attracted to bait or coming to its nest.

clappering: the production of mechanical sounds in storks (*Ciconia* spp.) by clapping the upper and lower bills together.

class: systematic unit below a phylum and above an order. In traditional classifications birds form their own class, Aves.

classification: the method of grouping taxa into a system based on phylogenetic relationships, which are often determined through sophisticated systematic study; *cf.* evolutionary systematics, phylogenetic systematics, taxonomy.

clavicle: collar bone, paired elements of the shoulder girdle in most vertebrates but in birds fused into a single bone, the wishbone or furcula, which acts like a spring during flight and in this way aids the energetics of flight. Missing or little developed in kiwis (Apterygidae) and some parrots (Psittacidae). Latin *clavicula*; *cf.* hypocleidium.

clavicular air sac: thin-walled sacs along the neck that are part of the respiratory system, *cf.* air sacs.

claviculo-coracoid fat mass: a bad term for furcula fat; *cf.* fat index.

claw: the horny appendage at the tips of the toes of all birds and of the fingers of a few, e.g. the Hoatzin chick (*Opisthocomus hoazin*).

cleaning symbiosis: relationship between two species wherein one feeds on the ectoparasites of the other, e.g. the African oxpeckers (*Buphagus* spp.) feeding on ungulates.

cleidoic: having eggs, including avian ones, enclosed in a protective shell or membrane that limits the exchange of water, gases, etc.

clicking: the noise made by an embryo in an egg from the moment it starts to breathe.

climatic rules: see Allen's Rule, Bergmann's Rule, Gloger's Rule.

climax: applied to a biological community when it has achieved a stable state in equilibrium with local conditions, considered the terminus of the process of ecological succession; in restoration, when a destroyed area is totally re-established with the optimal vegetation for the climate and soil; *cf.* ecological succession.

climax community: an ecosystem that can perpetuate itself, i.e. in equilibrium; *cf.* ecological succession.

cline: a gradual change of a species' characters across geographic areas; **clinal variation**; *cf.* deme, subspecies, Allen's Rule, Bergmann's Rule, Gloger's Rule.

clipping: cutting of the primaries of captive birds to prevent them from flying. Also termed brailing; *cf.* pinioning.

cloaca: pl. cloacae, a chamber in the lowest part of the gut into which nitrogenous waste and faeces as well as eggs or sperm are voided, and which is emptied through the vent. The cloaca has three compartments: coprodeum, urodeum, proctodeum.

cloacal bursa: a gland on the dorsal wall of the cloaca, at its junction with the vent, present in young birds only and the secretions of which stimulate the immune system. Also called bursa Fabricii or bursa of Fabricius.

cloacal aperture: the distal opening of the cloaca; also called vent.

cloacal protuberance: a bulbous appendage at the cloacal region visible in many passerines in the breeding season. Becomes developed in males (females have a smaller tapering off gradually to the vent), often making it possible to determine the sex of live birds. Its function is primarily to store spermatozoa; *cf.* seminal sac, vas deferens.

close ringing: in aviculture, the ringing of the tarsometatarsus of a young bird with a 'closed' ring too small to slip from its foot when full-grown.

closed season: the protected season for any hunted species.

cloud forest: montane forest situated between an elevation of 1,000 and 2,500m or even higher shrouded in fog most of the time. Mosses, ferns, and epiphytic growth predominate on and among the trees.

club: a gathering of non-breeding seabirds at the periphery of a breeding colony.

clumping: sitting so close together that individual birds are in physical contact.

cluster analysis: a method of constructing branching diagrams (dendrograms) to express overall similarities (or differences) among individuals in a set of samples.

clustered distribution: clumped distribution of individuals.

clutch: a complete set of eggs laid by a single female for reproductive effort.

clutch parasitism: a rare synonym for nest or brood parasitism.

CMS: abbr. Convention on the Conservation of Migratory Species of Wild Animals. Also called Bonn Convention.

cnemial crest: a crest (muscle attachment) on the front of the proximal end of the tibiotarsus, especially large in some diving birds, e.g. divers (Gaviiformes).

CNS: abbr. of central nervous system, the brain and spinal cord; *cf.* peripheral nervous system.

coalescent analysis: analyses focusing on the coalescent properties of DNA evolution between lineages in reverse, whereby common ancestry between two divergent lineages is the coalescent when looking backwards in evolutionary time.

coastal species: species depending heavily on land and rarely seen far from coastal areas, such as many pelicans (Pelecanidae) and gulls (Laridae); *cf.* pelagic.

coax: Latin = hip.

cob: a term for a male Mute Swan (*Cygnus olor*), the female being the 'pen'.

cobweb: a spider web, especially of small spiders.

coccidias: protozoan endoparasites, to which belong the well-known malaria parasite (*Plasmodium*). Some species are serious parasites in birds.

coccidiosis: disease caused by coccidians (*Eimeria, Isospora*) infecting the intestinal epithelium and giving rise to diarrhoea with bloody feces. It is pathogenic for goslings.

coccygeal: the place from which the nerve fibres run to the tail.

coccyx: terminal bone of the tail; pygostyle or pygostylus.

cochlea: the fluid-filled inner ear that transforms sound-wave stimuli into nerve impulses. (Latin *cochlea* = snail curled like a snail's shell in mammals but not in birds); *cf.* columella.

Cochleariidae: once the monotypic family for the Boat-billed Heron (*Cochlearius cochlearius*) now usually included in the heron family (Ardeidae).

cock: the male of the domestic fowl (*Gallus domesticus*) and other gallinaceous birds, sometimes applied to males of other groups.

Code, the: for short the International Code of Zoological Nomenclature abbr. ICZN.

coefficient of variation: the standard deviation x 100 divided by the sample mean.

coeliac: of or relating to the abdomen also spelled celiac.

Coelurosaurs: 'advanced', reptile-hipped, carnivorous dinosaurs (theropods), from the Jurassic and Cretaceous periods; as defined today, the group includes the maniraptorans and hence the only surviving dinosaurs, the birds. Formerly the term was used for a variety of small dinosaurs, including a number of Triassic forms.

coevolution: concurrent evolution of ecologically connected species, for example a predator and its prey, a pollinator and its flowering plant, or a brood parasite and its host.

cognition: includes perception, learning, memory, and decision making, all ways in which animals take in information and retain and decide to act upon it.

cognitive map: a mental map, the concept that migrating birds build their own map of the migration route based upon their experience.

cohesion species concept: a species concept emphasizing factors ('cohesion mechanisms') that keep genetic groups (species) together, as opposed to the emphasis on isolating mechanisms of the biological species concept; *cf.* recognition species concept and phylogenetic species concept.

cohort: 1) a group of birds of the same age (born in the same year). 2) systematic unit between subclass and superorder.

cold-blooded: having a body temperature determined primarily by the temperature of the environment, as opposed to endothermic. Also called ectothermic, poikilothermic.

Coleoptera: the order of beetles within the class Insecta.

colic ceca: Am., tubular, dead-end, appendage stemming from the lower intestine in birds, especially in terrestrial species. Usually paired, with one on each side of the lower intestine near the cloaca and varying in form from buds to long tubes. The function is still not fully understood, but in grouse it seems that the well-developed caeca enable bacterially aided digestion of plant material. Also called cecum, pl. ceca, in Europe caecum, pl. caeca.

colies: another name for mousebirds (Coliidae).

Coliiformes: an order containing a single family, the 6 species of mousebirds (Coliidae).

collar: 1) a band of contrasting colour around the neck; complete or partial. 2) an epidermal collar in a feather follicle responsible for the growth of the feathers.

collar bone: clavicle, paired elements of the shoulder (pectoral) girdle in most vertebrates but in birds fused into a single bone to form the wishbone or furcula. Missing or little developed in kiwis (Apterygidae) and some parrots (Psittacidae). Latin *clavicula*; *cf.* hypocleidium.

collision accident: the collision of a bird with a window, a vehicle, or some other man-made obstacle, usually injuring or killing the bird; *cf.* bird strike.

collum: Latin meaning neck, pl. *colli*.

colon: the part of the intestine in most birds between the caecae and the cloaca, also called large intestine or rectum.

coloniality: dense nesting within limited territories, opposite dispersed breeding.

colony: breeding assemblage of several pairs of a species in a limited area, where only the nest and its immediate surroundings are defended against other individuals.

coloration abnormal: see: albinism, partial albinism, leucism, melanism, schizochroism, lutinous, flavism, erythrism, gynandromorph.

colour: Am. **color**, the spectral composition of light as perceived by the eye.

colour dyeing: marking of birds by painting part of the plumage to permit recognition even at some distance.

colour morph: one of the plumage types in a species that is polymorphic in some plumage trait, independent of sex, age, or season; well-known examples of dimorphic species are Arctic and Pomarine skuas (*Stercorarius parasiticus* and *pomarinus*), Tawny Owl *Strix aluco*), and many others; sometimes called **colour phase**. Dichromatic is mainly used of sexual differences in colour.

colour ringing: the marking of birds with coloured leg and/or rings of plastic or metal, permitting individual identification usually for scientific purposes.

Columbiformes: the order of pigeons and doves comprising 308 species in the single family Columbidae. Even the extinct Dodos (*Raphus cucullatus* and *R. solitarius*) and the Solitaire (*Pezophaps solitaria*) are now also included in this order.

columella auris: the single bone in the inner ear of birds. Also called stapes.

coly: alternative name for a mousebird (Coliidae).

Colymbidae: synonym for Gaviidae the family of divers.

comb: the fleshy, naked, and often brightly coloured protuberance on the top of the head of male domestic fowl, or the naked patches over the eyes of some grouse (Tetraonidae); *cf.* caruncle, casque, dewlap, lappet, wattle.

comfort behaviour: behaviour that appears to increase the physical comfort of the performer, such as preening, oiling, head-scratching, bathing, dust and sun bathing, stretching, and shaking; *cf.* maintenance activity.

commensal: literally a table-sharer, a species that benefits food-wise from another species through participation in a commensal relationship; *cf.* carposis, symbiosis, epizoic, mutualism, and parasitism.

commensalism: symbiotic relationship in which one species benefits from a common food supply with another without unduly affecting the other species, e.g. vultures (Falconiformes) on a carcass from which the Lammergeier (*Gypaetus barbatus*) is able to obtain its specific food through the activities of the other vulture species, i.e. the bones; *cf.* mutualism.

Commission for the Conservation of Antarctic Marine Living Resources: a commission that works under conservation principles laid down in a convention ratified in 1982. Conservation measures adopted by CCAMLR are based on scientific advice and require enforcement to be effective.

commissura: Latin = joining together.

commissure: 1) the angle at which the two mandibles meet. More commonly called gape. 2) a band of nerve fibers.

Common Bird Census: a program developed by the British Trust for Ornithology and aiming at censusing breeding birds by use of the spot-mapping method.

common name: the popular name, as opposed to the scientific name. Also called vernacular name.

communal breeding: breeding in a group containing more than one male and one female, all reproducing sharing the same nest. Cases in which more than two individuals provide care to a single brood of offspring. Non-breeding birds, in this context called helpers and very often siblings from the last brood, assist in territory defence, nest building, and the rearing of the nestlings. Occurs in, e.g. Ostrich (*Struthio camelus*), Magpie Goose (*Anseranas semipalmata*), Hammerkop (*Scopus umbretta*), Eclectus Parrot (*Eclectus roratus*), Hoatzin (*Opisthocomus hoatzin*), anis (*Crotophaga* spp.), bee-eaters (Meropidae), kingfishers (Alcedinidae), wood hoopoes (Phoeniculidae), hornbills (Bucerotidae), honeyeaters (Meliphagidae), babblers (Timaliidae), fairy-wrens (Maluridae), Long-tailed Tit (*Aegithalos caudatus*), etc. Also called cooperative breeding.

communal laying: laying by more than one female in a single nest, often followed by shared incubation and caring for the nestlings; known in anis (*Crotophaga* spp.).

communal roost: a gathering of birds to spend the night together, as seen e.g. in Starlings (*Sturnus vulgaris*).

community: the coexistence and interaction of multiple species.

comparative morphology: the study of structural similarities and differences.

compass orientation: 1) orientation according to a compass direction; most birds appear to have an innate ability to orient their flight direction, and experienced individuals often have additional skills permitting them to navigate between familiar sites, also called directional orientation; *cf.* goal orientation, sonar orientation, visual or parallactic orientation, piloting. 2) also applied to the orientation of bower structures built by male bowerbirds (Ptilonorhynchidae).

compensatory: generally applied to factors causing mortality in a population and inferring an inverse relationship among these factors as all sources of mortality reduce a population to its carrying capacity, e.g. if predators did not remove prey from a population above its carrying capacity, individuals would die instead from factors such as starvation, parasites, or disease.

competition parapatry: competition between two species with nearly or completely identical ecological requirements and living in adjoining areas (parapatric), but with no hybridization; *cf.* ecological parapatry, hybridization parapatry, ecological replacement.

competitive exclusion: exclusion of one species by another from an area, because both species have similar requirements for some resource(s), and one has a competitive advantage over the other.

complete migrant: a species or population in which all individuals migrate, also termed obligate migrant; *cf.* irruptive migrant, partial migrant.

complete moult: a moult in which all feathers are replaced, with the occasional exception of a few contour feathers.

complex: in systematics often applied when there is some doubt about the interrelationships of the considered groups or species.

compressed: flattened from side to side.

compromise behaviour: also called ambivalent behaviour, a behaviour that is the outcome of two incompatible motivations, e.g. to flee or attack; *cf.* displacement behaviour.

Compsognathus: a small theropod dinosaur, known from a single fossil specimen that for many years was misidentified as an *Archaeopteryx*.

concave: having an outline curved inward, like the inside edge of a circle; *cf.* convex.

concha: 1) cavity of the external ear. 2) two scroll-like conchae in the nasal cavity; *cf.* septum.

conditioning: mainly used in connection with experimental learning, when a bird learns to associate a particular stimulus, e.g. a sound, with something else, e.g. the location of food.

Condor, The: an American journal published by the Cooper Ornithological Society since 1900.

condyle: a round knob at the end of a bone that fits into a socket of an adjacent bone. Latin *condylus*.

cones: cone-shaped light receptor cells of the retina sensitive only to high levels of stimulation and responsible for colour vision; most birds have both cones and rods, but rods are greatly reduced in diurnal birds; a Common Buzzard (*Buteo buteo*), for example, has one million cones per square millimetre. Latin *conus*; *cf.* rod, dichromatism, trichromatism, tetrachromatism, scotopic vision, photopic vision, fovea.

confidence interval: in statistical analysis an interval encompassing the true – but unknown – mean with a preset high probability (often 95%). The endpoints of the interval are the **confidence limits**.

confluent: flowing together.

conforming overlap: the pattern in which the greater wing coverts on both over- and under-wing overlap in the same way as the primaries and secondaries overlap, the opposite of contrary overlap.

Confuciusornis: the earliest known toothless bird, from the Jurassic-Cretaceous. Discovered in China.

congeneric: belonging to the same genus; **congener**; *cf.* conspecific.

congestion: a vague term for many differing types of respiratory distress in aviculture.

Coniferous Forest Biome: one of North America's nine ecological divisions or biotic communities mostly in southern Canada in a broad belt from west to east and dominated by spruce and fir.

coniform: pear-shaped, as the egg of a sandpiper, also called pyriform.

cons.: abbr. of the Latin *conservandum* = to be conserved; e.g. conserved name = *nomen conservandum*.

conservative character: a character that does not change much or at all in evolutionary time, e.g. the palate, form of nostrils, syrinx, pelvis, toes, and scales on the tarsus. Such characters are important as indicators of relationships among orders and families.

conspecific: belonging to the same species; *cf.* congeneric.

conspecific brood parasitism: laying of eggs in the nests of other members of the same species and leaving those others to raise the young; *cf.* interspecific brood parasitism.

constrictor: a muscle that compresses an organ or decreases the size of a cavity or opening.

consummatory act: the final act in an instinctive behaviour pattern or sequence.

contact call: a simple call used for keeping contact within the flock or pair.

contact species: applied to birds of species that, when resting, tend to have bodily contact, such as most parrots (Psittacidae), mousebirds (Coliidae), and white-eyes (Zosteropidae); the opposite are birds that maintain an individual distance.

contagious diseases: a common term for disease caused by fungi, bacteria, rickettsiae, and viruses spread through physical contact.

contest competition: 1) rivalry for a resource in which the winner denies the looser access. 2) competition for a resource that is not limited; *cf.* exploitation competition, interference competition.

continental drift: the tectonic movement of continental plates through geological time, causing the continents to move; formerly all continents were united during part of the

Permian-Triassic, 260-225 mya; *cf.* Gondwanaland, Laurasia, Pangaea.

continental shelf: area of shallow water surrounding continents and islands, at most a few hundred meters deep, as opposed to the 3-5 km deep ocean basins.

continental slope: the edge of a continental shelf where the sea bottom slopes down to the deeps of the ocean basin.

continuous step-wise moult: a type of moult in which during any month of the year there are some feathers in moult; *cf.* staffelmauser, transilient moult, or serially descendent moult.

contour feather: any feather with a closed vane, although some authors exclude wing and tail feathers (remiges and rectrices). Sometimes also called **contour plumage** or body feathers; *cf.* down, downy feather, semiplume feather.

contrary overlap: the pattern in which the greater wing coverts on both upper- and under-wing overlap in the opposite way to the primaries and secondaries, the opposite of conforming overlap.

control group: in a scientific study birds are often divided into two groups, one group on which the experiments are conducted and another group that is not experimented upon, the latter being called the control group.

controlled rest-phase hypothermia: a term for a shallow hypothermia, during which the body temperature is reduced by < 10° C below normal. Also termed rest-phase hypothermia.

Convention on International Trade in Endangered Species: abbr.: CITES. An international organisation regulating the import and export of rare and endangered plants and animals. Came into force in 1975. Also known as The Washington Convention.

Convention on the Conservation of Migratory Species of Wild Animals: abbr.: 'CMS', aims to conserve terrestrial, marine, and avian migratory species throughout their ranges. Also called Bonn Convention.

convergent evolution: the independent evolution of similar traits in different lineages, as a result of adaptations to similar foods, life styles, etc. Examples include striking plumage similarities in the American meadowlarks (*Sturnella*) and the African longclaws (*Macronyx*), the former belonging to the family of American blackbirds (Icteridae) and the latter to the family of pipits and wagtails (Motacillidae). Also called parallel evolution, homoplasy, opposite divergent evolution; *cf.* parallelism.

convex: an outwardly curved surface, like the outside edge of a circle; *cf.* concave.

convexus: Latin = rounded.

cooing ground: used to describe the courting ground of some American grouse (Phasianidae).

cooperative breeding: cases in which more than two individuals provide care to a single brood of offspring. Non-breeding birds, in this context called helpers and very often siblings from the last brood, assist in territory defence, nest building, and the rearing of the nestlings. Occurs in, e.g. Ostrich (*Struthio camelus*), Magpie Goose (*Anseranas semipalmate*), Hammerkop (*Scopus umbretta*), Eclectus Parrot (*Eclectus roratus*), Hoatzin (*Opisthocomus hoatzin*), anis (*Crotophaga* spp.), bee-eaters (Meropidae), kingfishers (Alcedinidae), wood hoopoes (Phoeniculidae), hornbills (Bucerotidae), honeyeaters (Meliphagidae), babblers (Timaliidae), fairy-wrens (Maluridae), Long-tailed Tit (*Aegithalos caudatus*), etc. Also called communal breeding.

cooperative interaction: defines interactions between individuals in which there are reciprocal benefits, as opposed to antagonistic interaction.

cooperative monogamy: a reproductive system in which but one pair within a larger group mate at a given time. e.g. as in Acorn Woodpeckers (*Melanerpes formicivorus*).

cooperative polyandry: cases in which a female lays her eggs in a nest and more than one male, with whom she has mated, helps her with the reproductive duties. Found in some Antarctic skuas (Stercorariidae).

cooperative polygamy: cases in which more than two members of a group copulate and contribute to the clutch. Found in, e.g. Smith's Longspurs (*Calcarius pictus*).

Cooper Ornithological Society The: American society that publishes *The Condor* (from 1900-present, formerly *Bulletin of the Cooper Club*, 1899), *Pacific Coast Avifauna* (1900-1974), and *Studies in Avian Biology* (1978-present).

co-ordinate: 1) in taxonomy meaning 'of equal nomenclatural status'. 2) a system such as latitude and longitude used to locate and define a geographic position.

coprodeum: the innermost part of the cloaca; *cf.* urodeum, proctodeum.

coprophagy: the eating of faeces, as when shearwaters (Procellariidae) eat whale feaces; adj. **coprophagous**. Used of an animal that feeds on faeces.

coproporphyrin III: a pink pigment, found in the feathers of some bustards (Otididae) and owls (Strigidae).

copulation: the sex act; syn. with coitus.

Coraciiformes: an order comprising 12 species of rollers (Coraciidae), 5 species of ground rollers (Brachypteraciidae), the Cuckoo-Roller (*Leptosomus discolor, incertae cedis*, Leptosomatidae), 91 species of kingfishers (Alcedinidae), 5 species of todies (Todidae), 10 species of motmots (Momotidae), 25 species of bee-eaters (Meropidae), the Hoopoe (*Upupa epops*), 8 species of wood hoopoes (Phoeniculidae), 49 species of hornbills (Bucerotidae), and 2 ground hornbills (Bucorvidae).

coracoid: the largest and strongest paired element of the shoulder girdle (pectoral girdle) of birds, between the breastbone and the shoulder joint. Latin *coracicus.*

coracoidal facets: the smooth-faced grooves at the anterior end of the sternum where the posterior end of each coracoid is connected.

corcoracids: a common name for the Australian mudnesters, comprising the White-winged Chough (*Corcorax melanorhamphos*) and the Apostlebird (*Struthidea cinerea*).

cordillera: a mountain system, including all of its features.

core area: 1) an area with relatively high species richness and endemism. 2) the part of the home range of a species in which it spends most of its time. Core means the central or inner part.

Corcoracidae: synonym for Grallina, the genus of magpie-larks within the family Monarchidae.

Corella: periodical for The Australian Bird Study Association.

coriolis force: a force resulting from the fact that the Earth is not stationary but rotates.

corium: the inner layer of the skin (dermis).

cornea: the transparent front of the eye that refracts light through the pupil to the lens and from there onto the retina at the back of the eye.

corneous sheath: the horny substance covering the bill. Also termed rhamphotheca, or rhinotheca for the maxillar and gnathotheca for the lower mandible.

corneus: Latin = of a horny substance.

corniplume: the 'horns' of feathers on the top of the head, e.g. of many owls (Strigidae).

corona: Latin = the crown.

coronal stripe: a streak on the crown running from the front to the nape; lateral coronal stripes are on both sides of the mid-crown, a mesial coronal stripe runs along the midline.

coronary arteries: vessels providing the heart's own blood supply.

corpus: Latin = body.

corpuscles: syn. with blood cells.

corpus striatum: part of the forebrain, consisting of hyperstriatum and neostriatum, controlling eating, eye, movements, song, and breeding.

corr.: abbr. of the Latin *correctus* = corrected (by).

correlation: a measure of the correspondence between two attributes, for example wing length and weight, or age and brood size.

corridor: 1) a constricted portion of a migratory route, or a fairly well-defined (narrow) path of migration, examples being at the Bosporus and Israel. 2) a spatial linkage that facilitates movements between habitat patches or – on a large scale and in a 'historical' perspective – between geographical areas.

cortex: the outer layer of something, for example 1) the outer layer of the brain. 2) the outer layer of a barb in a feather.

corticosterone: a steroid hormone produced in the adrenal glands and released to the blood in stressful situations, but also when adult birds have to cope with different energetic constraints such as breeding. However, its main function is in the control of metabolism.

cortisone: a hormone from the adrenal glands regulating blood sugar levels and liver sugar metabolism.

corvid: any member of the crow family (Corvidae).

Corvoidea: a superfamily comprising Australian robins (Petroicidae), logrunners (Orthonychidae), the Australian babblers (Pomatostomidae), and crows (Corvidae), birds of paradise (Paradisaeidae), woodswallows (Artamidae), the magpie larks (Grallina), butcherbirds (Cracticidae), whistlers (Pachycephalidae), and shrike-thrushes (Colluricinclidae).

cosmopolitan: worldwide (distribution).

costal: referring to the ribs or rib cage. Latin *costa*.

costal facets: the small pits on the lateral edges of the sternum where the ribs attach.

cotype: an outdated name for syntype. In taxonomy when a new species or subspecies is described on the basis of a voucher specimen, the term syntype is used for each specimen in the type series if no holotype has been designated; *cf.* holotype.

counteradaptation: if a species is, e.g. heavily parasitized, it will develop an aversion behaviour; this is to counteradapt; an adaptive response that is a reaction to the enhanced adaptive performance of a predator or parasite.

countercurrent exchange: exchange of matter (soluble) or energy (heat) between fluids flowing in opposite directions in adjacent, parallel pipes. May be surprisingly efficient. The principle has found many technical applications but is also well known in living organisms. Examples in birds are the exchange of gases between air and blood in the avian lung and the arrangement of vessels in the legs (the *rete mirabile*) that permits prevent cooling of the blood flowing to the feet and hence limits heat loss to the surrounding environment.

countercurrent heat exchange system: a heat-saving system in which in cold weather the arterial blood running to the legs, with the help of a sphincter muscle, can be directed into a network of small vessels intertwined with the backward-running veins and where heat exchange can thus occur. In this way the blood going to the legs is cooled, and the blood running back to the body is warmed.

countershading: a camouflage pattern in which the underparts are paler than the upperparts, thus reducing the shadow effect and making birds less visible to potential predators; also called obliterative shading.

counter-singing: duetting between male and female or, in rivalry, between two males; *cf.* antiphonal song, duetting.

court: 1) a small patch of ground often cleared of litter and debris and defended by a single male on a communal display ground. 2) the cleared terrestrial area of a male bowerbird (Ptilonorhynchidae); *cf.* hills, lek.

courting nest: some male wrens (Troglodytidae) build more nests on their territory to attract a female, and she chooses and adds lining to the one she considers the best.

courtship: any activity performed with the objective of forming or maintaining a pair bond, often involving displays or acoustical signals. Ritualised courtship displays tend to differ between related species and probably often serve as isolating mechanisms. Many courtship displays apparently originated from displacement activities, intension movements, or agonistic behaviours, which are types of behaviour exhibited in contexts completely unrelated to courtship.

courtship feeding: feeding of the female by the male in a mated pair of birds during the pre-laying and laying periods (sometimes even later during the breeding cycle). Occurs in a large number of bird species and may significantly add to the nutrition of the female during egg formation.

covariation: applied to attributes that vary together; *cf.* correlation.

covariance analysis: in statistics, normally called analysis of covariance. Testing of a dependent variable for homogeneity among group means (as in ANOVA) when groups differ in the independent variable (the 'covariate'); abbr. ANCOVA.

coverts: feathers covering the base of flight and tail feathers, both on the upper- and underside; see also ear coverts.

covey: a flock of quail, partridge, or other terrestrial game birds.

cracid: any member of the family of currasows, guans, and chachalacas (Cracidae).

cracticid: any member of the family of butcherbirds, Australian magpies, and currawongs (Cracticidae), all endemic to Australasia.

Crampton's muscle: a muscle that can change the curvature of the cornea in the avian eye; *cf.* Brucke's muscle.

cranial: pertaining to the head, or in the direction of the head; Latin *cranialis*; also called anterior, rostral (from Latin *rostralis*), or cephalica.

cranial kinesis: the ability to move the upper mandible; *cf.* hinge.

craniofacial hinge: the connection between upper bill and forehead, more or less flexible in most birds so that they may lift the upper bill to some extent, most flexible in parrots (Psittacidae). Also called hinge frontonasal or naso-frontal hinge.

cranium: the bones that enclose the brain, which are fused in birds; by many authors used synonymously with skull.

crash: a precipitous decline of a population.

crèche: a 'nursery' for mobile chicks such as those of the Common Eide

(*Somateria mollissima*) and some or all species of boobies (Sulidae), penguins (Spheniscidae), pelicans (Pelicanidae), flamingos (Phoenicopteridae), and terns (Sternidae); also called nursery group; **crèching behaviour.**

creek: 1) bay. 2) Am. and Australian a brook or stream.

crepuscular habits: active at dawn and dusk, rather than in full darkness or daylight; *cf.* nocturnal, diurnal.

crest: group of elongated feathers on the crown of a bird's head; may be raised depending on species; no sharp distinction from a tuft.

Cretaceous: the last period of the Mesozoic era, 144-65 million years BP, at the end of which all non-avian dinosaurs disappeared. The epoch is divided into Early Cretaceous 146-98 million years BP and Late Cretaceous 97-65 million years BP.

cricket: grasshopper-like insects of the order Orthoptera.

crippled-bird act: a distraction behaviour seen in some ground-nesting birds, in which the bird leads a predator away from the eggs or chicks by acting sick and unable to fly. Also called broken-wing display or trick, or injury feigning; *cf.* diversionary display.

crissum: undertail coverts, especially when these are distinctively coloured, and the area around the vent.

crista: Latin = comb, crest.

critical: a criterion used by BirdLife International for a species showing a reduction of population of more than 80% over the last ten years or in three generations.

critical period: 1) a term for the period in which a chick can be imprinted, the period of susceptibility. Also called sensitive phase or period. 2) used for any critical period, moulting time, hunting time etc.

cronistic behaviour: Am. kronistic, eating one's own dead or moribund nestlings; **cronism.**

crop: a thin-walled, often bi-lobed dilatation of the upper food canal (oesophagus) found in many birds, used for temporary storage of food before it is passed on to the stomach, or while it is being transported; also called ingluvies; *cf.* sublingual pouch.

crop milk: a secretion from the crop of pigeons (Columbidae), the Emperor Penguin (*Aptenodytes fosteri*), and the Greater Flamingo (*Phoenicopterus rubber*), with which their chicks are fed. Also termed pigeon milk.

crop worm: a roundworm (nematode) *Capillaria contorda* whose larvae can block the trachea and cause the death of infested birds.

cross: a hybrid between two different species, subspecies, or genotypes.

cross-fostering: raising chicks of one species by foster parents of another species, used as a technique to study inherited and learned behaviour, or to bring a species back from the brink of extinction; an example of the latter was the Black Robin (*Petroica traversi*).

crow's beak bone: syn. with coracoid.

crowing: the call of a male chicken (*Gallus gallus*) or Ring-necked Pheasant (*Phasianus colchicus*).

crowing area: Am. term for the defended territory of the male Ring-necked Pheasant (*Phasianus colchicus*), also called **crowing ground.**

crown: 1) the top of the head, between the eyebrows, the part nearest the bill being the forehead. 2) the canopy and foliage of a tree.

crural: pertaining to the leg, as in **crural feathering** or **crural tract** (*pterylae cruralis*) on the thighs.

crus: the shank or tibiotarsus.

crustacean: any member of the arthropod class Crustacea (crabs, lobsters, crayfish, shrimps, woodlice, barnacles, and many others).

crypsis: concealment.

cryptic coloration: protective colouring that conceals the bird in its habitat, also called camouflage. The opposite of phaneric coloration; *cf.* countershading, procryptic coloration, anticryptic coloration, deflective coloration, epigamic coloration.

cryptic phylogroup: a population or other evolutionary unit (e.g. species, subspecies) recognised only through phylogenetic analysis of biochemical evidence, e.g. sequence data.

cryptic species: two or more very similar but not interbreeding species.

cryptoptile: 1) hypothetical down-like or filamentary forerunners of modern feathers in the ancestors of birds. 2) rare term for the first filaments from the feather papillae of young birds.

cubitals: old term for secondaries.

cubital band: a dark band in the wing between the carpal joint and elbow, e.g. in some immature terns (Sternidae).

cubitum: Latin = elbow.

Cuculiformes: an order comprising 138 species of cuckoos in the family Cuculidae. Turacos (Musophagidae) and the Hoatzin (Opisthocomidae, *Opisthocomus hoatzin*) were until recently included in this order.

cues: a stimulus, usually environmental, that elicits a certain response, e.g. a certain day length that triggers reproductive activity or migration in many bird species.

culmen: the ridge of the upper mandible or maxilla, between the tip of the bill and the base of the skull or the cere; also used for the straight-line distance between these points, a common measure of bill length.

cuneate: wedge-shaped, Latin = *cuneus*

cup nest: cup-shaped or shallow saucer-like nest built by, e.g. many songbirds; *cf.* adherent nest, platform nest pensile cup nest, pendulous nest.

cupula: Latin = cup shaped.

curator: a keeper of a department of a museum whose most important job is to manage the growth and maintenance of the collections.

cursorial: being adapted for running on the ground, like the Ostrich (*Struthio camelus*) and many other birds. From Latin *cursus* = a running, rapid motion

Cursoriidae: outdated family now recognised as a subfamily Cursoriinae of the family of coursers and pratincoles (Glareolidae).

curvatura: Latin, curving, arching, e.g. the curvature of the wing.

cuticula gastrica: the hard inner wall of the gizzard. Also called koilin layer or gastric cuticle.

cuticle: the outermost surface of an egg shell, which protects the embryo from microbes and upon which colour and patterning are laid down during laying; *cf.* testa.

cutting edge: the edges where the two mandibles meet. Rarely called commissure or tomium.

cyanin: the blue and green pigment in many eggshells.

cybernetics: the science of communication and control in systems, including living organisms.

cycle: periodic change of something, e.g. an annual cycle of breeding, moult, migration, wintering, territory establishment, etc., or regular variation in numbers of animal species from year to year, often predictable, a well-known example is the 3-4 year cycle of lemmings (*Lemmus lemmus*) and the vole (genus *Microtus*). In moult terminology a cycle means a complete sequence of moult; *cf.* periodism, fluctuation, oscillation.

Cyclarhidae: outdated family comprising the genus *Cyclarhis* in the vireo family (Vireonidae).

cygnet: a young swan, genus *Cygnus*.

cytochrome *b*: a protein used in cell respiration; the DNA sequence of the gene coding for the protein is commonly used in systematic studies of relationships among organisms.

cytogenetics: the study of the heredity of the cell.

cytology: the study of the structure, function, and formation of the living cell.

cytoplasm: the contents of a living cell inside the cell membrane, with the exception of the nucleus.

cytus: Latin = cell, cyte.

D

dabble: the method by which a duck reaches food in shallow water without diving.

dabbling: a foraging technique in which a bird moves its bill from side to side on the water surface to catch small animals and vegetation.

dabbling duck: any member of the tribe Anatini within the Anatidae (ducks and geese); these waterfowl rarely dive for food, as opposed to the various groups of diving ducks.

dabchick: common name for most species of *Tachybaptus* grebes (Podicipedidae).

dacnis: ten species of the genera *Dacnis* and *Xenodacnis*, both in the tanager family Thraupinae within Emberizidae.

dactyl: finger or toe. Also called digit or phalange.

daily periodicity: endogenous rhythm of approximately one year's duration, controlling breeding, moult and migration; *cf.* circannual cycle or rhythm.

dambo: a grassy tropical African habitat that seasonally becomes a marsh.

dancing ground: a place where grouse of the genera *Bonasa* and *Tympanuchus* dance their displays, also called booming ground because of their long-carrying vocal sounds.

Dansk Ornitologisk Forening: abbr. DOF. The Danish Ornithological Society. Published *Dansk Ornitologisk Forenings Tidsskrift* since 1906.

Darling Effect: the stimulation of breeding in a pair by similar activity among other conspecific pairs nearby; causes synchronisation of breeding through reciprocal stimulation in colonial birds, also called the Fraser Darling effect.

darter: Am. anhinga, any member of the family Anhingidae.

Darwin, Charles Robert: English naturalist (1809-1882) who in 1859 introduced the theory of the evolution of species by means of natural selection.

Darwinism: the theory of evolution by natural selection and common descent, first made public by the joint presentation on 1 July 1858 of a paper by C. R. Darwin and A.R. Wallace at the Linnean Society, and in more detail by the first edition of Darwin's book *The Origin of Species* of 24 November 1859. Also called Darwinian evolutionary theory; *cf.* neo-Darwinism.

Darwin's finches: general name for the 14 Galapagos finches of the subfamily Geospizinae (Emberizidae), for the role they came to play in stimulating Darwin's ideas of evolution by natural selection.

data deficient: a criterion used by BirdLife International for a taxon with inadequate information about status; *cf.* not evaluated.

dawn chorus: bird song at its peak at dawn around sunrise.

DDE: a breakdown product of DDT with harmful effects to ecosystems; accumulated in fatty animal tissues and excreted very slowly. Among other things known to cause eggshell thinning in birds, especially in birds of prey (Falconiformes) by which some populations were severely affected before DDT was banned or restricted.

DDT: an organochlorine pesticide, now banned in many countries because of its harmful effects on natural ecosystems, but still in use in many tropical countries; *cf.* DDE.

de-: prefix from Latin *de* meaning away from, denoting removal of.

death rate: the proportion of individuals of a population or cohort dying per period, properly defined as the instantaneous rate, although the term is frequently used also of, e.g. annual mortality. Also called mortality rate; *cf.* recruitment rate.

DEB: abbr. for daily energy budget.

debris: vegetable and/or animal remains.

deceptive display: a distraction behaviour seen in some ground-nesting birds in which the bird leads a predator away from its eggs or chicks by acting sick and unable to fly; also called distraction display or behaviour, deflection display, broken-wing display or trick, crippled-bird act, wounded-bird act, or injury feigning.

deciduous: shedding leaves before the onset of winter, such as most broadleaved trees; the opposite of evergreen.

deciduous forest biome: one of North America's nine ecological divisions, or biotic communities, that covers much of the eastern USA.

decompose: break down, decay, or rot; fungi and bacteria actively breaking down organic material.

decoy: an artificial duck or other bird used as a lure; also a trap formerly often used to catch ducks in a long tapering tunnel.

decurved: curved downward.

deductive method: in scientific research the formulation of theories or hypotheses that are used to make predictive statements that are then tested; also called hypothetico-deductive method.

deferens: carrying down.

deferent duct: syn. with vas deferens, the sperm-carrying duct from testes to cloacae; also called vasa deferentia or ductus deferens.

deficiency disease: disease caused by the lack of something (e.g. certain aminoacids, vitamins, or minerals).

definitive alternate: Am. for Eur. adult summer (or breeding) plumage; 'definitive' because the bird does not change its plumage with age thereafter; *cf.* definitive basic.

definitive basic: Am. for Eur. adult winter (or non-breeding) plumage; 'definitive' because the bird does not change its plumage with age thereafter; *cf.* definitive alternate.

definitive plumage: Am. for adult plumage which does not change further with age.

deflection display: syn. for injury feigning, a form of distraction behaviour found in many species, especially ground-nesting birds, in which the bird appears to be sick and unable to fly until the predator is diverted away from the nest or chicks; also called diversionary display, broken-wing display or trick, crippled-bird act, or injury feigning.

deflective coloration: 'surprise coloration', e.g. the white wing spot of many pittas (Pittidae), which is hidden when the wing is closed but suddenly appears as a white flash when the wings are spread, to the confusion of predators; *cf.* cryptic coloration, epigamic coloration.

degree of confidence: the probability (very often 95%) applied when determining a confidence interval, the interval in which a quantitative assertion can be considered true in, e.g. 95% of cases; *cf.* confidence limits, degree of freedom.

degrees of freedom: in statistics, the number of observations or measurements upon which a parameter's estimate is based minus the number of parameters being estimated. The more degrees of freedom, the more precise the parameter estimate.

dehydration: removal of water from a substance, e.g. many migrating birds die in deserts due to dehydration.

Deinonychus: a dromaeosaur from the middle Cretaceous with terrible claws.

delayed density dependence: when a population density relates to previous densities rather than to present ones, e.g. numbers of predators fluctuate relative to numbers of prey but decline or increase somewhat later than the decline/increase of their prey; *cf.* inverse density dependence.

delayed plumage maturation: delayed acquisition of adult plumage by sexually mature birds, e.g. among bowerbirds male Satin Bowerbirds (*Ptilonorhynchus violaceus*) do not attain their first adult plumage until their seventh year.

delta: 1) a triangular area, e.g. a river delta. 2) a letter in the Greek alphabet.

deltoideus: the proximal clavicle or wishbone muscle that flexes the shoulder and rotates the wings outward.

deme: 1) a homogenous and interbreeding population. 2) or a subpopulation of less than subspecies rank. More often used by botanists; *cf.* population.

democoenosis: refers to both a population and its living place (demotope) and their interrelations.

demography: the study of population structure and dynamics (birth and death rates, sex and age ratios, age-specific rates of fecundity, etc.); adj. **demographic**.

demographic stochasticity: random events affecting demographics, e.g. an entire generation being the same sex; *cf.* stochastic, environmental stochasticity.

demotope: the living place of a population.

dendrite: nerve ending, fine root-like process on a neuron at which the neuron receives signals from other neurons; *cf.* sensory neurons, motor neurons, Grandry's-, Herbst's-, Merkel's corpuscles.

dendrogram: a diagram of phyletic relationships, drawn like a branching tree.

dens: a toothlike process.

density compensation: a term most often used for island species or populations that increase in abundance in the absence of competitors.

density dependence: a necessary characteristic of any mechanism regulating the size of a population such as predation, disease, parasites, or competition for food.

density independent factors: natural disasters such as extreme winters and other severe weather, food shortage, etc.

dentary: 1) the distal bone of the lower mandible in birds. 2) and the sole bone in the mandible of mammals; *cf.* premaxilla, surangular.

denticulatus: Latin = finely notched.

deoxyribonucleic acid (DNA): the genetic material in a cell, composed of the nucleotides adenosine phosphate, guanosine phosphate, cytidine phosphate, and thymidine phosphate, which occur in two interlocking, complementary strands forming a double helix. The genetic information lies in the sequence of the nucleotides.

dependent variable: loosely, a function of something, the something being the independent variable; in an x-y graph or scatterplot the independent variable is generally given by the horizontal axis (x-axis, abscissa), the dependent variable by the vertical axis (y-axis, ordinate); *cf.* independent variable.

depigmentation: removal of pigments; primaries and secondaries with partial white areas in one or some feathers. Often seen in birds in captivity. Cause unknown but possibly due to lack of vitamins; *cf.* albino, partial albinism, leucism.

deplume: a term in falconry for a raptorial bird plucking the feathers of its prey.

depressor mandibulae: the muscle on the ventral and lateral surface of the mandible that lowers the lower jaw and opens the mouth.

derived activity: movement derived from other types of behaviour; *cf.* displacement behaviour, intention movements.

derived character: a character present in some members of a taxonomic group but not in the last common ancestor of that group; also called an apomorphy; the opposite of an ancestral (primitive) character or plesiomorphy.

dermal: adjective pertaining to dermis or to skin.

dermal papilla: a small collection of cells at the base of the feather follicle that produces the feather; *cf.* papilla.

dermatitis: inflammation of the skin.

dermatology: the study of the skin and of skin diseases.

dermestic or **dermestid beetles**: beetles of the family Dermestidae, some of which are feared by museum curators because they eat skin and feathers of preserved bird specimens while others are used to clean flesh from skeletons (under great safeguards) and thus also called museum beetles.

dermis: the inner layer of the skin below the epidermis; also called corium; *cf.* hypodermis.

dertrum: a rarely used term for the curved or hooked tip of the upper mandible, specifically for that found in some pigeons (Columbidae) and plovers (Pluvialinae).

descendent: pertaining to the numbering of flight feathers, or their sequence of moult, and meaning from the innermost feather away from the body. Now the preferred numbering method for the primaries; secondaries are always counted ascendent, from the outermost towards the body; *cf.* transilient.

descendens: Latin = descending.

deserter species: a host species that deserts a nest parasitized by a brood parasite and builds another.

designation: a term used in taxonomy for the description of a type specimen (or designation of a syntype, lectotype, paratype, etc. in the absence of a holotype) or the definition of a contested type locality.

desmognathous: Greek *desmos* = a bond, pertaining to a bony palate characterized by fused maxillopalatine bones and small and tapering vomers; found in ducks (Anatidae), parrots (Psittacidae), birds of prey (Falconiformes), and owls (Strigiformes); this type is one of four palatal structures traditionally recognized in avian classificatory studies; *cf.* schizognathous, dromaeognathous, aegithognathous.

determinate layer: a species that lays a fixed number of eggs in a clutch, as opposed to an indeterminate layer that is able to replace lost or experimentally removed eggs from a single clutch, at least to some extent.

deterrent display: display behaviour performed to deter an intruding animal.

detritus: dead and decomposing vegetable and/or animal matter.

Deutero-Oscines: suborder comprising all passeriform birds not included in the suborder Passeres (Oscines); not widely recognized today because the group is unlikely to be monophyletic.

Deuterostomia: in taxonomy one of the two great subkingdoms, so named because the embryo's blastopore develops to become the anus, with the mouth formed as a later, secondary opening; opposite to the Protostomia, in which the blastopore becomes the mouth (in reality both mouth and anus, through lateral fusion of the blastopore lips).

Deutsche Bund für Vogelschutz: [German Federation for Bird Protection], became in 1990 Naturschutzbund Deutschland [German Nature Protection Federation]. Situated in Bonn.

Deutsche Ornithologen-Gesellschaft: abbr. DO-G. Published: *Journal für Ornithologie* since 1853, since 2004 called Journal of Ornithology and solely written in English. Oldest ornithological society in the world.

Devonian period: a period from c. 400 to 360 mya when the first fishes ventured out of the water onto the land.

dewlap: lose skin hanging below the throat.

dexter: Latin = right; *cf. sinister.*

dho-gaza: a ringing/banding term for the placement of a live or stuffed owl near a mist net in order to attract birds for capture.

diagnose: 1) character of sufficient distinctiveness to allow identification. 2) to determine the cause of something, e.g. a disease. Adj. **diagnostic.**

diakinesis: a stage of meiosis.

dialect: a geographic song variation.

dialyt binoculars: field glasses with a roof prism arrangement that greatly reduces weight.

diaspore: a winged seed.

diastataxy: a condition of the wing in which the fifth upper secondary greater covert has no corresponding fifth secondary flight feather, as opposed to eutaxy in which the fifth secondary and its greater covert is present.

Diatrymiformes: order of fossil flightless birds, related to cranes and rails, known from Oligocene to Pliocene deposits in North America and Europe.

dichopatric: populations so geographically isolated that gene flow between them is impossible.

dichotomous key: a tool for the identification of organisms by focusing on pairs of contrasting morphological characters.

dichotomy: a division into two parts or categories, for example a node with two branches in a cladogram, as opposed to a polytomy; adj. **dichotomous.**

dichromatism: 1) a dimorphism specifically with respect to colour, used mainly in terms of sexual differences in colour; adj. **dichromatic.** 2) colour vision based on two different classes of colour-sensitive cells (cones) in the retina; *cf.* monochromatic, trichromatism, tetrachromatism.

dicotyledon: a plant with two seed-leaves, belonging to the Dicotyledones (one of the two great divisions of Angiosperms, the other being the Monocotyledones).

didactylous: having only two dactyls (fingers or toes), such as the Ostrich (*Struthio camelus*).

diel: a 24-hour period, usually encompassing one day and one night. A term often used in avian physiology.

dieldrin: an organochlorine pesticide.

diencephalon: the posterior part of the forebrain, consisting of epithalamus, thalamus, and hypothalamus; *cf.* telencephalon.

differential exploitation: using different resources, as often seen in sympatric species living in the same habitat.

differential migrant: a species or population performing a differential migration involving a temporal or geographical segregation of the sexes or age-classes outside the breeding season; one example is the Long-eared Owl (*Asio otus*), in which young birds and females tend to migrate farther southwards in winter than adult males; *cf.* complete migrant, irruptive migrant, partial migrant.

differentiate: to distinguish (between objects, groups, etc.).

diffraction: the interference of waves from a single source, in optics causing dark and light bands or coloured spectra of different shades.

diffuse: 1) of matter in solution, to move from a point of higher concentration to one of lower concentration solely by random movements. 2) not sharply defined.

digestive energy: energy that is absorbed from the action of intestinal digestion; *cf.* metabolism.

digestive system: comprising the mouth, the gullet, the food canal (esophagus), crop, proventriculus, gizzard, duodenum, gastrointestinal tract, and small and large intestines. Also all associated glands secreting digestive enzymes, such as the pancreas and gall bladder. Also called alimentary canal. See also: alimentary system, liver, islets of Langerhans, ileum, cloaca, vent.

digit: a toe or finger. 1) first foot digit = hind toe, second d. = inner toe, third d. = middle toe, and fourth d. = outer toe. 2) in birds the remnants of three finger digits are present, digit one or alular d. (the thumb in humans), second d. or major d., and third d. or minor d. Also called phalanges or dactyl.

digital: pertaining in ornithology to the digits; also syn. for digital primary. Latin *digitus*.

digital primaries: the primaries attached to the wing digits, as opposed to the carpometacarpus.

digitigrade: walking on the toes.

dihedral: wings held up in a V form when gliding, seen, e.g. in the Rock Pigeon (*Columba livia*).

dihybrid: offspring of parents heterozygous at two genes.

dilution: 1) another term for leucism, or pale plumage colour, **dilute albino.** 2) also used in chemistry for a solution of diminished concentration.

dimorphism: appearing in two distinct forms, differing in size, plumage, or other characteristics. Many species are sexually dimorphic (males and females differing); dichromatism is a dimorphism applying to (plumage) colour specifically; **dimorphy**, adj. **dimorphic, dimorphous**; *cf.* monomorphic, polymorphic.

dinosaur: any member of Dinosauria, the major group of archosaurs that dominated terrestrial ecosystems throughout the Mesozoic; only one lineage, the birds, survived into the Tertiary.

dioxin: tetrachlorodibenzoparadioxin, a very poisonous and persistent substance.

diphtheria avian: disease caused by protozoan infection giving creamy white necrotic material in the mouth, pharynx, inner nares, and oesophagus. Also called trichomoniasis, frounce, or dove disease.

diploid: having two sets of similar (homologous) chromosomes and genes (the condition in all higher animals), in contrast to the haploid state of the germ cells (in birds the ova and sperm), having only a single set of chromosomes.

diploid number: the number of chromosomes in the diploid cell, usually written 2*n*.

dipping out: what birdwatchers are said to be doing when they have the opportunity to see a rare bird, but miss it.

dip-scooping: a feeding behaviour of pelicans (Pelecanidae) whereby they either swim forward to dip their bill and pouch into the surface water or, like ducks (Anatidae), dabble head down and tail up to catch prey below the surface or at the bottom in the water.

Diptera: the insect order of flies, mosquitoes, and gnats with only a single pair of wings.

dipterocarp: a tree of the family Dipterocarpaceae, of south-east Asia, having two-winged fruits. Adj. dipterocarpaceous.

direct calorimetry: measurement of the energy released when a specific food item is oxidized; *cf.* indirect calorimetry.

direct competition: competitive relationship in which individuals compete through direct interactions for a resource; *cf.* indirect competition.

directed song: male song directed to a female; *cf.* undirected song, subsong.

direct head-scratching: head-scratching in which the foot is raised directly to the head; the opposite of indirect head-scratching, in which the foot is raised over the wing.

directional orientation: when a certain compass orientation is maintained during migration utilising a given external reference such as the earth's magnetic field, also called compass orientation; *cf.* goal orientation, parallactic or visual orientation, piloting.

directional selection: evolutionary selection causing a directionally consistent change in the phenotype of a population through time, e.g. selection for larger body size.

directional statistics: are for analysing data that involve angles or directions, commonly used in studies of orientation.

directive mark: the colourful or marked mouth lining of a nestling that signals its location to a provisioning parent.

disassortative mating: mating between individuals of unlike phenotype in a polymorphic population.

disc: the circlet of feathers around the face, especially in owls (Strigiformes). Also spelled **disk**.

discontinuity: in an ecological context meaning the gaps between the disjunct subpopulations of a population not occurring continuously over an area, usually so that little or no gene flow occurs between the subpopulations.

discriminant analysis: abbr. DA, a multivariate statistical method used to learn the extent to which populations or groups diverge from each other, often with the goal of finding a new composite variable (linear combinations of the original variables) that separate previously identified groups. A function that maximally discriminates between groups is often the goal of such analyses. Also called **discriminant function analysis**, although discriminant functions are a product of the analyses, not the starting point.

discus: Latin = disc, discus.

disinhibition: a behaviour completely irrelevant to the situation and the current activity of an animal, e.g. when two fighting birds suddenly start to preen; more commonly called displacement behaviour (activity).

disjunct distribution: the distribution of a species when it is not continuous over an area but rather confined to separated sub-areas; the subpopulations may or may not be genetically isolated from each other; *cf.* fragmentated distribution.

diskette: a small, thin magnetic circular plate, within a protective plastic case, upon which computer-generated data are stored. Also called floppy disk.

dismigration: centrifugal movements, particularly of juveniles, that lead to their dispersion.

dispersal: 1) movements between breeding seasons without a fixed direction or distance, either of young birds from their birth site to their first breeding site (natal dispersal), or of breeders from one breeding site to another (breeding dispersal). 2) more generally of any movements apart from migration, e.g. postbreeding dispersal from the end of the breeding season until the onset of migration. 3) range extension; *cf.* quasi-dispersal.

dispersal barrier: anything obstructing the dispersal of organisms; for birds it could be an ocean, a major desert, a mountain range, etc., depending on the species; also called **ecological barrier**.

dispersed lek: a lek in which the displaying males are separated by some distance, often out of sight of each other, but within earshot.

dispersion: 1) the spatial pattern or distribution of (or within) a local population. 2) in statistics, the distribution about the mean, or how individuals are spread, e.g. randomly or clustered.

dispersion coefficient: a measure of the spread of data about the mean, or with

reference to some other theoretically important threshold or statistical point, e.g. the standard deviation.

displacement behaviour: a behaviour completely irrelevant to the situation and the current activity of an animal, e.g. when two fighting birds suddenly start to preen; also called **displacement activity**, allochthonous activities, disinhibition, vacuum activity, intention movements, redirected activities; *cf.* intention movements, redirected activity

displacement chase: an aggressive activity involving a bird evicting a conspecific from a defended site or area.

display: a ritualised behaviour (postures or movements, often combined with vocalization) used in specific situations, such as courtship, threat, territory announcement, etc.

disruptive coloration: a plumage coloration that breaks up an animal's outline so much that predators have difficulty seeing the bird in its natural habitat; *cf.* countershading.

disruptive selection: selection for the extremes of phenotype in a single interbreeding population having polymorphism for a trait(s), e.g. selecting against medium-sized individuals and thus giving rise to a bi-modal size distribution, such as in the West African Black-bellied Seedcracker (*Pyrenestes ostrinus*).

distal: away from the center of the body; also called terminal, as opposed to proximal or basal.

distance: in systematics a term for the difference between two operational taxonomic units (OTUs) in genetic or phenetic terms.

distance animal: one that typically maintains distance between itself and conspecifics, e.g. gulls and terns (Laridae); opposite contact animal.

distance data counts: a census technique in which the distance to which birds are seen or heard is recorded. The resulting data may be analysed using the software DISTANCE, available at: http://www.ruwpa.st-and.ac.uk/distance.

distraction behaviour: a behaviour seen in some ground-nesting birds, in which the bird leads a predator away from its eggs or chicks by acting sick and unable to fly; also called **distraction display**, deflection display, broken-wing display or trick, crippled-bird act, wounded-bird act, or injury feigning.

distantia: Latin = distance between two points.

distress call: a call given by a bird captured by a predator (or being in some other dangerous situation); different from the normal alarm call.

diurnal: active during the day, opposite to nocturnal.

diurnal birds of prey: an older term for birds of prey (Falconiformes), which are generally active during daylight hours, in contrast to owls (Strigiformes), that were formerly called nocturnal birds of prey.

diurnal migrant: a bird that migrates during the day.

diurnal rhythm: a biological clock following a cycle of about 24 hours in the absence of external stimuli; also called circadian rhythm.

diver: Am. loon, the five members of the genus *Gavia*, comprising the family Gaviidae.

divergent evolution: evolution of dissimilar characters by related taxa; *cf.* ecological divergence, speciation.

diversionary behaviour: movements and/or vocalizations that function to distract a predator away from the performer's nest or offspring; a more developed form is distraction behaviour.

diversion line: a geographic feature diverting migrating birds from their preferred direction, for example a water body, a mountain range, or a desert; *cf.* leading line.

diversity index: a descriptive statistic in ecology, designed to describe both species richness and the evenness of species abundances in a community or sample.

diverticulum: a blind-ended tube or sac opening off a canal or cavity, e.g. the crop.

diving duck: a duck that dives for food, as opposed to a dabbling duck that obtains food on or near the water surface.

divorce: the breaking of a pair bond not caused by the death of one or both sexes.

DNA: abbr. for deoxyribonucleic acid. James Watson and Francis Crick discovered in 1953 that the genetic material consisted of DNA, so that the amino acid sequences of proteins are determined by base sequences in the DNA of the cell nucleus. Minor amounts of functional DNA are also found in mitochondria; *cf.* mitochondrial DNA.

DNA-DNA hybridization: molecular technique used to estimate the evolutionary distance between taxa. The method is based on the fact that the stability of an experimentally created hybrid double-strand of DNA (a heteroduplex) is inversely related to the difference between the two source DNAs (i.e. the genetic distance between the source species). The degree of stability of the heteroduplex is measured as the so-called melting point, which increases with the similarity of the DNA of the two organisms. This method has been most useful in examining the relationships between higher taxa such as families and orders. The technique was pioneered in a major undertaking by C. G. Sibley and J. A. Ahlquist; *cf.* biochemical data, mitochondrial DNA, nuclear DNA, nucleotide sequence analysis.

DNA fingerprinting: the generation of individually unique patterns of DNA fragments, in avian science especially used to identify paternity but not considered robust in systematics. Also called genetic fingerprinting, RAPD (randomly amplified polymorphic DNA), and also applied sometimes to microsatellite loci used for individual identification.

DNA sequencing: determining the individual base composition of the nucleotides along a strand of DNA; i.e. the sequence of the four types of nucleotides making up DNA: adenine (A), cytosine (C), guanine (G), and thymine (T). In the two strands in a DNA molecule (double helix), an A nucleotide in one strand always pairs with a T nucleotide in the other, and a C always pairs with a G. If the nucleotide sequence in one strand was …AGGGTCCTA…, then the complementary strand would be TCCGAGGAT.

Dodo: extinct, flightless bird (*Raphus cucullatus*) from Mauritius, by most authors now placed in the order Columbiformes. Extinct in 1662. The Dodo has become synonymous with the concept of extinction, hence the proverb 'as dead as a Dodo'.

domed nest: a cup with an attached dome overhead and with a side entrance characteristic of, e.g. pittas (Pittidae) and the Long-tailed Tit (*Aegithalos caudatus*); *cf.* globular nest.

domestic: being domesticated by humans.

domicile: the part of a bird's range that it most often frequents by day and sleeps and breeds in which it; also known as the home range.

dominance hierarchy: a social organization within which individuals differ in status, creating a rank or 'pecking order'.

dominant: 1) commonly applied as one individual being dominant over another or others. 2) a gene is dominant if its effects are expressed in an organism even though it has received it from only one of its parents (i.e. expression occurs in a heterozygote); *cf.* recessive.

dormitory nest: a nest used only for roosting at night as, e.g. in many wrens (Troglodytidae).

dorsal: on the dorsum, or back, or the upperparts of the body, opposite to ventral. Latin *dorsalis; cf.* lateral.

dorsalis scapulae: the long muscle on the lateral surface of the shoulder bone (scapula).

dorsal segment of rib: the upper segment of a rib nearest the dorsal vertebrae. Also called vertebral rib; *cf* sternal rib.

dorsal tract: the dorsal feather tract from the base of the skull to the base of the tail. Also called spinal tract; *cf* pterylography.

dorsal vertebrae: the vertebrae between the neck and the three lowest lumbar vertebrae; the ribs are connected to the dorsal vertebrae. Also called back vertebrae; *cf.* os dorsale.

dorsum: Latin = pertaining to the back or entire dorsal surface of the body; *cf.* ventrum.

dotted: an egg with small spots evenly distributed over the whole surface.

double-brooded: (normally) laying two clutches in a breeding season.

double-clutching: 1) pertaining to a breeding system in which a monogamous female lays two clutches in quick succession, the first being incubated by the male and the second by the female. May be an evolutionary forerunner of polyandry. Found in, e.g. Red-legged Partridge (*Alectoris rufa*) and Temminck's Stint (*Calidris temminckii*). 2) Also used by conservation biologists for the practice of removing the first eggs of declining species, to rear them artificially, and causing the bird to lay replacement eggs.

double scratch: a behaviour of some ground-feeding birds in which they jump forward then jump backward dragging both feet, displacing ground litter to expose food, e.g. by Fox Sparrows (*Passerella illaca*) and Song Sparrows (*Melospiza melodia*).

doubly labelled water technique: a method to estimate metabolic rate, in which doubly labelled water is injected at the start of the experiment and blood is analysed at the end, typically after a few days. Both hydrogen and oxygen atoms of the water are isotopically labelled (hence 'doubly'), the usual hydrogen (^{1}H) being partly replaced by tritium (^{3}H or T) and the usual oxygen (^{16}O) by ^{18}O.

dove disease: a fatal disease caused by an endoparasitic protozoan (*Trichomonas gallinae*) in the throat, lungs, and liver. Found in doves and pigeons (Columbidae) and hawks and falcons (Falconiformes) that eat them.

down: fluffy (vaneless) feathers; apart from the absence of hooks on the barbs, down is characterized by having no or at most a reduced shaft (rachis), never as long as the longest barb; *cf.* semiplume, body down, natal down, neossoptile, neoptile, trichoptile, powder down.

drag: the friction between a flying bird and the air it displaces; *cf.* thrust.

dragonfly: any member of the insect order Odonata, including dragonflies and damselflies; winged and carnivorous insects with aquatic larvae.

drake: the male duck, swan, or goose.

drawtube: a telescope without prisms, in which the tube can be slid back and forth to focus on an object.

dread: the communal alarm behaviour of colonial or amassed birds, e.g. terns (*Sterna* spp.), suddenly flying up and circling in silence. Also called panic.

drift migration: a migration forced by adverse climatic conditions such as a storm, gale, or hurricane, **drifting species**.

drive: 1) a bird-catcher's driving birds towards a trap or net. 2) the innate drives that force a bird to behave in a certain way.

dromaeognathous: Greek *dromaios* = a runner, pertaining to a bony palate characterized by large and imperfectly fused vomers; found in ratites (Struthioniformes) and tinamous (Tinamiformes); this type is one of four palatal structures traditionally recognized in avian systematics. Also called paleognathous; *cf.* desmognathous, schizognathous, aegithognathous.

Dromaeosaur: a theropod from the early Cretaceous, maybe modern birds' closest relative.

Dromornithidae: outdated family of gigantic birds in Australia, which became extinct during the last ice age. Now placed with the ducks, geese, and swans in the Anseridae, order Anseriformes.

drop net: a trap made of a net suspended by a frame set to drop on a target bird when a pull-cord is activated. Also called **drop trap**.

dropping: another name for the faeces or excrement of a bird.

dropsy: accumulation of watery body fluid in the body cavity or in tissue, the cause can be heart, kidney, or lung disease.

drumming: a common term used for various mechanical (non-vocal) sounds produced by some birds, such as the sound made by the vibration of the outer tail feathers during aerial displays in many species of snipe (*Gallinago*), the sound produced by the wings of displaying Ruffed Grouse (*Bonasa umbellus*), and the well-known bill drumming of woodpeckers (Picidae). Also known as instrumental song. The sound made by snipes is also called bleating or winnowing.

drumstick: the tibiotarsus and attached flesh of a (cooked) bird.

duck decoy: 1) a wire structure erected over a body of water that increasingly narrows to a terminal trap, ducks being driven into it. 2) Am. an artificial duck used as a lure in hunting; *cf.* Heligoland trap.

duck plague: a viral disease limited to ducks, geese, and swans (Anatidae), particularly prevalent where birds gather in high density; cannot be transferred to humans. Accidentally introduced to America from Europe in 1967. Also called duck viral enteritis.

duck sickness: a severe and often fatal type of food poisoning caused by a toxin from *Clostridium botulinum*, an anaerobic bacteria living in soil. Ducks (Anatidae) and pheasants (Phasianidae) are most often affected. A more usual term is botulism.

duck tegmen: the shiny patch on the underside of a duck primary.

duck viral enteritis: abbr. DVE, a viral disease limited to ducks, geese, and swans (Anatidae), particularly prevalent where birds gather in high densities; cannot be transferred to humans. Accidentally introduced to America from Europe in 1967. Also called duck plague.

duck viral hepatitis: a disease involving haemorrhagic necrosis of the liver with an associated high mortality rate. Ducklings are most commonly affected.

duckling: a young duck.

Ducks Unlimited: an American organisation founded in 1937 that works for the restoration of duck-supporting wetlands.

ductless glands: all glands that secrete hormones to the blood, i.e. the pituitary, pineal, thyroid, parathyroid, adrenal, testes, ovaries, and the pancreatic islets of Langerhaus, also termed endocrine glands.

ductulus: Latin = a small duct.

ductus deferens: the sperm-carrying duct from testes to cloaca; also called vas deferens; *cf.* cloacal protuberance.

dude: slang: in birding for a casual and inexperienced birdwatcher.

duetting: the act of a usually rather stereotyped song simultaneously or alternately by both members of a mated pair in such a way that phrases from the two birds are interwoven, making it difficult to hear that two birds are involved. Mainly known in some tropical forest birds having monogamous pair bonds of life-long duration; *cf.* antiphonal singing.

dummy: an artificial egg used, e.g. in research of host rejection behaviour or a stuffed bird placed near a nest to study how the breeding birds react.

dummy nest: an incomplete nest, play nest, or sleeping nest, well known in e.g. the House Wren (*Troglodytes aedon*).

dumping: laying eggs in other bird nests, also called **dump-laying** or egg dumping.

dump nest: a nest in which more than one female has laid eggs.

duodenum: the expanded U-shaped upper part of the intestine, just behind the stomach or gizzard that envelopes the pancreas.

dura mater: the thin outer layer of tissue covering the brain, the inner lay er being the pia mater; collectively, the two layers are called meninges.

dusky stripes: dusky stripes in the feathers of some individuals belonging to the pitta family, Pittidae, a primitive character state within a group inherited from a common ancestor and conserved in some of the members of the group; carries no information about evolutionary relationships within the group (plesiomorphic); *cf.* pealea phenomenon.

dusting: a behaviour in many respects resembling bathing, in which a bird lets dry earth or sand penetrate the plumage; probably helps in general feather maintenance and may serve to reduce ectoparasites. Also termed **dust-bathing**; *cf.* sunning.

dynamic pressure: the pressure of movement.

dynamic programming: the conceptualized strategy of optimising the timing of migration (e.g. moult and fattening) through allowing environmental cues to modify genetic 'programming.'

dynamic soaring: non-flapping flight extracting energy from horizontal airstreams, particularly the wind speed gradient above the ground or sea (wind near the surface is slowed down). No birds seem to use this technique in its pure form, but elements of it are apparent in the flight of albatrosses, other large petrels (Procellariiformes), and many pelicans (Pelecanidae).

dysplasia: abnormal development of a tissue.

dystrophic: of a lake rich in organic matter and usually brown but with low nutrient content and few animals.

E

ear: the anatomy for hearing; see: auditory meatus, auditory tube, basilar membrane, cochlea, columella auris, endolymph, lagena, otolith, perilymph, periotic, pharynx, sacculus, semicircular canals, tympanic membrane, utriculus, vestibule.

eardrum: membrane in a hearing organ. Also called tympanic membrane.

ear-spot: a contrasting spot of feathers in the ear region, particularly seen in some gulls (Laridae).

ear stones: small pieces of calcium carbonate in the cochlea of the ear.

ear-tuft: elongate and erectile feathers that resemble ears, as in some owls (Strigidae) and grebes (Podicipedidae) and in the Horned Lark (*Eremophila alpestris*); may be erectile for display, e.g. in the fairy wrens (Maluridae).

ecarinate: having no keel: the opposite to carinate.

eccentric moult: from the centre outwards; only applied to the primaries, syn. for descendent primary moult; *cf.* descendent, ascendent.

ecdysis: the shedding of old feathers for replacement by new ones; *cf.* endysis.

echolocation: navigation using echoes of emitted sounds, in principle like sonar and analogous to radar; especially well known in microchiropteran bats, a sophisticated system that is based on high-frequency (ultra-sonic) pulses and is used not only for orientation but also for detecting and homing in on prey. A few cave-dwelling bird species also use echolocation, based on pulses of lower frequency that can be heard as clicks: the Oilbird (*Steatornis caripensis*) and cave-breeding species of swiftlets (*Aerodramus*).

eclipse plumage: cryptic plumage like that of females, borne for a short time after breeding by many male ducks (Anatidae), helping to conceal them from predators during moult when they are flightless. Similar cryptic male plumages in otherwise conspicuously coloured birds are also found in some sunbirds (Nectariniidae), fairy-wrens (Maluridae), and weaverbirds (Ploceidae).

eco-: a prefix derived from the Greek word *oicos*, = house or dwelling place.

ecocline: 1) variation in a character corresponding to an ecological or geographical cline, in which contiguous populations exhibit local adaptation to the geographically varying ecological conditions. 2) also a geographical gradient of communities associated with elevation or a co-varying cline of species composition and environmental variation.

eco-ethology: behavioural research from an ecological perspective.

ecogenesis: development of an ecosystem in an area formerly lacking life, for example due to volcanic activity. Also applied to differentiation between two lineages due to selection, and to ecologically-generated morphological patterns in geographic space.

ecogeographic rules: generalisations describing commonly seen phenotypic patterns that have environmental (climatic) correlates across the geographic distribution of living organisms. A related but narrower term is zoogeographic rules. Three well-known examples are Allen's, Bergmann's, and Gloger's Rules.

ecogeography: using plants and animals as an ecological description of the landscape; *cf.* biome, biocoenosis, landscape ecology.

ecological balance: stability in an ecological system. Also termed **ecological equilibrium**.

ecological barrier: anything obstructing the dispersal of organisms; for birds it could be an ocean, a desert, a mountain range, etc., depending on the species; also called **dispersal barrier**.

ecological biogeography: a scientific discipline studying the factors determining the distributions of species.

ecological compatibility: the ability of different species to coexist in the same area; mainly applied to closely related species that avoid competition by utilising slightly different resources, for example by inhabiting different microhabitats; *cf.* ecological isolation.

ecological divergence: the acquisition of dissimilar ecological characteristics by related species; *cf.* divergent evolution.

ecological diversity: the diversity of ecosystem(s) of any given area, e.g. forest and desert.

ecological efficiency: the efficiency by which energy is transferred from one trophic level to the next.

ecological guilds: group of species utilizing similar food resources in similar ways within an area, e.g. swallows (Hirundinidae) and swifts (Apodidae) feeding on flying insects.

ecological isolation: reproductive separation of populations due to ecological barriers.

ecological niche: a conceptualization of the role of a species and the multidimensional biological space it occupies in an ecosystem, e.g. a species' foraging niche. Although each species is generally considered unique, complexities can include temporal, age/sex, and geographic shifts within species.

ecological parapatry: a sharp ecological shift occurring between two populations, e.g. meadow/forest, or forest/savannah, sometimes reinforced by competition between them; *cf.* competition parapatry and hybridization parapatry.

ecological radiation: evolutionary diversification of a taxon over a relatively short time, leading to several new forms with different ecological adaptations; a classic example is Darwin's finches (Geospizinae) of the Galápagos Islands, thought to have evolved from a single colonizing population that arrived there no more than five million years ago, and perhaps as recently as one million years. Usually called adaptive radiation.

ecological separation:the separation of two or more populations owing to their different ecological adaptations rather than geographical distributions.

ecological species concept: the concept that a species is a lineage or set of lineages occupying a unique ecological adaptive zone; *cf.* biological species concept, phenetic species concept, recognition species concept.

ecological succession: a long process in which one association of plants and animals is gradually replaced by another, and so on, until in some cases the ecosystem remains relatively stable and is considered a climax community.

ecological valence: the range of fluctuation of an environmental factor that can be tolerated by an organism or population.

ecologue: taxa sharing a comparable ecology or niche.

ecology: the study of the interrelationships between animals and plants and the environment; *cf.* bionomics; autecology, synecology.

Ecology: a publication from the Ecological Society of America, Durham, North Carolina, USA.

economic defendability: the concept of examining an animal's defence of a resource in terms of biological benefits and costs.

ecoparasite: a parasite with one or a few related host species. Also spelled oecoparasite.

ecospecies: a group of different populations that can freely interbreed but which differs sufficiently from other such groups to inhibit gene flow; similar to biological species.

ecosphere. That portion of the upper crust of the Earth and the lower portion of the atmosphere that is inhabited by plants and animals.

ecosystem: a community of living organisms, including the non-living components of the environment with which they interact (soil, water, light, etc.). Also called biocenosis, biocoenosis.

ecotone: The edge, boundary, or transition between two adjacent biotic communities, e.g. the edge of forest and grassland. Also called edge habitat; *cf.* edge effect.

ecotoxicology: the study of the effects of pollution on ecosystems.

ecotype: refers to a local variation in plumage or other morphological features induced by the environment.

ectepicondyle: the smaller of the two expansions on the distal end of the humerus; *cf.* entepicondyle.

ectethmoid: a bony plate in the forepart of the eye sockets (orbits) of the skull.

ecto-: a prefix from Greek *ekto* = outside.

ectoderm: the outer of the three germ layers of the early animal embryo, differentiating into epidermis (skin) and nervous tissue; *cf.* endoderm, mesoderm.

ectogenetic: changes directly induced by the environment.

ectoparasite: a parasite living on the body surface of the host, by some authors also a blood-sucker such as a mosquito that only briefly visits its victim; the most common ectoparasites of birds are mites (Acarina) such as feather mites (Analgesidae), itch mites (Sarcoptidae), nasal mites (Rhinonyssidae), red mites (Dermanyssidae), ticks (Ixodidae), and insects, the most important of which are feather lice and lice (Phthiraptera), louse flies (Hippoboscidae), and fleas (Siphonaptera).

ectothermic: cold-blooded, having a body temperature determined primarily by the temperature of the environment, as opposed to endothermic; n. **ectothermy**. Also called poikilothermic.

ectropodactyl: a foot on which the 1st and 4th toes can be rotated into an external lateral position; *cf.* anisodactyl, zygodactyl, heterodactyl, syndactyl, pamprodactyl.

edaphic: relating to the soil or substratum.

edaphon: a soil-dwelling organism.

edema: Eur. oedema: a condition characterized by the presence of an excessive amount of fluid in the affected part of the body. Adj. **edematous**.

edge effect: the fact that more bird species are found at the edge of a habitat (transition zone between habitats, or ecotone) than inside either adjacent habitat, because birds with different preferences meet there.

E-DNA: the form adapted by synthetic DNA lacking guanine, with 7.5 base pairs per turn; *cf.* A-DNA, B-DNA, Z-DNA, deoxyribonucleic acid.

effective population size: abbr. N_e, the size of an 'ideal population'.

efferens: away from.

e.g.: Latin *exampli gratia* = for example.

egg: the shell, yolk, and albumen of the external reproductive cell(s) of birds within which the zygote develops; *cf.* air chamber, albumen, allantoic, amniotes, blastoderm, chalazae, chorioallantois, germinal disc, shell membranes, vitelline membrane, yolk.

egg-breaker: a sharp projection on the tip of the upper mandible of hatching chicks of most bird species, used to break the egg shell. It is lost a few days after hatching. More often called egg tooth.

egg burial: burial (in the nest lining) by the nest owner of an egg laid by another bird.

egg-capping: a term for the slipping of a hatched egg's shell over an intact egg.

egg dumping: laying eggs ('dumping' them) in other birds' nests, also called dump-nesting; *cf.* brood parasitism.

egg form: the shape of the egg; see: elliptical, cylindrical, oval, pyriform, and spherical.

egg markings: the patterns of eggs, e.g. blotched, capped, dotted, marbled, overlaid, scrawled, splashed, spotted, streaked, vermiculated, wreathed.

egg pricking: making a small hole in the shell of a bird's egg, thereby causing the death of the embryo; used in control of some bird populations, where pricking the eggs in a signifi-

cant proportion of the nests is an effective method, because the parents will continue to incubate the clutch instead of laying a new one.

egg tooth: a sharp projection on the tip of the upper mandible (rhinotheca) of hatching chicks of most bird species, used to break the egg shell. It is lost a few days after hatching. Also called egg-breaker, caruncle, or hatching tooth.

egg volume index: length x breadth^2.

Egretta: the periodical of the Österreichische Gesellschaft für Vogelkunde (the Ornithological Society of Austria). Published since 1958. Also a genus of herons (Ardeidae).

eidos: the type.

Elapaio, The: the Hawaiian ornithological periodical. Published by the Hawaii Audubon Society.

electrocution: killing by electricity; in birds usually because they collide with, or otherwise touch, more than one wire of a transmission line.

electrophoresis: separation of different proteins or pieces of DNA in an electric field in a gel or polymer matrix.

elephant bird: any member of Aepyornithidae, an extinct family of large, flightless birds living in Madagascar until as recently as c. 1,000 years BP. Various fossils from other parts of the world have been ascribed to the family, but no certain evidence exists that they ever occurred outside Madagascar.

elevational migrant: bird performing elevational migration between breeding areas at higher elevations and winter areas at lower elevations.

elevational migration: migration between higher and lower elevations in mountainous regions, usually by birds having high-altitude breeding areas and low-altitude non-breeding areas, also referred to as altitudinal migration; *cf.* latitudinal migration.

elfin forest: a high-elevation, wind-swept, stunted, humid forest, the trees of which are short, gnarled, and twisted and in which epiphytes are often common.

ellipse: an oval; a form similar to a flattened circle.

ellipsoidal: an oblong oval form of the egg, **ellipsoid**, Latin *ellipsoideus*; *cf.* oval, pyriform, spherical, subelliptical.

elliptical: having the shape of an ellipse; *cf.* subelliptical, oval, pyriform, spherical.

elliptical migration: migration in which a species or population returns in spring to its breeding area by a different route than that taken in autumn, i.e. some kind of circular route, also called loop migration; seen in e.g. Ruddy Turnstone (*Arenaria interpres*), Red-backed Shrike (*Lanius collurio*), or Sand Martin (*Riparia riparia*).

elliptical wings: a term for short and broad wings.

El Niño/Southern Oscillation: (abbr. ENSO) a climatic phenomenon appearing every 4 to 6 years, linked to a temperature difference between the surface waters of the Indian and Pacific oceans. It causes drought or torrential rain in Indonesia and Australasia and, through the retreat of cold surface water to greater depths in the region of the Humboldt Current, leads to severe crashes in seabird populations in Ecuador and Peru. The ENSOs of 1982-83 and 1997-98 were extremely severe. Although the effects are particularly strong in the tropical Pacific, ENSOs are a global phenomenon; *cf.* La Niña.

emarginate: of a feather, particularly a primary, meaning that one of the vanes narrows abruptly (has a notch) near the tip; also called notched.

emberizid: pertaining to the bunting family (Emberizidae), also including towhees, juncos, and most American sparrows.

embryology: the study of the development of the embryo from the single-celled egg to the hatched chick.

embryonic period: the time between the laying and hatching of an egg.

emergent layer: the tallest trees that rise above the main canopy in a rain forest.

emigrant: a human or an animal that moves out of the area under consideration and settles permanently in another area (in which it is an **immigrant**).

empirical: based on observations and experience, in contrast to theory.

empirical modeling technique: estimating bird density using field methods similar to index counts, but with an analytic component that models variation in a species' detectability in order to obtain estimates of density.

Emu: the journal for the Royal Australasian Ornithologists' Union (RAOU), founded in 1900 and since 2001 known as *Emu Austral Ornithology.* Also the common name of the second largest living bird, the Australian Emu (*Dromaius novaehollandiae*).

Enantiornithes: a subclass of fossil birds from the Cretaceous. Also called opposite birds because their metatarsal was fused with the tarsometatarsus from the proximal end to the distal end, the direction opposite to that of modern birds.

encephalitis virus: a virus transferred to birds and other animals by blood-sucking arthropods. Can also infect humans. One of several types of arbovirus (or arthropod-borne virus).

endangered: a formal category of populations or species that have reached very low numbers, used in USA law for management of flora and fauna and separately formulated by IUCN and used by BirdLife International for a species with more than a 50%

population decline during the last ten years, or during three generations; *cf.* critically endangered, vulnerable, lower risk.

endaspidean: the term applied to a tarsus in which the anterior and internal sides of the sheath have large scutes and the external side is bare or with small scutes only; *cf.* exaspidean, holaspidean, ocreate, pycnaspidean, taxaspidean.

endemic: 1) adj. of a formally recognized taxon with a distribution restricted to the area under consideration; the term is often applied to species with a limited geographical distribution. 2) n. an infection well distributed in an avian population but not causing heavy losses. Also called enzootic; *cf.* epidemic.

Endemic Bird Area: abbr. EBA, defined by BirdLife International as an area encompassing the entire range of two or more restricted-range species; *cf.* restricted range species.

endo-: prefix from Greek *endon*, meaning inside, within, or inwards.

endocrine glands: all ductless glands secreting hormones to the blood, i.e. the pituitary, pineal, hypothalamus, thyroid, ultimobranchial body, parathyroid, thymus, and adrenal glands, the islets of Langerhans in the pancreas, the bursa of Fabricius, and the testes and ovaries.

endocrine system: organ system consisting of widely separated endocrine glands; *cf.* nervous system, circulatory system, respiratory system, and urogenital system.

endocrinology: the study of the endocrine glands and their secretions.

endoderm: the inner of the three germ layers of the early animal embryo, differentiating into the alimentary canal (the gut) and associated glands. Also called entoderm; *cf.* ectoderm, mesoderm.

endogamy: mating within the group; *cf.* inbreeding, assortative mating.

endogenetic: changes caused by internal factors; the opposite of exogenous, adj. **endogenous**.

endolymph: fluid in the semicircular channels of the inner ear that maintains equilibrium; *cf.* perilymph.

endoparasite: a parasite living inside its host, in the gut, body cavity, blood, or any other site. Most avian endoparasites are unicellular organisms (protozoa) or belong to one of the roundworms (Nematoda), Acanthocephala, tapeworms (Cestoda), or flukes (Trematoda); *cf.* ectoparasite.

endoskeleton: an internal skeleton, as found in all vertebrates; *cf.* exoskeleton.

endothermic: warm-blooded, having a relatively constant body temperature most often exceeding the ambient temperature, as opposed to ectothermic; **endothermy**. Also called homeothermic, homoiothermic. Only birds and mammals are warm-blooded.

endrin: an organic solid poison of odourless white crystals, banned in many countries.

endysis: the development of new feathers in moult; *cf.* ecdysis.

energy: in avian biology, the capacity to do work in thermal, kinetic, or chemical terms.

energy budget: or energy expenditure, the balance of energy input and energy utilization; *cf.* basal metabolic rate, metabolic rate, standard metabolic rate.

ENSO: abbr. El Niño the Southern Oscillation. A climatic phenomenon appearing every 4 to 6 years, linked to a temperature difference between the surface waters of the Indian and Pacific oceans. It causes drought or torrential rain in Indonesia and Australasia and, through the retreat of cold surface water to greater depths in the region of the Humboldt Current, leads to severe crashes in seabird populations in Ecuador and Peru. 1982-83 and 1997-98 were extremely severe. Although the effects are particularly strong in the tropical Pacific, ENSOs are global phenomena.

ntepicondyle: the larger of the two expansions on the distal end of the humerus; *cf.* ectepicondyle

nteritis: a viral disease limited to ducks, geese, and swans (Anatidae), particularly prevalent where birds gather in high densities; cannot be transferred to humans. Accidentally introduced to America from Europe in 1967. Also called duck plague.

nterohepatitis: a protozoan (*Histomonas meleagridis*) that attacks the liver and caecum of many birds, e.g. Turkeys (*Meleagris gallopavo*) and other gallinaceous birds, resulting in a high mortality rate. Also called blackhead disease, histomoniasis, heterakiasis, or histomoniasis.

ntoderm: the inner of the three germ layers of the early animal embryo, differentiating into the alimentary canal (the gut) and associated glands. Also called endoderm; *cf.* ectoderm, mesoderm.

ntoglossal: within the tongue, such as the bones that support the tongue; *cf.* hyoid horns, hyoid apparatus.

ntomophagy: feeding upon insects, adj. **entomophagous**; *cf.* insectivorous.

ntomophilous: plants adapted for pollination by insects.

nvironment: the envelope of biotic and abiotic conditions surrounding an organism. A broader definition than habitat.

nvironmental stochasticity: random changes in the environment, e.g. fires and hurricanes; *cf.* stochastic, demographic stochasticity.

nzootic: an infection well distributed in an avian population but not causing heavy losses. Also termed endemic and the opposite of epidemic or epizootic.

enzyme: a protein that functions as a biological assistant (catalyst); all metabolic processes are governed by enzymes that are remarkably specific compared with normal industrial catalysts.

Eoalulavis: an 'opposite bird' from the Cretaceous, found in Spain; had a well-developed alula.

Eoaves: infraclass containing the order Struthioniformes and Tinamiformes.

Eocene: epoch 57-35 mya in the Tertiary period.

epaulet: shoulder patch, e.g. the red epaulets of the Red-winged Blackbird (*Agelaius phoeniceus*).

epi-: prefix from Greek *epi* = upon or above.

epibranchial: the paired slender bones posterior to another terminating the tongue bones; *cf.* basihyal, basibranchial, ceratonranchial, epibranchial.

epideictic: of communal displays or manoeuvres, particularly those performed at special times, such as at dawn and dusk.

epidemic: an infection causing heavy losses in a population. Also termed epizootic. The opposite of endemic or enzootic.

epidermal collar: part of the developing feather papilla from which most structures in the growing feather originate at the feather's base.

epidermis: the outermost cell layer of an organism; in vertebrates the 'skin' is multilayered, in land-vertebrates (amniotes) being composed from the outside of stratum corneum, stratum transitivum, stratum intermedium, and stratum basale; *cf.* dermis.

epididymis: pl. epididymides, convoluted tubules on the dorsal side of the testes where the mature spermatozoa reside.

epigamic: of any character that attracts and stimulates members of the opposite sex during courtship. Common examples in birds are special sounds (song) and plumage markings, often playing an important role in epigamic display; *cf.* gamosematic.

epigamic coloration: colours having an epigamic importance, in birds most often seen in males and used by females when choosing a mate. An example of an **epigamic character**.

epigamic display: display playing a role in courtship and pair formation.

epigamic selection: type of natural selection in which traits are selected solely on the basis of the advantage they give in competition for mating; most often the competing sex is male, the choosing sex female. Especially in polygamous and lekking bird species, sexual selection has promoted the evolution of very peculiar and extravagant traits (plumage and other ornaments, displays, and other behaviours). More common called sexual selection; *cf.* founder effect, genetic drift, natural selection, runaway selection.

epigenetic: the study of the interaction of genetic factors from fertilization to adulthood; *cf.* ontogeny.

epinagthism: term for an overdeveloped upper mandible; *cf.* prognathism.

epiphenomenon: something produced as a side-effect to a process.

epiphysis: the pineal body (gland) within the forebrain.

epiphyte: a non-parasitic plant growing on another plant. Groups containing many epiphytic species are, e.g. the orchids, ferns, mosses, and lichens.

episematic: applied to traits such as special marks, colours, or behaviours that help an animal to recognise conspecifics; *cf.* antepisematic, proepisematic, pseudepisematic, aposematic.

epistatic interaction: interaction of genes at different loci.

epithalamus: part of the forebrain; *cf.* thalamus, hypothalamus, diencephalons.

epithelium: sheet of tightly connected cells, with one side free and the other resting on a basal membrane of connective tissue. Lines body cavities and covers surfaces.

epithet: in taxonomy the second (species) name in a scientific binomen and the last two (species, subspecies) names in a trinomen.

epizoic: living on the surface of another animal without being parasitic; **epizoon**; *cf.* commensal.

epizootic: epidemic disease amongst (crowded) animals.

epoch: in geology and paleontology subdivision of a period; *cf.* era, period.

epomidis: a dark rufous colour phase found in the Senegal Coucal (*Centropus senegalensis*).

eponymous name: a name incorporating that of a person, e.g. as in the scientific name of a bird.

equilibrium: describes a stable system in which, for example, a population achieves stability in size through the balancing of birth and immigration with death and emigration, or in which the number of species in a community is stable through balanced extinction and colonization.

era: any of the major intervals in geological time, such as Mesozoic and Cenozoic; subdivided into periods and further into epochs.

erectile: capable of being raised to an upright position.

erne: a vernacular name for the European Sea Eagle (*Haliaeetus albicilla*)

eruptive species: a species in which regular and abrupt increases in population occur, typically resulting in mass movements. Population increase es follow one or more consecutive seasons with unusually favourable breeding conditions because of abundant food, and mass mortality occurs when conditions subsequently deteriorate over large areas. Most such species are specialised on fluctuating or cyclically varying foods, such as certain fruits or seeds, or small rodents in northern areas. Examples are Pallas's Sandgrouse (*Syrrhaptes paradoxus*), Bohemian Waxwing (*Bombycilla garrulous*), Brambling (*Fringilla montifringilla*), and some northern owls, e.g. Snowy Owl (*Nyctea scandiaca*). More often called irruptive species; *cf.* gradation-bird.

rysipelas: disease caused by the bacterium *Erysipelotrix rhusiopathiae* which can long persist in soil. Can be a serious problem in zoos and bird parks.

rythrism: abnormal pigmentation in which red and chestnut replace other pigments. Erythrism in eggs is due to a lack of or reduced amount of blue pigment; *cf.* flavism.

ythrocyte: red blood cell; *cf.* leucocyte, thrombocyte.

ythromelanin: pigment in feathers, giving red, red-brown, or chestnut colours.

ythropoiesis: the production of red blood cells.

cape distance: the minimum distance a bird will allow a potential predator to approach before fleeing.

cape movement: a movement of short to intermediate geographic distance to avoid harsh environmental conditions, including drought, storms, and cold.

ophageal fluids: Am. for crop milk, pigeon milk, i.e. the secretions from the crop by which pigeons and a few other birds feed their chicks. Eur. oesophageal.

ophagus: Am. for oesophagus; the part of the food channel between the pharynx and the stomach, in birds often having a sack-like widening, a crop, in which food can be stored temporarily.

ESS: abbr. evolutionarily stable strategy. A strategy (for optimizing evolutionary fitness) that cannot be bettered by an alternative strategy.

established population: a self-sustaining population, as opposed to a sink population or habitat.

estradiol: a hormone from the ovary that together with progesterone stimulates nest building in female birds.

estrogen: Am. for oestrogen, a female sexual hormone; *cf.* testosterone.

estuary: a river mouth with tidal mud flats, alternately being flooded and exposed, providing rich feeding grounds for shorebirds. Adj. **estuarine**.

et al.: from Latin *et alia* = and others.

Ethiopian region: zoogeographical region comprising sub-Saharan Africa, Madagascar, and southern Arabia. Also called Afrotropical Region. Some authors exclude Madagascar and treat it as a separate region, the Malagasy faunal region; *cf.* the Nearctic, Neotropical, Palearctic, Oriental, and Australasian regions.

ethology: from Greek *ethos* = habit or custom, the science of animal behaviour.

ethological barrier: reproductive isolating mechanism based on behaviour, e.g. in courtship being species specific.

eucalyptus: a flowering evergreen tree of the genus *Eucalyptus*, found in Australia.

eukaryote: a member of the Eukaryota, one of three major subdivisions of life on Earth. The other two are Archaea and Eubacteria. Eukaryota includes all organisms having cells with a membrane-bounded nucleus. Also rarely spelled **eucaryote**.

eukaryotic: one of the two main types of cells, it has a complex internal structure, including internal organelles and a nucleus; *cf.* prokaryotic.

eumelanin: a common pigment in feathers, giving black, dark brown, or grey colours; *cf.* melanin, pheomelanin, carotenoid.

Euparkeria: a thecodont from the Triassic period, perhaps an ancestor of dinosaurs.

Eurasia: the continent of Europe and Asia combined.

EURING: a data bank started in 1979 containing recoveries in codes from birds ringed in Europe. The system has undergone a major revision and extension resulting in the EURING EXCHANGE CODE 2000, where it is also possible to study many other aspects such as survival rates and natal dispersal or even capture methods. Biometric data are planned for future research. More on the websites: www.euring.org or www.vogel-trekstation.nl.

euryoecious: term (adj.) applied to organisms able to live in a wide spectrum of habitats: the opposite of stenoecious.

euryphagous: term (adj.) applied to organisms that use a wide variety of foods, in contrast to a food specialist; **euryphagy**; using a wide range of types of food; *cf.* omnivorous, oligophagous, stenophagous.

eurytopic: being habitat tolerant, able to adjust to large environmental fluctuations.

euryzonal: an animal living in mountains and occurring through a broad range of elevations, in contrast to a stenozonal.

eustachian tube: the canal connecting the middle ear with the pharynx. Also termed pharyngotympanic tube or auditory tube.

eusyantrope: a species living together with humans, such as the House Sparrow (*Passer domesticus*); the opposite of exanthrope; adj. **eusyantropous.**

eutaxy: the condition that the fifth secondary is present and has a corresponding greater covert, as opposed to diastataxy. All passerines are eutaxic.

eutrophic: rich in nutrients, mostly in connection with fresh-water habitat; *cf.* mesotrophic, oligotrophic.

eutrophication: the enrichment of water with nutrients, either from natural causes or as a result of human activities; may lead to an overproduction of algae to the extent that decomposing algae use virtually all oxygen in the water column, making the water body uninhabitable for aerobic life; also called overthrow, capsizing, or tipping of balance.

evaporative cooling: heat loss through vaporization of water; *cf.* panting, gular fluttering.

evo-devo: abbr. of evolutionary developmental biology.

evolution: any changes in organism occurring through genetic inheritance across generations; generally gradual and occurring through mutation and natural selection; descent with modification. Applied to organism characteristics (e.g. phenotypic and molecular traits (e.g. DNA sequence); *cf.* macroevolution, microevolution.

evolutionary species concept: abbr. ESC, defines a species as a lineage of descendant populations with its own evolutionary tendencies and history unlike the biological species concept does not explicitly consider gene flow or reproductive isolation; *cf.* biological species concept, phylogenetic species concept.

Evolutionary Synthesis: the scientific revolution of the 1930s and 1940s that combined classic Darwinian principles of evolution with the findings of genetics, systematics, and paleontology. Also called Modern Synthesis or New Syntesis.

ex-: prefix from Latin meaning from or according to.

exanthropous: adj. applied to a species living away from human settlements and cultivated land, the opposite of eusyanthropous or synanthropous. Also called hemerophilous.

exaptation: when an ancestral character becomes modified for a new purpose. Also called preadaptation.

exaspidean: applied to describe a tarsus on which the anterior and external sides of the sheath have large scutes and the internal side is bare or with small scutes only; *cf.* endaspidean, holaspidean, ocreate, pycnaspidean, taxaspidean.

excavator: a hole-nesting bird that makes its own hole, such as woodpeckers (Picidae), or a tunnel, such as Collared Sand Martin (*Riparia riparia*), as opposed to non-excavators such as, e.g. Starling (*Sturnus vulgaris*) that use existing holes.

excl.: abbr. of Latin *exclusus* = excluded.

excluded name: a scientific name excluded from the provision of the International Code of Zoological Nomenclature, e.g. owing to hypothetical concepts or hybrid specimens.

excretion: ridding the body of waste material, including the removal of waste products from the blood by the excretory system (the kidneys).

excretion, extrarenal: excretion taking place outside the kidneys; a well known example is the removal of excess salt by the salt glands (nasal glands) in seabirds; these glands are situated in the skull in the region of the orbits and are connected to the nasal cavity, from which the salt solution flows through the nares or the mouth.

excretory system: another name for the urinary system. Consists of paired kidneys and uretes; *cf.* urogenital system.

exo-: prefix from Greek *exo* = without, acting outside, opening to the outside.

exoccipital: a paired bone at the posterior end of the skull.

exocrine: a gland whose secretion is drained by ducts; *cf.* endocrine gland.

exogenous: originating outside the entity under discussion, for example an organism.

exoparasite: syn. with ectoparasite, a parasite living outside the body of the host, by some authors also a bloodsucker such as a mosquito that only briefly visits its victim; the most common ectoparasites of birds are mites (Acarina) such as feather mites (Analgesidae), itch mites (Sarcoptidae), nasal mites (Rhinonyssidae), red mites (Dermanyssidae), ticks (Ixodidae), and insects, the most important of which are feather lice and lice (Phthiraptera), louse flies (Hippoboscidae), and fleas (Siphonaptera).

exoskeleton: external skeleton, as characteristic of all arthropods, e.g. beetles, often found in bird's pellets.

exotic: a species introduced to a new place it is not natural to.

exovation: the process of hatching.

exploded lek: lek in which the displaying males are separated by some distance, often out of sight of each other, but within earshot; syn. dispersed lek.

exploitation competition: competitive relationship in which an individual or species uses a resource more efficiently than another individual or species; *cf.* interference competition.

exploratory behaviour: investigation of a novel environment. Behaviour performed in the absence of a releaser. Also termed appetitive behaviour.

extirpation: a surgical operation in which an organ or part of an organ is removed to study subsequent behaviour of the animal and thus obtain information about the function of the removed organ, e.g. used in brain research.

extant: of a species living at the present time, as opposed to extinct.

extensor: a muscle whose contraction opens a joint, and so for example straightens a limb; opposite of flexor.

extensor brevis: a muscle on the tarsometatarsus.

extensor carpi radialis: a wing muscle on the radius that extends the hand.

extensor metacarpi radialis: a muscle on the radius in the wing that extends the hand.

extermination: elimination of a population or species.

external lateral xiphoid: the process on the anterior end of the sternal notch. Also called lateral caudal process.

exteroceptive: all external senses such as smelling, vision, hearing, tasting, and balance.

extinct: of a species, not existing anymore; operationally defined as (a species) not found in the wild during the last 50 years; *cf.* extant, extirpated.

extirpated: the condition of being locally extinct from an area formerly occupied.

extra-: prefix from Latin = outside, located outside.

extralimital: occurring outside of the typical range, e.g. of an organism not belonging to the area's fauna; also an organism found outside its natural geographical range, either as a vagrant or after having become established recently; *cf.* allochthonous, autochthonous.

extra-pair copulation: abbr. EPC, copulation outside of a mated pair in a monogamous species; *cf.* extra-pair fertilization.

extra-pair fertilization: abbr. EPF, extra-pair copulation leading to fertilization of one or more eggs.

extra-pair helper: a non-breeding bird who assists a breeding pair in feeding their young or providing care in other ways; in most studied cases helpers are earlier offspring of the breeding pair, or at least close relatives; also called auxiliary.

extra-pair paternity: paternity by any male other than the mother's pair bonded mate.

extrarenal excretion: excretion taking place outside the kidneys; a well known example is the removal of carbon dioxide in the lungs, and the elimination of excess salt by the salt glands (nasal glands) in sea birds.

extratropical: outside the tropics.

extrinsic: existing or originating outside an individual, group, or system.

extrinsic factors: factors exterior to an organism, such as food supply, predation, or disease.

extrinsic muscles: muscles originating and inserting on the trachea; *cf.* intrinsic muscles.

eyas: also spelled **eyass**, pl. eyasses, hawk or falcon nestling; mainly a falconry term.

eye: the organ of vision; *cf.* choroid, ciliary body, cones, cornea, fovea, interorbitale septum, lens, nictitating membrane, orbit, pecten, pupil, retina, rod, scleral ossicles.

eyebrow: another name for the superciliary.

eye cup: the soft part in front of the lenses of field glasses that enables a person with glasses to use a pair of binoculars.

eyelash: bristles (feathers) forming a structure similar to the mammalian eyelash (of hair). Found in a few groups of birds, e.g. Ostrich (*Struthio camelus*) and hornbills (Bucerotidae), many cuckoos (Cuculidae), and some hummingbirds (Trochilidae).

eyelid: birds have three eyelids: an upper and lower eyelid and a nictitating membrane.

eyeline: a narrow stripe running from the base of the bill through the eye, distinct from the superciliary above the eye; also called eye stripe.

eye peeking: the opening of one eye from time to time by a sleeping bird to obtain information about its surroundings.

eyepiece: the part of the binoculars or spotting scope that the eyes are put to in use.

eyerim: the ring around the eye, consisting of flexible, feathered, or bare skin; also called orbital ring, and periophthalmic ring.

eye-ring: a ring of feathers or swollen skin forming a marking around the eyes, also called periophthalmic ring; *cf.* eyerim.

eye-spot: eye-shaped pattern, like the spots in the 'tail' of a Peacock (*Pavo cristatus*) or the eye-like spots in the nape of some birds, e.g. the American Kestrel (*Falco sparverius*).

eye stripe: a narrow stripe running through the eye, distinct from the superciliary above the eye; also called eyeline.

Eyrean Fauna: the fauna of the arid interior part of Australia; *cf.* Bassian Fauna, Torresian Fauna.

eyrie: the nest of a large bird of prey (Accipitridae). Also spelled **eyry**, aery or aerie.

F

F_1: first offspring or first generation from a cross between parents of different genotypes.

face: the lores, orbital area, and cheeks, combined; *cf.* nape, forehead, and crown.

facial disc: the disc-like face of owls and harriers, enhancing hearing. Also spelled **facial disk.**

facial ruff: the outer part of the facial disc in owls.

facial shield: a plate on the forehead of, e.g. coots (*Fulica* spp.).

factor analysis: statistical methods that examine multivariate data sets to identify and determine the importance of a presumed subset of the variables in explaining observed variance.

facultative: flexible, the opposite of obligate; able to exist under more than one set of environmental conditions; for example a facultative anaerobe, an organism that is tolerant of, but not dependent on, oxygen; or a facultative brood parasite, a species that may sometimes lay its eggs in the nests of other birds but is fully capable of rearing a brood itself.

facultative hypothermic responses: an adaptive response to decreases in ambient temperature (e.g. nightly or seasonal) that enables organisms such as swifts (Apodidae), nightjars (Caprimulgidae), and hummingbirds (Trochilidae) to become torpid. Some authors include torpor and rest-phase (controlled) hypothermia under the term.

facultative learning: learning by imitation, e.g. as in European tits (*Parus* spp.) that started to drink milk by pecking open the foil tops of milk bottles; *cf.* obligate learning.

facultative migration: formerly called weather migration. Migrating in response when to prevailing conditions, especially food supplies and their winter distribution vary greatly from year to year.

facultative parasite: a parasite that is not necessarily exclusively confined to its host during its life cycle, living under broader environmental conditions, such as cuckoo species that can raise young but will often try to lay their eggs in the nests of other birds; or ticks, which in their life cycles do not live their whole life on the host (obligate parasite), but are more independent of the host; *cf.* temporary parasite.

facultative partial migration: a population in which some individuals migrate annually, while others do not, e.g. if circumstances such as a food shortage triggers migration; *cf.* partial migration and obligate partial migration.

faecal sac: Am. fecal sac; a gelatinous capsule containing the excreted droppings, or faeces, of a nestling. Permits the parent(s) to more easily carry the droppings away from the nest and thus keep the nest clean; characteristic of passerines.

faeces: Am. feces; excrement.

faeder: a male bird looking like a conspecific female. An alternative mating strategy in which a female-like male steals copulations with visiting females. A phenomenon only found in the Ruff (*Philomachus pugnax*).

Fahrenheit: abbr. F, a temperature scale in common use in English-speaking countries, especially in the USA. The freezing point of water (0° C) is at 32° F, the boiling point (100° C) is 212° F, so that Fahrenheit is converted to Celsius by subtracting 32 and multiplying the result by 5/9.

falcate: sickle-shaped.

falcon: 1) any member of the family Falconidae. 2) a falconer term for the female falcon, the male being the tiercel.

falconry: or falconery, the art of hunting with trained raptors.

Falconiformes: order comprising seven species of New World vultures (Cathartidae), 64 species of falcons (Falconidae), and 233 species of Osprey, kites, hawks, and eagles (Accipitridae).

fall: 1) Am. for autumn. 2) a sudden arrival of a large number of migratory birds at a single site due to weather conditions, also called **fallout**.

fall shuffle: a game biologist term for the dispersal of young birds in the autumn (Am. fall), especially applied to the Ruffed Grouse (*Bonasa umbellus*).

false crop: an expansion of the gullet (esophagus) on the left side of the vertebral column in the Redpoll (*Acanthis flammea*).

false ribs: the two ribs not attached to the breastbone.

family: in taxonomy the level between order and genus, a group of closely related genera; scientific names of families of animals (but not plants) always end with -idae. A family can comprise one, a few, or many subfamilies or genera, *cf.* class, phylum, kingdom.

fancier: a follower of some activity or thing, e.g. a pigeon fancier.

FAO: abbr. Food and Agriculture Organization of the United Nations.

FAP: abbr. of fixed action pattern. A behaviour invariant and independent of external stimuli.

fascia: tissue that binds muscle fibres together; *cf.* tendon, aponeurose.

fascis: Latin = a small bundle.

fat index: 1) the ratio of the dry weight of all fat in a body (including under the skin and in the body cavity) to that of non-fat biomass. Also called **fat load**. 2) a 'fat score' of some type, usually taken through examination of fat deposits in live birds by subjective visual assessment through the skin, e.g. of the furculum.

fault bar: a narrow, often translucent transverse band found in individual feathers of birds, e.g. common in crows (Corvidae), as a result of physical stress during the feather's growth, e.g. through handling. It is the result of abnormally formed or missing barbules that weaken feathers, making breakage more likely. Also called hunger streak, hunger fault, hunger trace, starvation mark, subordinate bar, feather mark, and by veterinarians stress band. When formed as spot, called **fault spot** or **fault hole.** In error also called fundamental bar. This lack of consistent terminology has led to some confusion in the literature.

fauna: all animals of an area; *cf.* biota, flora, avifauna.

faunal regions: geographically defined areas containing closely associated animals and plants. The six such regions usually recognized include th

Australasian-, Ethiopian-, Nearctic-, Neotropical-, Oriental-, and Palearctic regions (or realms) (the last also spelled Palaearctic). The Antarctic and the oceans represent additional regions. Also called zoogeographic regions.

Fauna Norvegica, Serie C, Cinclus: periodical published by Norsk Ornitologisk Forening: abbr. NOF. Published since 1979-; formerly *Cinclus* 1978.

Fauna Preservation Society: a society founded in 1909 in London with the purpose of protecting all of the world's animals. Publishes *Oryx*.

faunistic: pertaining to the fauna.

F-distribution: probability distribution playing an important role in statistics. Named in honor of R. A. Fisher.

feather: a keratinous structure characteristic of birds; *cf.* periderm, contour feather, down, flight feathers, placode, filoplumes, bristles, powder down, calamus, rachis, scapus, umbilicus, barb, barbule, hooklet, vane, afterfeather, aftershaft.

feather comb: the toothed edge of the claw of the middle toe, like a comb and used in preening. Found, e.g. in nightjars (Caprimulgidae), herons and bitterns (Ardeidae), and the Barn Owl (*Tyto alba*). More commonly called pectinate claw.

feather fly: member of the family Hippoboscidae, flattened ectoparasitic flies with a leathery surface and well-developed claws, mostly wingless, at least after having settled on a host. Also called birdfly, flat-fly, hippoboscid fly, ked-fly, louse-fly, spider-fly, and tick-fly; *cf.* ectoparasites.

feather follicle: the basal part of a feather that is within a bird's skin.

feather louse: pl. lice, belonging to the family Mallophagidae, flattened and wingless ectoparasite, that sucks blood from feathers and skin. Some species live within the feather shaft. Vectors of a number of avian diseases. Feather damage caused by them may reduce winter survival because it causes heat loss. Also called bird louse, chewing louse, or body louse.

feather mark: a narrow, often translucent, transverse band found in individual feathers of common in birds, e.g. crows (Corvidae), as a result of physical stress during the feather's growth, e.g. through handling. It is the result of abnormally formed or missing barbules that weaken feathers, making breakage more likely. Most commonly called fault bar, but also hunger streak, hunger fault, hunger trace, starvation mark, subordinate bar, and by veterinarians stress band. When formed as spots called fault spot or fault hole.

feather mites: of the families Analgoidae, Freyanoidae, and Pterolechoidae. Most are commensals, not parasites, mainly restricted to flight feathers and living upon the algae, fungi, bacteria, and pollen thereon; *cf.* itch mites, nasal mites, red mites.

feather pecking: when one bird pecks at and pulls out the feathers of conspecifics.

feather sheath: the sheath around a growing feather (a 'pin').

feather tract: a tract or area of skin growing contour feathers, also called pteryla (pl. pterylae). In most bird families contour feathers are restricted to such areas, but in ratites (Struthioniformes) and penguins (Spheniscidae) feathers are dispersed evenly all over the body.

fecal sac: Am. for faecal sac, a gelatinous capsule containing the excreted droppings, or faeces of a nestling. This permits the parent(s) to more easily carry the droppings away from the nest and thus keep the nest clean; characteristic of passerines.

feces: Am. for faeces, excrement.

fecundity: the reproductive success or the number of chicks successfully raised or fledged per year. Also called birth rate; *cf.* fertility, age-specific fecundity.

feedback mechanism: a general mechanism operative in many life processes, where the result of a process influences the process itself, directly or indirectly; *cf.* cybernetics.

feeding territory: in most birds the feeding and breeding territory are identical, or the feeding area is the larger, and such combined territories are strongly defended against conspecifics. However, in some birds, such as the Common Cuckoo (*Cuculus canorus*), food may be obtained many kilometres from the 'breeding territory', and such 'feeding territories' are not defended against conspecifics.

female choice: in sexual selection it is most often the female that selects one of several available males for mating, rather than the opposite; therefore the female is also typically the choosy sex.

femoral tract: a feather tract situated on and behind the thigh. Also called *pterylae femoralis*. **femur**: pl. femora, the thigh bone, adj. **femoral**.

fen: a waterlogged area with peaty soil; *cf.* marsh, bog, wetland.

fenestra: a vacant space or 'window' in a bone, e.g. at the posterior end of the breastbone (sternum); *cf.* metasternum.

fenestra ovale: an oval opening in the wall of the internal ear.

Feng-Huang: a Chinese version of the Phoenix but resembling a peacock.

Fenno-Scandia: in biogeography Finland, Kola Peninsula, Karelia, and the Scandinavian Peninsula except Scania (Skåne).

feral: of a domesticated species that has established a population in the wild, e.g. feral pigeon (domesticated form of the Rock Dove, *Columba livia*).

fertility: the ability to reproduce, measured as the number of offspring per year or lifetime; *cf.* fecundity.

fetus: an embryo, especially when fairly advanced in development.

fibrosis: thickening of connective tissue.

fibula: one of the two bones of the leg below the knee, in birds a thin bone on the back of the tibiotarsus usually ending as a thin splint two-thirds of the way down from the knee.

fide: Latin = according to.

field glasses: an optical instrument consisting of two small telescopes joined together to provide magnification over distance for both eyes, also called binoculars.

fight or flight response: in animal behaviour and physiology, when confronted with a threat an animal can choose to either face it (fight) or avoid it (flee, or flight).

filament: thread, thread-like object, adj. **filamentous**.

Filaroidea: a group of endoparasitic roundworms; some species parasitize birds.

filial imprinting: when a bird raised by another species learns its foster parents' social behaviour during the first days of life, critical for such learning; *cf.* sex imprinting.

filoplume: a hair-like feather either completely lacking a vane or with only a small tuft of barbs at its tip. Often longer than neighbouring contour feathers. Found in most families but absent in flightless birds; most extreme in the Hairy-backed Bulbul (*Hypsipetes criniger*). May be associated with sensory receptors in the skin; *cf.* bristle, semiplume.

filter-feeding: the straining process by which birds such as dabbling ducks feed on abundant small aquatic organisms.

finger: 1) a digit of the hand. 2) the tip of the longest primaries (often emarginated), which become widely separated during flight, e.g. of a raptor.

first adult: of plumage, the first plumage obtained during the life of a bird that is identical to the adult plumage of its species; *cf.* first winter, first basic.

first alternate: Am. term for first summer or first breeding plumage.

first basic: Am. term for first winter or first non-breeding plumage.

first non-nuptial: older Am. term for first winter plumage.

first nuptial: An old term for first summer plumage; *cf.* first alternate.

first prebasic molt: Am. term for post-juvenile moult. First moult into immature plumage or adult plumage if no immature stages exist between juvenile and adult.

first prebreeding moult: in Am. called first (second, etc.) prealternate moult.

first winter: of a juvenile bird that has a partial post-juvenile moult; *cf.* first adult.

Fisher's exact test: A statistical test for independence in a 2×2 table, in which the null hypothesis is that the row and column classifications are independent. Probabilities are calculated based on the hypergeometric distribution. This test is particularly useful if cell frequencies (entries) are small, so that alternatives (*G*-test, chi-squared test) are inappropriate.

Fisher's fundamental theorem of natural selection: theory according to which the average fitness of the individuals in a population increases at a rate equal to the fitness variance of the population. The theory implies that average fitness always increases and that genetically determined variance in fitness is required for selection to cause evolutionary change. Commonly visualized through Wright's 'adaptive landscape', or 'adaptive topography', and serving as a focal point for distinction between the effects of sexual and natural selection.

Fisher's runaway model: males with special exaggerated traits that have some selective advantage not attributable to female choice. Females that mate with such males produce more offspring. The sons inherit the male trait and daughters inherit the female preference for the trait. This process leads to an accelerating enhancement through positive feedback from generation to generation, hence the term "runaway".

Fish Hawk: old name for the Osprey (*Pandion haliaetus*).

fissipalmate: of a swimming foot that instead of webs between the toes has lobes or fringes along the toes, as in grebes (Podicipedidae), coots (*Fulica* spp.), and some other waterbirds.

fissura: Latin = cleft.

fist: a falconry term for the gloved hand of a falconer.

fitness: 1) the quality of a genotype. 2) a measurement of an individual's ability to survive and reproduce. 3) quantification of the contributions of one genotype versus another to subsequent generations; *cf.* phenotype.

fixation: 1) in taxonomy, determination of the type species of a genus or a subspecies or determination of a type specimen. 2) in ethology a term used for an abnormal social bond between two individuals of different species. 3) in genetics, when an allele becomes 'fixed' in a population and other alleles have disappeared.

fixed action pattern: abbr. FAP, an innate behaviour independent of learning. When first started by a releasing stimulus it is played out to the end regardless of any response that may occur.

flange: the swollen, light-coloured margins of the mouth in juvenile birds.

flank: the sides of the body between the ribs and the pelvis, largely hidden in birds by the wings when held against the body.

flapping flight: animal flight in which thrust is generated by wing movements, as in 'normal' bird flight. Also called powered flight; *cf.* gliding flight, soaring flight, dynamic soaring.

flat fly: member of the family Hippoboscidae, flattened ectoparasitic flies with a leathery surface and well-developed claws, mostly wingless, at least after having settled on a host. Also called birdfly, featherfly, hippoboscid fly, ked-fly, louse-fly, spider-fly, and tick-fly; *cf.* ectoparasites.

flavism: a rare abnormality of plumage coloration in the wild in which there is an excess of yellow; also called xanthochroism. Found in the Canary (*Serinus canaria*) and Budgerigar (*Melopsittacus undulatus*).

flavus: Latin = yellow, golden.

flea: blood-sucking ectoparasite of the insect order Siphonaptera; laterally flattened and a good jumper but unable to fly. Can be a vector for pathogenic microbes.

fledgling: a young bird that has just fledged, a slightly vague term usually meaning 'has become fully feathered', 'has left the nest', or 'has attained the ability to fly'. Usually not used of flightless or precocial species. Also spelled **fledgeling**.

fledgling period: the period from leaving the nest to becoming independent of parents.

fledging success: the percentage of young surviving to fledging.

flexi cardiulnaris: a muscle on the posterior part of the ulna in the wing.

flexor: muscle whose contraction causes a joint to close, as in the bending of a limb; opposite extensor.

flexor carpi ulnaris: a muscle located beneath the ulna in the wing.

flexor cruris lateralis: a muscle on the thigh and used in avian classification by Alfred Henry Garrod.

flexor digitorum profundus: a wing muscle atop the ulna that flexes the hand; *cf.* extensor metacarpi radialis.

flexor digitorum superficialis: a muscle over the ulna of the wing that closes the hand; *cf.* extensor metacarpi radialis.

flight bathing: bathing in flight, as may be seen in certain terns (Sterninae) and frigatebirds (Fregatidae) and in flying foxes (Mammalia, Chiroptera) that take a dip whilst skimming a water surface; *cf.* in-out bathing, plunge-bathe, rain-bathing, stand-in bathing, stand-out bathing, and swim-bathing.

flight distance: the minimum distance a bird allows a human (or other threat) to approach before taking flight. Also called flushing distance.

flight feathers: collective term for the primaries and secondaries (the remiges). Some authors also include the tail feathers (rectrices). Compared with other contour feathers they are stiffer and longer, have very little or no basal down, and no afterfeather.

flipper: the modified wing of a penguin (Spheniscidae).

floater: a bird without a territory, generally able to quickly and opportunistically occupy a vacancy among its territorial conspecifics; floaters occur when suitable habitat is saturated and they can appear in breeding or non-breeding systems.

flock: a temporary association of animals, e.g. feeding, sleeping, or migrating together; *cf.* group.

floppy disk: a common device used to store electronic data, comprised of a small, thin, magnetic circular plate within a protective plastic case. Also called diskette.

flora: all plants of an area; *cf.* fauna, biota, avifauna.

flotation method: the placing of an egg into water to determine its age since laying; *cf.* candling eggs.

fluctuation: irregular, random variation (in, for example, the population density of some species); sometimes also applied to more regular, e.g. cyclic variations; perhaps best known are the 3- to 4-year cycles of lemmings and voles; *cf.* cycle, oscillations.

fluctuating asymmetry: small, random deviations from symmetry in characters between the right and left sides of bilaterally symmetrical organisms. Departures from symmetry have been linked to environmental stress and inbreeding.

fluke: endoparasitic flatworm belonging to the class Trematoda; those parasitizing (water-) birds generally have one or more intermediate hosts, often a fish, snail, annelid, crustacean or other arthropod.

fluorescent plumage colour: plumage that absorbs ultraviolet radiation and re-emits it as visible radiation, producing a 'glowing' appearance in green, blue, yellow, orange, or red; presumably playing a role in sexual selection, e.g. mate-choice; *cf.* ultraviolet plumage colour.

flush: 1) when a bird runs or takes flight to escape a threat; to frighten a bird out of cover. 2) an explosive population increase; the opposite of a crash.

flush and rush: a term for foraging by hopping and running, ambushing, or chasing prey out from cover; *cf.* peer and pounce.

flushing distance: the minimum distance a bird allows a human (or other threat) to approach before taking flight. Also called flight distance.

flush-pursuit foraging: a tail-spreading behaviour that assists in startling and flushing potential prey that are then pursued and captured in flight. A behaviour seen in the American redstarts, genus *Myioborus*, all with contrastingly coloured black and white and pale red tails.

fluttering: rapid movements, for example of the wings; largely the same as quivering; *cf.* gular fluttering.

flyway: a fairly well-defined (narrow) path along a migratory route; for example in North America there are four distinct migrating routes or corridors that waterfowl follow: Atlantic, Mississippi, Central, and Pacific flyways; *cf.* corridor, mass resting area.

foliage-gleaning: feeding upon food items (insects) on leaves; *cf.* bark-gleaning.

folium: Latin = a leaf or a leaf-like structure.

folivory: leaf eating, as in the Hoatzin (*Opisthocomus hoatzin*); adj. folivorous.

folklore: a mixture of traditional and popular beliefs, customs, legends, myths, and fables among common people.

follicle: 1) a small sac, gland, or cavity. 2) also the basal section of a feather imbedded in the feather socket in the skin. 3) a developing oocyte; *cf.* papilla, dermal papilla, placode.

follicle stimulating hormone: abbr. FSH, a gonadotropic hormone secreted by the pituitary that causes growth and development of sex organs; *cf.* luteinizing hormone.

follicular cells: cells surrounding the egg (oocyte) in the ovary and secreting oestrogens.

folliculus: Latin = small sac or bag, **follicle**.

food canal: the esophagus and intestine from mouth to cloaca, the alimentary canal.

food chain: ecological generalisation describing the feeding relationships among organisms in an ecosystem, wherein primary producers (autotrophs, primarily photosynthetic plants) provide food for consumers such as herbivores and, through them to successive levels of consumers (heterotrophs) to decomposers.

food hoarding: food-storing or food caching for later use.

food parasitism: a relationship in which members of one species obtain some or all of their food by robbing other animals of the same or other species; frigatebirds (Fregatidae) and skuas (Stercorariidae) are specialised food parasites on various seabirds; *cf.* kleptoparasitism.

food pass: the delivery of food to one's mate or offspring.

foot: pl. feet; 1) a measurement = 304.8 mm = 12 inches. 2) in birds, the toes at the end of a leg.

foot pox: a viral disease causing swellings on the toes. Also called avian pox.

foraging strategy: the method(s) used by birds to obtain food.

foramen: pl. foramina; a hole, usually in a bone and most often enabling a nerve or tendon to pass through it.

foramen magnum: the major opening at the base of the cranium, through which the spinal cord passes into the brain case.

foramen triosseum: the opening between three bones, the clavicle, scapula, and coracoid, through which the tendon from the major elevator of the wing (the supracoracoideus) passes to the humerus. Also called supracoracoid foramen or triosseal canal.

forb: a non-grassy, broad-leaved, herbaceous plant.

forbivory: feeding upon broad-leaved plants as does the Hoatzin (*Opisthocomus hoazin*), adj. **forbivorous**; *cf.* folivory.

forearm: the part between the upperarm (humerus) and hand (manus) consisting of ulna and radius.

forebrain: the frontal cerebral hemisphere controlling behavioural instincts, instructions, sensory organs, and learning; *cf.* midbrain, hindbrain.

forecollar: a band or collar of contrasting colour, across the foreneck of a bird.

forehead: the part of the crown nearest the base of the upper mandible.

forelimb: an anterior limb of a quadrapod, e.g. a wing; see: humerus, brachium, ulna, ulnare, radius, radiale, antebrachium, carpal, carpometacarpus, digit, alular digit.

foreneck: the throat.

forest floor: the ground of a forest with soil and litter of dead leaves and other plant debris.

fore-stomach: proventriculus, the glandular stomach anterior to the gizzard.

forked tail: a tail with its middle feathers much shorter than its outer ones, seen in, e.g. the forktails (genus *Enicurus*) of the family Muscicapidae and the Barn Swallow (*Hirundo rustica*); *cf.* square tail, streamers.

form: a neutral term for distinguishable entities, such as species, subspecies, etc. Often used where uncertainty exists regarding the taxonomic status, or where a more specific taxonomic designation is not desirable or practical.

formation flight: flight in formations such as the V-shape seen in geese, swans, and cranes, particularly during their migrations.

Formenkreis: an outdated taxonomic term introduced by the German ornithologist Kleinschmidt in 1900, the nearest modern synonym being superspecies.

Formicidae: the ant family; not to be confused with Formicariidae, the family of ant thrushes and antpittas.

fossa: pl. fossae, a pit or trench-like depression in a bone, e.g. the single or double excavation or depression at the proximal end of the upper arm (humerus) found in many oscine and all suboscine perching birds, plus the whole woodpecker (Piciformes) and kingfisher orders (Coraciformes). It is a feature often used in classification.

fossil: a plant or an animal or its skeleton, or an impression or trace of same, preserved in and as stone, amber, or tar, or, rarely, as a dried or frozen 'mummy', the latter more correctly classified as a subfossil.

fossorial: adapted for digging; of birds that make their nest by digging a burrow in soil, such as bee-eaters (Meropidae) and kingfishers (Alcedinidae).

fossula: small depression.

foster parent: the host of a young brood parasite that it is rearing.

founder effect: a genetic consequence of a small number of founders of a new population bringing with them only a limited portion of the genetic diversity present in the parent or source population. Reduced genetic variation is particularly likely in island populations, and this has been hypothesized to be one of four processes promoting speciation; *cf.* genetic drift, natural selection, sexual selection.

founder effect speciation: rapid divergence of a new population from the parent population.

fovea: pl. foveae; a small pit or depression. The most well-known fovea (the one meant when the word is used without a qualifier) is a depression in the retina of some vertebrates, including all birds, where receptors (mainly or exclusively cones) are especially tightly packed, resulting in this being the location of greatest visual acuity. Many birds have two foveae, one central and one temporal, the latter used in binocular vision; *cf.* fossa, *fossula*.

fowl cholera: a bacterial disease caused by *Pasteurella multocida*, causing many bloody spots on the skin and necrosis of the liver. Found in many bird families but most often in waterbirds. Also called avian cholera or avian pasteurellosis.

fowl pest: a term embracing both fowl plague and Newcastle's disease.

fowl plague: a viral disease in poultry, often fatal.

fowl pox: a viral disease causing skin lesions beginning as vesicles or blisters and spreading to become pockets of fluid, swelling, and later scab formation, most often seen in pigeons in which it causes wart-like growths on the head and feet. Also called avian pox.

fowl typhoid: a disease caused by bacteria of the genus *Salmonella*, giving diarrhoea. The bacteria are excreted with the droppings. Liver and spleen become white- or grey-spotted. Another form affects the mucous membranes of the mouth and upper respiratory tract. Also called salmonellosis, bacillary white diarrhoea, infectious enteritis, or paratyphoid infection.

fragmented distribution: a geographic distribution that is intermittent, thus causing disjunct patches of a species' range; *cf.* disjunct distribution.

Fraser Darling Effect: the stimulation of breeding in a pair by similar activity nearby among other conspecific pairs; causes synchronisation of breeding through reciprocal stimulation in colonial birds, also called the Darling effect.

frass: insect excrement and other matterett behind, especially by larvae.

fratricide: literally the killing of brother(s), but in practice used for the killing of siblings (nest mates) regardless of sex; cf. siblicide, cainism.

free-martin: egg with two yolks from which two embryos may develop; in mammals, the sterile female twin of a male, sterility caused by hormonal effects from the male during development *in utero*. Also called freemartin.

French moult: an abnormality in which growing feathers are stunted and fall out before fully grown. Most often seen in Budgerigars (*Melopsittacus undulatus*).

fret mark: a narrow, often translucent, transverse band found in individual feathers of birds, e.g. common in crows (Corvidae), as a result of physical stress during the feather's growth, e.g. through hunger. It is the result of abnormally formed or missing barbules that weaken feathers, making breakage more likely. Also called fault bar, hunger streak, hunger fault, hunger trace, feather mark, starvation mark, subordinate bar, and, by veterinarians, stress bands. When formed as spots called fault spot or fault holes.

friction barbules: special barbules on the inner vanes of the outer primaries that reduce separation of the feathers during flight.

Friedman test: a non-parametric statistical method for randomized blocks used in lieu of the two-way analysis of variance (ANOVA).

fright moult: Am. fright molt, the shedding of feathers as a defense when attacked, to distract or confuse the attacker. Usually only tail and rump feathers are shed. Also termed shock moult.

fringe: sometimes used to describe a narrow area of contrasting colour at the tip of a feather that does not extend onto its sides, often giving a scaly appearance to the plumage.

fringillid: any member of the finch family (Fringillidae).

frizzle fowl: a breed of chicken in which a feather mutation causes body feathers to curl toward the head, giving the bird a 'frizzled' appearance.

frond: a leaf, especially of a palm or fern or any leaf-like structure.

frons: forehead, Latin *frontis*.

front: 1) the forward side of an animal or structure. 2) in meteorological terms an abrupt change in atmospheric conditions. 3) can also be used to refer to boundaries between water masses.

frontals: a pair of medially fused bones forming the anterior part of the brain case. Latin *frontalis*.

frontal shield: an area of bare, horny, or fleshy, often colourful, skin on the forehead, immediately above the base of the upper mandible.

frontonasal hinge: the flexible connection between bill and skull occurring in some birds, especially in parrots (Psittaciformes). Also called hinge.

frounce: a protozoan infection causing creamy white necrotic material in the mouth, part of the upper alimentary canal (pharynx), inner nares, and oesophagus. Also called trichomoniasis, diphtheria, or dove disease.

frugivorous: feeding on fruit.

FSH: abbr. of follicle-stimulating hormone, which is secreted by the pituitary and causes the growth and development of sex organs; cf. LH.

F-test: a test for the departure of the variance ratio of two samples from unity.

fuel load: commonly applied to the fat stores accumulated by a migrating bird and enabling it to fly for a long time without interruption, so covering a long distance, sometimes over hostile terrain such as an ocean or desert.

fulmar oil: an evil-smelling, oily, stomach-derived substance that occurs in most Procellariiformes which, e.g.

Fulmars (*Fulmarus glacialis*), can projectile 'vomit' as a defence strategy. Also called stomach oil.

functional response: when an animal shifts diet to exploit a food type that has become more abundant.

fundamental bar: any of the bars seen on flight and tail feathers when held at a certain angle relative to the light (not visible in all species). Each consecutive pair of bars – one light and one dark –represents 24 hours' growth of a feather. According to some authors the varying width of growth bars is caused by day-to-day variations in the nutritional state of the bird while the feather was growing. More commonly called growth bar.

fungus: pl. fungi, any taxon of Fungi, one of the major divisions of life and today usually considered a kingdom. Fungi are heterotrophs, and most are decomposers of detritus, although many are parasites. Most are multicellular. A fungal disease is often called a mycosis.

furca: Latin = fork.

furcula: bone consisting of the fused clavicles, making a flexible structure that acts like a spring during flight; popularly called wishbone or merrythought. Latin *furculum*.

furculum: a term often used in bird-ringing literature for the hollow area between the two fused clavicle bones (branches of the furcula) often examined in order to assess the bird's amount of deposited fat. Also called tracheal pit.

fuscus: Latin = dark coloured or black.

fusiform: the form of an egg that is slightly longer than a subelliptical egg.

fusiformis: Latin = form like a spindle.

G

gaggle: a flock of geese on the ground; *cf.* skein.

gall bladder: a sac in or near the liver that stores bile, which aids in digestion.

gallery forest: a narrow strip of trees along water courses traversing non-forested habitats.

galli: mainly used for members of the pheasant family (Phasianidae), but also for megapodes (Megapodiidae) and curassows (Cracidae).

Galliformes: order comprising 22 species of megapodes or moundbuilders (Megapodiidae), 50 species of curassows, guans, and chachalacas (Cracidae), 6 species of guineafowl (Numididae), 32 species of New World quails (Odontophoridae), and 180 species of turkeys, grouse, pheasants, and partridges (Phasianidae).

gallinaceous: belonging to Galliformes.

Galloanserae: a parvclass containing Galliformes and Anseriformes.

game bird: 1) a bird that may legally be hunted. 2) another word for gallinaceous bird.

gamete: a mature, haploid, reproductive cell (egg or sperm).

gametogenesis: the formation of gametes.

gamma diversity: the diversity of species within a given geographical area; *cf.* alpha diversity, beta diversity.

gamosematic: pertaining to characters or behaviours that assist pair members to find each other.

gander: male goose.

ganglion: pl. ganglia, a functional aggregate of nerve cells in the peripheral nervous system. Also called nerve knot; *cf.* nuclei.

gap-crossing: any movements by animals across areas of inhospitable habitat, such as a river or other gap between forested habitats.

gape: the mouth.

gape flange: the fleshy mouth opening formed in the angle between the two mandibles, often yellow in young birds; also called rictus commissure; *cf.* directive mark.

gapeworm: the endoparasitic roundworm (nematode) *Syngamus trachea* found in the trachea (rarely the bronchi) of birds and causing severe and often fatal respiratory problems.

gaping: 1) the begging behaviour of a chick opening its mouth wide. 2) a term for the action of a Starling (*Sturna vulgaris*) or Worm-eating Warbler (*Helmitheros vermivorum*) putting its closed bill into a substrate in which prey may be located, such as soil or a curled dead leaf, and then powerfully opening it, to create an opening.

Garuda: a fabulous bird in the Hindu religion and mythology; also a national symbol in Indonesia; *cf.* Gerda.

gas exchange: exchange of gases between blood and air in the lungs.

gastral ribs: abdominal ribs, found in *Archaeopteryx* and many other dinosaurs (but not recent birds), and some crocodiles and lizards.

gastric cuticle: the internal hard surface of the muscular stomach or gizzard, especially well-developed in seed-eating birds. Also called cuticula gastrica or koilin.

gastric mill: outdated term for the gizzard.

gastrocnemius: a muscle on the tibiotarsus connected to the toes by a tendon and typically made up of three parts (pars lateralis, intermedia, and medialis); in some suboscines a fourth part is present (pars supramedialis); *cf.* peroneus longus.

gastrointestinal tract: alimentary canal, the organ system that takes in food, digests it to extract nutrients and energy, and excretes the left over waste (from mouth to cloaca in birds).

Gause's Rule: ecological generalisation saying that related species sharing the same area will differ with respect to habitat preferences or feeding habits; i.e. will occupy different niches.

Gaviiformes: order comprising five species of divers or Am. loons (Gaviidae).

gel electrophoresis: separation of different proteins or pieces of DNA in an electric field in a gel matrix.

gender: any of the classes masculine, feminine, or neuter. Not a syn. of sex.

gene: a unit of heredity, transmitted from parents to offspring; actually a functional DNA sequence, usually coding for a specific protein

gene flow: the exchange of genetic material between separate populations and subpopulations due to dispersal and interbreeding.

gene pool: all the genes and gene variants of a given population at a specific time.

generalist: an organism eating a wide variety of food, or having a broad habitat preference; the opposite of a specialist.

generic name: the scientific name of the genus to which an organism belongs.

genetic bottleneck: loss of genetic variation due to a period of very low population size, often leading to inbreeding depression; *cf.* inbreeding.

genetic code: the hereditary, biochemical basis for the structuring of an organism; the sequence of nucleotides making up strands of DNA that code for proteins, i.e. in coding DNA, every three nucleotides code for a specific amino acid. The rule by which a nucleotide sequence is translated into an amino acid sequence, i.e. the conceptual wordbook telling how "nucleic acid language" is translated into "protein language". It turns out that triplets of nucleotides correspond to single amino acids, so that 61 of the 64 possible triplets (given that there are four kinds of nucleotide) code for the 20 amino acids (with 1-6 different triplets for each amino acid), while the remaining 3 triplets function as "stop codes".

genetic death: a term for a genotype of little or no fitness, caused, for example by mutation or the hybrid crossing of evolutionarily disparate lineages.

genetic distance: the difference between corresponding genes (or the entire sample genome) of two taxa.

genetic drift: changes in gene frequencies within a small population caused by random events and not by selection, mutation, or immigration. Also called random drift. One of four processes thought to drive the development of new species; *cf.* founder effect, natural selection, sexual selection.

genetic fingerprinting: the generation and analysis of individually unique patterns of DNA fragments, in avian science especially used to identify paternity but not considered robust in systematics. Also called DNA fingerprinting, RAPD (Randomly Amplified Polymorphic DNA).

genetic isolation: absence of gene flow between the population in question and other populations; generally considered favourable to differentiation; *cf.* ecological separation.

genetic program: the information coded in an organism's DNA.

genetics: 1) the science of biological heredity, or how and why morphological and behavioural characters are transferred from parents to offspring. 2) the study of molecular and genetic evolution at the level of the gene.

gen. et sp. nov.: Latin *genus et species nova* = new genus and species.

genital organs: (outer) sex organs. Latin *genitalis.*

genome: all genetic information or DNA of an organism.

genotype: the genetic make-up of an individual; *cf.* phenotype.

genotypic variation: the genetic variation occurring among individuals within a species or population.

gens: pl. gentes, subpopulation of a brood parasite, such as a cuckoo, specialized on a particular host species; a term with no formal taxonomic significance. Latin *gens*: pl. *gentis* = generation.

genus: pl. genera, a group of similar species considered more closely related mutually than any of them is with other species; in classification a unit ranking between species and family. The first name in the scientific bi- or trinomen is the generic name, i.e. refers to the genus, e.g. *Fringilla*; *cf.* family, order, class, phylum and kingdom.

geoffroyism: a term for adaptive response.

geographic isolation: isolation (of populations, species, etc.) from each other by geographic barriers, e.g. oceans, mountain ranges, deserts, or other barriers inhospitable to dispersal. Such isolation is commonly considered a crucial step in species formation; *cf.* allopatric speciation, isolating mechanism.

geographic range: the collective range of all individuals of a species, although usually excluding vagrants.

geographical speciation: speciation in mutually isolated populations, i.e. genetic divergence over time until they would no longer interbreed if they got into contact with each other. More commonly called allopatric speciation.

geomagnetism: the Earth's magnetic field.

geophagy: the ingestion of soil.

Gerda: a fabulous bird from Malaysian mythology whose origin was Garuda, of Hindu religion and mythology.

Gerfaut, le: periodical published since 1919 by Institut Royal des Sciences Naturelles de Belgique (IRSNB).

germ: a common name for a microorganism, often one that causes disease.

germ cell: a sex cell from which gametes are derived. Latin *german, germinis.*

germinal disc: the site in the egg where the embryo will develop, only visible as a white spot in the unfertilized egg; also called the blastula or **germinal spot.**

germinal vesicle: nucleus of animal oocyte, especially used of the enlarged nucleus of the oocyte during a certain stage of meiosis.

germline: in embryology the cells from which ova and sperm (gametes) are produced; also spelled **germ-line**; *cf.* somatic cell.

gerontology: the study of aging; *cf.* senescence.

giardiasis: in birds, a rare protozoan infection caused by *Giardia* found, e.g. in passerines, parakeets (Psittacidae), and toucans (Ramphastidae); more commonly occurring in mammals, including humans, whence it is often termed **giardia** or beaver fever.

gibber or **gibber desert**: Australian plains of gravel and pebble stone pavement with minimal vegetation; inhabited by Gibberbird (*Ashbyia lovensis*), family Meliphagidae.

GIS: Geographic Information System; computer hardware and software for analysing geographically referenced features.

gizzard: the muscular stomach, having an outer muscle layer and a hard inner surface (called *cuticula gastrica*, gastric cuticle, or koilin layer), which breaks down food mechanically. Often contains small stones (grit) swallowed by the bird to aid in breaking down food; *cf.* proventriculus.

gizzard worm: an endoparasitic roundworm (nematode) that causes destruction of the horny inner coat of the gizzard, often leading to the death of the bird.

glacial period: a period of global cooling during which there is an extension of ice caps and glaciers at high latitudes and elevations, resulting in a drier climate and lowered sea-levels worldwide; *cf.* interglacial period.

glacial refugium: pl. glacial refugia, areas where species may survive during ice ages.

gland: an organ that secretes either through an opening or into the blood. Latin *glans*, pl. *glandis*.

glandula picorum: a salivary gland in woodpeckers (Picidae) secreting a sticky fluid that enables the birds to catch insects with the tongue.

glandular stomach: syn. with proventriculus, part of the stomach anterior to the gizzard, especially well developed in fish-eating birds and birds

of prey. It secretes mucus, acid, and enzymes for digestion.

gleaning: in birds, the act of searching for and taking prey from leaves, bark, and branches; *cf.* sally gleaning.

glenoid: or glenoid cavity, the socket for the upper arm (humerus) and the coracoid formed by the coracoid and the scapula. Also called **glenoid fossa** or **glenoid cavity**.

gliding flight: unpowered flight, gliding on outstretched motionless wings; speed will decline in level flight but may be maintained if descending, i.e. at the expense of height and gravitational energy; *cf.* flapping flight, soaring.

glissando: in vocalizations, the sliding of one tone into the next in a scale-like passage.

globular nest: a round nest completely enclosed and usually with a round hole as a side entrance, characteristic of most wrens (Troglodytidae); *cf.* domed nest.

globulin: a protein that is insoluble in water but soluble in salt solutions and that coagulates when heated.

globus: Latin = round body.

Gloger's Rule: the zoogeographical rule that birds and mammals tend to be darker in warm, humid environments and paler in cool, dry environments; *cf.* ecogeographical rules.

glomus seminale: seminal vesicle or sac where sperm is stored.

glossa: pl. glossae, an old term for tongue, of Greak origin.

glottis: the slit-like opening into the gullet (larynx).

GLS: abbr. for generalized least squares, in statistics, a method that generalizes the least squares method of fitting curves to data, suitable for data lacking independence or with unequal variance.

glucagon: a hormone produced in the pancreas increasing blood sugar con centrations by mobilizing carbohydrate reserves, especially liver glycogen; *cf.* insulin.

glucocorticoid: a hormone released by the adrenal cortex in response to stressful stimuli.

gluconeogenesis: in physiology, the synthesis of glucose from foods other than carbohydrates.

glycogen body: a gelatinous mass rich in the nutritive sugar glycogen, found in the rhomboid sinus.

gnathotheca: a now rather uncommon term for the horny covering of the lower mandible; *cf.* rhamphotheca, rhinotheca.

GnRH: abbr. of gonadotropin-releasing hormone, a hormone produced by the hypothalamus that triggers the release of gonadotropins such as luteinizing hormone (LH) and follicle-stimulating hormone (FSH), involved in gonadal development and regulation.

goal area: main site occupied between the two migratory steps, see also intermediate goal areas.

goal orientation: orientation towards a goal, or a sequence of goals, by migrating birds, using some internal compass and visual or other information to keep the direction and compensate for lateral displacement; *cf.* compass orientation, parallactic orientation, piloting.

goatsucker: Am. name for a nightjar, family Caprimulgidae. Aristotle related that it was popularly thought that nightjars milked goats, a perception probably derived from seeing these birds catch insects against the pale ventral pelage of goats under low light conditions.

gobbling ground: Am. term for the display arena of the Lesser Prairie Chicken (*Tympanuchus pallidicinctus*).

goitre: pathologic enlargement of the thyroid gland.

gonads: common name for the internal sex organs of males and females.

gonadotropin-releasing hormone: a hormone produced by the hypothalamus that triggers the release of gonadotropins such as luteinizing hormone (LH) and follicle-stimulating hormone (FSH), involved in gonadal development and regulation.

Gondwana: a prior land mass formed by the present South America, Africa, Madagascar, India, Australia, New Zealand, and Antarctica until it began to break up and drift apart 160 mya; also called **Gondwanaland**; *cf.* Laurasia, Pangaea.

gonochoristic: of populations/species having individuals of separate sexes, i.e. having male and female individuals, which is the normal condition in higher animals.

gonys: the keel-like ridge of the ventral surface of the lower mandible, formed by the two rami, very evident in gulls and terns (Laridae).

good genes: a term for a male with high quality secondary sexual characters such as a long tail, a large badge or bright plumage colours, which give the choosy sex (the female) good information about the genes of the male that is advantageous to the offspring; *cf.* runaway selection.

goodness of fit test: any of several statistical tests, such as a chi-squared or *G*-test, that compares the frequency of observed values against an expected frequency to obtain a probabilistic estimate of their differences.

good sons: a term used for offspring that have inherited good genes from the parents.

gorget: a throat or breast band of brilliant colouring, e.g. in some hummingbirds (Trochilidae).

gosling: a goose chick.

gout: a disease in which the kidneys fail to adequately eliminate nitrogenous waste from the bloodstream, causing insoluble urates such as uric acid crystals to build up in various parts of the body.

gouty swelling: ivory-coloured bead-like pimples mainly around the joints of the legs.

GPS satellite telemetry: Global Positioning System, a navigating and surveying system based on reception of signals from satellites giving the precise coordinates.

gradation: applied to a species or population with fluctuating numbers, having a maximum and a minimum, or bottom, in its cycles, each stage of which is called a gradation; or one can speak of a **gradation cycle, gradation rhythm**, or **gradation sequence.**

gradation-bird: a species with fluctuating population sizes, such as the Black Grouse (*Tetrao tetrix*). Species in which the fluctuations ('gradations') lead to mass movements are called irruptive or eruptive species; *cf.* invasion species.

graded display: a display that is variable in strength, depending upon the motivation of the individual; e.g. the degree to which a crest is raised.

graded return: return of the first-year birds from their winter range when it occurs late or the birds stop partway to pass the summer at suitable sites away from their future breeding range; species exhibiting graded return generally first breed at an age of two or more years; *cf.* retarded return.

gradient map navigation: bird navigation that is goal oriented and where the birds exploit the gradients of at least two physical/chemical variables to find their way.

graminivorous: grass-eating, as e.g. geese.

Grandry's corpuscles: elaborate sensory nerve fibres found in the mouth and bill of owls (Strigidae) and ducks (Anatidae); *cf.* Herbst's corpuscles, Merkel's corpuscles.

granivorous: seed-eating. Note, however, that most granivorous birds feed their nestlings a more protein-rich diet, most often comprising insects.

granulate: covered with small tubercles.

granulocyte: white blood cell with granules in the cytoplasm.

grasp rejector: a host that takes the parasitic egg in the bill as a rejection behaviour, *cf.* puncture rejector, deserter, acceptor.

grassland biome: one of North America's nine ecological divisions or biotic communities, primarily the interior plains.

gravity: the force by which bodies are drawn towards the centre of the earth.

gray: Am. for grey.

Great Chain of Being: an historic philosophy that all organisms are part of a single linear scale of ever-growing perfection, e.g. from atoms to man. 'It received its final death blow when Cuvier (1812) asserted emphatically that there are four distinct phyla of animals, no more and no fewer, and that there was absolutely no connection among them' (Mayr 1982:201). Also called *scala naturae.*

great circle route: the shortest possible route between two points on the surface of Earth.

Greater Antilles: a group of islands in the West Indies comprising Cuba, Hispaniola, Jamaica, and Puerto Rico; *cf.* Lesser Antilles.

greater coverts: the row of large coverts that cover the bases of the primaries and secondaries. Compound word where 'coverts' forms a part are by some authors spelled with a hyphen.

greater primary coverts: the row of large coverts that cover the bases of the primaries

greater secondary coverts: the row of large coverts that cover the bases of the secondaries.

Greater Sunda Islands: include Sumatra, Java, Borneo, and Sulawesi; *cf.* Lesser Sunda islands.

greater wing coverts: the largest wing coverts covering the bases of the primaries and secondaries both on the upper- and under-wing; separately termed greater primary coverts, and greater secondary coverts (or only secondary coverts); *cf.* median wing coverts, lesser wing coverts.

gregarious: living in a group. Also called sociable.

grey matter: Am. **gray matter**, tissue composed of nerve cell bodies without a myelin sheath; *cf.* white matter.

grid square: a geographical square in an atlas project in which an area is subdivided by a square grid, e.g. 10×10 km.

gristle: tough, flexible, and usually whitish tissue, generally cartilage or ligaments, that join bones together or attach muscle to bones; *cf.* tendon.

grit: gizzard stones or pebbles for grinding food.

grooming: term most often used for mammals; preening, keeping the hairs or feathers in good condition, by birds usually by use of the bill but often also including the feet and claws.

gross moult: a term signifying that only the moult of wing and tail feathers has been examined by an ornithologist.

ground speed: speed (of a flying object) relative to the ground; *cf.* air speed.

group: an assemblage of animals remaining together over an extended period of time, e.g. when more than one pair attends and defends a territory at a nest or a small group invades a new area; *cf.* flock.

group predation: predation by predators hunting in a group.

group selection: natural selection operating at the level of the group rather than at the level of the individual, and in which characters may evolve that are detrimental to individuals but enhance the fitness of the group; *cf.* kin selection.

growth bar: any of the bars seen on flight and tail feathers when held at a certain angle relative to the light (not visible in all species). Each consecutive pair of bars – one light and one dark – represents 24 hours' growth of a feather, dark bars laid down during the day and light bars during the night. According to some authors the varying width of growth bars is caused by day-to-day variations in the nutritional state of the bird while the feather was growing. Formerly called fundamental bar.

Grube Messel: a former oil-shale mine, located near Frankfurt am Main, Germany, where many fossils have been found; *cf.* Solnhofen Lithographic Limestone.

Gruiformes: order comprising 26 species of bustards (Otidae), three species of mesites (Mesitornithidae), two species of seriemas (Cariamidae), the Kagu (*Rhynochetos jubatus*), the Sunbittern (*Eurypyga helias*), 141 species of rails, waterhens, and coots (Rallidae), three species of finfoots (Heliornithidae), three species of trumpeters (Psophiidae), 15 species of cranes (Gruidae), the Limpkin (*Aramus guarauna*), and 16 species of buttonquails (Turnicidae).

G-test: statistical test of independence in two-way tables, an alternative to the classical chi-squared test.

guano: compacted faeces of colonial seabirds, accumulated over many years; historically, and to some extend even today, an important source of nitrogen for agricultural fertilizer and mined as such especially in Peru.

guano bird: a bird whose excrement is used commercially in the form of guano; most notably the Guanay Cormorant (*Phalacrocorax bougainvillii*).

guild: a group of bird species that exploits the same habitat in similar ways, e.g. granivorous birds in grassland or piscivorous birds in a freshwater habitat.

gular fluttering: a cooling method, in which the increase of heat loss is achieved by opening the bill and vibrating muscles and bones (hyoid apparatus) in the throat, especially by colonially-nesting waterbirds in hot climates (note that birds lack sweat glands); *cf.* upper critical temperature, panting, evaporative cooling.

gular pouch: a pouch between the rami of the lower mandibles and upper throat found, e.g. in pelicans (Pelecanidae).

gullet: the anterior part of the food channel, also called upper oesophagus.

gulper: a fruit-eating bird that swallows whole fruit; *cf.* seed disperser, seed predator.

gut: the intestines.

guttate: speckled, spotted, or shaped like a drop.

gymnopaedic: of a naked or nearly naked newly-hatched chick, also called nidicolous or psilopaedic, the opposite of ptilopaedic; *cf.* nidicolous, nidifugous, altricial, precocial.

gymnosperm: a woody plant lacking flowers; *cf.* angiosperm.

gynandromorph: an animal having both ovary and testis, in sexually dichromatic species characterised by having one side of the plumage coloured as a female and the other as a male, changing abruptly along the mid-line; *cf.* hermaphrodite, pseudogynandromorph .

gypsotropic: of alkaline lakes with low availability of phosphates.

H

H5N1: a highly pathogonic avian influenza. Avian influenza, caused by a RNA influenza A virus effects birds and mammals; waterbirds (e.g., ducks, geese, and shorebirds) are typical hosts, but the virus can infect atypical hosts such as landbirds (e.g. chickens) and mammals (e.g. pigs, seals, mink) and there become more virulent. Pathogenicity depends on the strain of the virus, and highly pathogenic (HP) strains can cause severe economic damage in the poultry industry. Strains are named on the basis of their hemagglutinin (H) and neuraminidase (N) subtypes. Epidemic and pandemic human influenza episodes have frequently stemmed from avian influenzas that have apparently undergone subsequent mutations in another mammalian host.

ha: hectare; 1 ha = 10,000 m^2.

habitat: the specific environment in which an organism lives, in birds often described as the specific plant community inhabited; *cf.* biotope.

habitat conception: an innate ability to recognise suitable habitat, as in migrants temporarily stopping at resting grounds in response to appropriate structure, density, and/or height of vegetation.

habitat fragmented: a habitat, e.g. a forest, that is broken up into discrete, often small and isolated patches.

habitat generalist: an animal having a broad habitat preference or tolerance; as opposed to a specialist.

habitat segregation: division of environmental resources between sexes, age groups, or species, by utilization at different periods or by using different microhabitats.

habitat selection: preference for a certain habitat.

habitat specialist: an animal that can only live in one or a few types of habitat; as opposed to a habitat generalist.

habits: behavioural patterns of an organism.

habituation: the modification of an otherwise reflex behaviour to do otherwise as a result of experience as, for example, birds feeding on roads despite vehicular traffic.

hacking: Am. for the gradual release of a captive-bred raptor into the wild, during which it is fed for some period to give it the opportunity to learn to cope by itself; **hack site**.

hackles: long, slender feathers on the neck, as in the Vulturine Guineafowl (*Acryllium vulturinum*).

haemal: to do with blood.

haematocrit: the ratio of the volume of red blood cells to the total volume of blood.

haemoglobin: the red pigment protein in blood that binds oxygen, increasing the blood's capacity to dissolve oxygen far above that of pure water; also called erythrocytes. Am. hemoglobin.

Haemoproteus: genus of parasitic Sporozoa, transmitted by blood-sucking flies; fatal to young pigeons and quails.

haemorrhage: profuse bleeding.

haemorrhagic septicaemia: a bacterial disease caused by *Pasteurella multocida*; symptoms include small blood spots on the skin and necrosis of the liver. Found in many birds, but most often in waterbirds. Syn. fowl cholera, avian cholara, and avian pasteurellosis.

haemulus: pl. haemuli, Am., microscopic third-order barbs, or hooks that, together with first- and second-order barbs (barbicels), hold a feather firm and give it strength. Eur. hamulus.

haggard: a falconry term for a raptor taken from the wild as an adult.

hairworm: a long and slender worm of the phylum Nematomorpha with a smooth surface lacking rings. Many members of this group are endoparasites in arthropods. Also called treadworm; *cf.* roundworm.

Haldane's Rule: reduced fertility and reduced viability in hybrids are often expressed in the heterogametic sex (in birds the female).

hallux: the first toe (digit) of the foot, in birds usually directed backwards; absent in many running birds.

halotropic: an organism that is attracted to or lives in a saline environment, e.g. the sea; adj. halobiotic.

hammock: a clump of woody vegetation on slightly raised ground in otherwise lower and wetter habitat (e.g. mangrove, cypress swamp, or sawgrass marsh).

hamulus: pl. hamuli, microscopic third-order barbs, or hooks that, together with first- and second-order barbs (barbicels), hold a feather firm and give it strength. Am. haemulus.

hand: the outer section of the wing where the primary feathers are attached. Also called manus.

handicap signal: a signal that reflects individual quality, e.g. the red or yellow integument pigmentation caused by carotenoids.

HANZAB: abbr. for Handbook of Australian, New Zealand, and Antarctic Birds.

haploid: a haploid cell has only one set of chromosomes. In multicellular animals (metazoans) only the gametes are haploid, whereas the somatic cells have two sets of chromosomes (i.e. they are diploid).

haplotype: 1) the single species included in a genus at the time of its designation, thus becoming the type species of the genus. 2) the constellation of allees present at a particular region of a chromosome. 3) a plant living in saline conditions.

hard-billed bird: a seed eater, as opposed to a soft-billed bird.

Harderian gland: tear gland in the orbit of the eye. Also called **Harder's gland**. Birds also have another tear gland, called the lachrymal gland.

harem polygyny: a polygynous mating system in which the male defends a 'harem' of females against other males. Females leave the harem after copulation and rear the offspring alone. Occurs in tinamous (Tinamidae) and the Greater Rhea (*Rhea americana*), in which the male can have up to 15 females in his harem, and in some pheasants (Phasianidae); *cf.* polybrachygamy.

Haribon Foundation: the BirdLife partner in the Philippines, founded in 1972.

Hastings rarities: a long series of bird rarities reported from Hastings in Sussex, UK, between 1892 and 1930. After examination it was concluded in 1962 that it was a case of fauna fraud and that the records were fictitious; as a result 16 species were deleted from the British list.

hatching: emerging from the egg.

hatching asynchrony: asynchronous hatching of a clutch, the term generally limited to cases in which the interval between hatching eggs is at least one day; common in bird species depending on an unpredictable food source in which it is considered an adaptive trait, a mechanism for regulating brood size according to food availability; *cf.* hatching synchrony, siblicide.

hatching muscle: a muscle, *musculus complexus*, in the neck of a hatchling, helping it to break out of the egg shell and disappearing soon after hatching.

hatching success: the percentage of eggs surviving to hatching.

hatching synchrony: synchronous hatching of a clutch, meaning that the eggs hatch at approximately the same time because incubating began at the laying of the last egg; *cf.* hatching asynchrony.

hatching tooth: a sharp projection on the tip of upper mandible of many hatchlings used to break the egg shell from within and then lost within a few days after hatching. Also called egg-breaker, caruncle, or most commonly egg tooth.

hawking: 1) a falconry term for hunting with trained falcons and other raptors. 2) a bird flying from a perch to capture prey on the wing (e.g. flying insects).

hawk mimicry: mimicry found in the members of the cuckoo genus *Cuculus*: they look similar to hawks.

head: the part of the body above the neck; *cf.* auriculars, cere, chest, chin, commisure, crown, culmen, eyerim, eye ring, eye stripe, forehead, gonys, lores, malar stripe, maxilla, moustachial stripe, nape, narial feathers, nostril, operculum, pilium, rhamphotheca, rictal bristles, superciliary stripe, supraorbital ridge. See also skull.

heart: a muscular organ that pumps blood. See: atrium, ventricle, interatrial septum, interventricular septum.

heat exchanger: counter-current system, in which heat is exchanged between two blood flows; *cf.* rete mirabile, tibiotarsal rete, sphincter muscles.

hectare: abbr. ha; 1 ha = 10,000 m^2.

hedgehog stage: nestling stage in some birds, in which the otherwise naked chick has spiny pinfeathers, the sheaths encasing the growing feather; seen in, e.g. in kingfishers (Alcedinidae).

heel pad: a term for the thickenings on birds' feet, each separated by furrows, also called digital pads or only pad in some nestlings, e.g. in the order Coraciiformes and Piciformes.

Heligoland trap: a wire-net trap, a long cage with up to 20m wide 'wings' at the opening and gradually narrowing until it ends in a catching box. Mostly used to catch ducks and shorebirds. First developed at Heligoland to catch birds for food consumption, but now used only to catch birds for ringing. Also spelled **Helgoland trap**.

helminths: common term for the following endoparasites: roundworms (Nematoda), thorny-headed worms (Acanthocephala), tapeworms (Cestoda), and flukes (Trematoda).

helper: a non breeding bird that assists a breeding pair in raising their young. Cooperative breeding has been recorded in about 250 bird species, and helpers are usually found to be closely related to the breeders. Also called extra-pair helper or auxiliary.

hematozoon: a parasite living in the blood. Also spelled **hematozoan**.

hemerophilous: an association between a human and another species, n. **hemerophily**; *cf.* synanthropous, hemerophobous.

hemerophobous: a species avoiding human settlements and cultivated land, also called exanthropous; *cf.* eusyanthropuus, hemerophilous.

hemi: prefix meaning half.

hemipode: common name for any member of the button quails (Turnicidae).

Hemiptera: important order of insects, also called bugs, all lacking a true larval and pupal stage.

hemoglobin: Am. for the red pigment protein in blood that binds oxygen, increasing the blood's capacity to dissolve oxygen far above that of pure water; *cf.* erythrocytes. In English spelled haemoglobin.

hen: a female bird; may be applied to any species, but most often seen in connection with domestic fowl and a few other species or groups.

Henle's loops: the part of the excretory units of the kidney (nephrons) in which water is reabsorbed.

Hennigian systematics: derived from Willy Hennig's (1966) establishment of clades, or monophyletic groups, that include all the descendants of a common ancestor. Concerned with phylogenetic branching patterns, but not usually with identifying ancestors.

hepatic: 1) liver-coloured, i.e. dark brownish red. 2) applied to the red-brown colour morph found in some cuckoo species, which is also called the **hepatic phase** or rufous phase.

hepatic portal system: the blood supply to the liver from the intestine; *cf.* renal portal system.

hepatitis: inflammation of the liver.

hepatoenteric ducts: ducts that transport bile from the liver to the small intestine. Occur only in bird species lacking a gall bladder.

herbaceous: not woody (referring to plants).

herbicide: a chemical toxic to plants and used to kill weeds.

herbivore: an animal that eats plants, adj. **herbivorous**. Also called primary consumer; *cf.* phytophagous, carnivore.

Herbst's corpuscle: a tactile corpuscle with elaborate sensory nerve fibers, found in great numbers at the bill tip of shorebirds (Scolopacidae), such as snipe (*Gallinago*) and sandpipers (*Calidris*), helping them to detect prey in soil or mud. Widely distributed in the avian skin in association with feather follicles and with the muscles of the feathers; also found at the tip of the tongue of woodpeckers (Picidae); *cf.* Merkel's corpuscles, Grandry's corpuscles.

herd: a flock of swans, genus *Cygnus*, on the ground.

heredity: the passing on of specific characters or traits from one generation to the next.

heritability: the proportion of phenotypic variation that is genetically inherited.

hermaphrodite: an individual with both male and female sex organs and with plumage characters of both sexes. Also referred to as a bisexual, adj. **hermaphroditic**; *cf.* gynandromorphy, parthenogenesis.

herpes virus: certain type of virus; one variant causes a serious disease with death of cells (necrosis) in the liver in some birds (falcons, owls, parrots, pigeons).

herpetology: the study of reptiles and amphibians.

herpetivorous: feeding on reptiles, frogs, and toads; *cf.* zoophagous, carnivorous.

Hertz: abbr. Hz, unit equivalent to cycles per second and used in connection with various kinds of wave motion (sound, radio, etc.); *cf.* kilohertz.

Hesperornis: a genus of toothed, flightless, swimming birds known from the Cretaceous of North America.

Hesse's Rule: in warm-blooded animals the forms living in cooler climates have heavier hearts than those in warmer areas.

heterakiasis: disease caused by the protozoon *Histomonas meleagridis* that attacks the liver and caeca of, e.g. gallinaceous birds, resulting in gastric disturbances, anorexia, and diarrhoea, often with high mortality. Also called histomoniasis, blackhead disease, or enterohepatitis.

hetero-: prefix from Greek *heteros* = other, different, or other than usual.

heterochrosis: abnormal coloration, **heterochroism**; *cf.* albinism, partial albinism, leucism, melanism, schizochroism, lutinous, flavism, erythrism, gynandromorph.

heterochrony: relative differences in development between the sexes, either by slowing down or speeding up.

heterocoelous: saddle-shaped, for example the centrum end of an avian vertebra.

heterodactyl: a foot condition in which toes 1 and 2 are directed backwards and toes 3 and 4 forwards. Only known in trogons (Trogonidae), adj. **heterodactylous**; *cf.* anisodactyl, syndactyl, pamprodactyl, and zygodactyl.

heteroduplex: an experimentally created hybrid double strand of DNA.

heterogametic: used of taxa having two types of gametes.

heterogametic sex: the sex possessing one copy of each of the two sex chromosomes, the special chromosomes that determine sex in the majority of the metazoans (and some other organisms); the other (homogametic) sex has two copies of one of the sex chromosomes, whereas homozygotes for the other sex chromosome never

occur. In the well-known XY system in mammals, females are homogametic, having two X chromosomes and so always produce eggs with one X chromosome, whereas males are heterogametic and have one X and one Y chromosome, hence producing spermatozoa with either an X or a Y chromosome. The sex chromosomes in birds are called Z and W, and females are the heterogametic sex (WZ), while males are homogametic (ZZ); *cf.* homogametic sex.

heterogamy: 1) an uncommon term for disassortative mating, or the mating of unlike individuals. 2) more often applied to the uniting of unlike gametes, of taxa having different types of reproduction in successive generations (e.g. parthenogenetic and sexual). 3) or of a plant producing gametes of both types from a single flower type.

heterogeneous: made up of diverse components; also used in genetics of populations to indicate the presence of genetic variation; n. **heterogeneity**.

heterogeneous aggregation: mixed species assemblage for purposes other than feeding and lacking social organization, e.g. roosting; the opposite of homogeneous aggregation.

heterogeneous summation: in stimulus-response behaviour, heterogeneous stimuli can work together to produce a stronger response than a single stimulus.

heterogyny: a species having two kinds of females, **heterogynism**, adj. **heterogynous**.

heteromorphic: 1) of an organism that has different forms at different stages of its life cycle, as in many insects and some plants. 2) the sex in which the sex chromosomes differ, as in female birds that have WZ compared with males that have ZZ. Also called heterogametic.

heterospecific: pertaining to a different species; opposite of conspecific.

heterotroph: an organism requiring organic compounds as a carbon source to grow and reproduce; adj. **heterotrophic**; *cf.* autotroph.

heterozygote: a diploid cell (individual) having two different alleles at a given locus as opposed to homozygous.

hibernation: the inactive state in which some animals pass winters. Hibernation is fairly common in mammals, in which the body temperature may fall almost to the ambient (although not below freezing). Rare in birds, with only a few nightjar species (Caprimulgidae) known to hibernate; best known in the Common Poorwill (*Phalaenoptilus nuttallii*). Other birds may become torpid for short periods, with reduced body temperature and metabolism; most hummingbirds (Trochilidae), for example, spend the night in such a state. By some authors syn. with torpor; *cf.* hypothermia, torpor.

hide: *n.* 1) a structure built for and used as a hiding place to watch or photograph birds; Am. blind. 2) a skin removed from an animal for treatment and preservation, e.g. to make leather or furs; generally applied to the skin of heavier animals and of mammals in particular. 3) as a verb: to conceal oneself or an object.

hierarchical method: classification based on a sequence of ranked categories.

hierarchy: a dominance system, a social organization within which individuals differ in status, creating a rank or 'pecking-order'.

high-aspect-ratio wings: long, narrow wings without appreciable gaps between the tips of the primaries (unslotted), highly specialized for gliding, found in albatrosses (Diomedeidae),

shearwaters and petrels (Procellariidae), gulls (Laridae), and many other birds.

high-speed wings: tapered and pointed wings, often with a backward-tending direction; found in ducks (Anatidae), terns (Sterninae), falcons (Falconidae), and swifts (Apodidae).

hill: term sometimes used of the display arena (lek) of the Ruff (*Philomachus pugnax*).

hindbrain: the posterior brain or *Medulla oblongata* that controls the nervous system; *cf.* forebrain.

hind limb plexus: the nervous system of the pelvis and legs; *cf.* wing plexus, lumbasacral plexus.

hinge (frontonasal): the connexion between upper bill and forehead, more or less flexible in most birds so that they may lift the upper bill to some extent, most flexible in parrots (Psittacidae) Also called craniofacial hinge or naso-frontal hinge; *cf.* mesokinesis, rhynchokinesis.

hippo: 1) an abbr. applied by ringers to members of the warbler genus *Hippolais*. 2) more commonly used as a nickname for the hippopotamus (*Hippopotamus amphibious*).

hippoboscid fly: member of the family Hippoboscidae, vertically flattened ectoparasitic flies with a leathery surface and well-developed claws, superficially resembles a house fly, mostly wingless, at least after settling on a host. Also called birdfly, feather-fly, flat-fly, ked-fly, louse-fly, spider-fly, and tick-fly; *cf.* ectoparasites.

hippocampus: 1) a paired structure on the dorsal forebrain important for orientation and spatial memory, and other long- or short-term memory processes. Also called **hippocampal complex.**

Hirudidae: a family of leeches, not to be confused with the swallow family Hirundinidae.

hirundine: a member of the swallow family (Hirundinidae).

histogram: a type of bar graph or chart denoting frequencies of classes within a continuous variable; column widths can vary but edges touch to denote contiguousness, and column area is proportional to frequencies.

histology: the study of tissues.

histomoniasis: disease caused by the protozoan *Histomonas meleagridis* that attacks the liver and caecum of birds, e.g. Turkey (*Meleagris gallopavo*) and other gallinaceous birds; causes a high mortality rate. Also called blackhead disease.

histopathology: the study of abnormal tissues.

histoplasmosis: fungal disease of the lungs, caused by *Histoplasma capsulatum*, that does not affect birds but can be spread by them.

hoarding: storing food, as seen in some birds, mainly passerines. Especially well developed in nutcrackers (*Nucifraga*, Corvidae) and some tits (Paridae), but also woodpeckers (Picidae).

hock: the joint of the avian leg between the tibia and the metatarsus, pointing backward.

Holarctic: a zoogeographical region comprising the northern parts of the Old and New worlds (the Palearctic and Nearctic combined).

holaspidean: having the broad plantar surface of the tarsometatarsus covered by a single series of broad, often rectangular, scutes; *cf.* endaspidean, exaspidean, ocreate, pycnaspidean, taxaspidean.

hole nest: a nest either excavated by the user, such as most woodpecker species (Picidae), or such holes adopted by other species, such as the Stock Dove (*Columba oenas*), which takes over holes made by Black Woodpeckers (*Dryocopus martius*).

holo-: a prefix from the Greek *holos* meaning whole or entire.

Holocene: the post-glacial geological epoch, beginning about 10,000 years ago.

holophyletic: the same as monophyletic as this term is used in cladistics (and in almost all modern works in systematics): a holophyletic group consists of all descendants from their last common ancestor.

holorhinal: having posteriorly rounded nostril openings without a deep cleft on the bony structure, the state found in grouse and pheasants (Phasianidae) and in rails (Rallidae); *cf.* schizorhinal.

holothecal: refers to the tarsus of an adult bird when the usual scales are fused into one smooth sheath or 'boot'; juveniles of holothecal species may have scutellae tarsi, but these scutes soon fuse; *cf.* laminiplantar, scutellate.

holotype: in taxonomy the specimen designated to 'represent' the species when it was named and described for the first time; also called type specimen; *cf.* lectotype, paratype, neotype, syntype, protype, pseudotype.

homeostasis: self balancing, the tendency of a biological system to resist change and to maintain itself in a stable, steady state. Also spelled homoeostasis.

homeothermic: warm-blooded, able to maintain a high and constant body temperature; also spelled homoiothermic. Also called endothermic.

home range: the area within which a bird lives, whether defended or not; *cf.* territory.

homing: the ability to find 'home', by migrating birds in spring or by pigeons transported far from their loft.

homo-: prefix from Greek *homo*, meaning alike, the same, similar.

homoeostasis: self balancing, the tendency of a biological system to resist change and to maintain itself in a stable, steady state. More often spelled homeostasis.

Homo erectus: extinct hominid known from fossils from 1.75-0.25 mya, in Africa and eastern Asia (and perhaps Europe). May be a direct ancestor of modern humans.

homogametic sex: the sex possessing two copies of one of the two sex chromosomes, the special chromosomes that determine sex in the majority of the metazoans (and some other organisms); the other (heterogametic) sex has single copies of both sex chromosomes. In the well-known XY system in mammals, females are homogametic, having two X chromosomes and so always produce eggs with one X chromosome, whereas males are heterogametic and have one X and one Y chromosome, hence producing spermatozoa with either an X or a Y chromosome. The sex chromosomes in birds are called Z and W, and females are the heterogametic sex (WZ), while males are homogametic (ZZ); *cf.* heterogametic sex.

homogamy: assortative mating, like with like; opposite to heterogamy.

homogeneous: similar in nature.

homoiothermic: warm-blooded, able to maintain a high and constant body temperature; also spelled homeothermic. Also called endothermic.

homologous: having the same evolutionary and structural derivation, n. **homology**; *cf.* analogous, homoplasy.

homonym: a scientific name applied to more than one taxon, meaning that all but the oldest are invalid; *cf.* synonym.

homoplastic: applied to traits that are similar in form and structure but not in origin.

homoplasy: resemblance caused by parallel or convergent evolution, giving rise to similar traits in two or more

unrelated evolutionary lineages; *cf.* parallelism.

Homo sapiens: the scientific name for the modern human first recorded as existing c. 150,000 years ago.

homoxenia: when two brood parasites share the same host species, adj. **homoxenic.**

homozygosity: possessing the same alleles at a locus.

homozygous: applied to an individual that has identical alleles at a given locus. The opposite of heterozygous.

honest advertisement model: traits that are highly correlated with overall fitness, such as fighting abilities or disease resistance, which are used by females in male choice.

honeycomb fungus: a fungal disease, most often seen in chickens and turkeys, but also occurring in pigeons (Columbidae) and passerines (Passeriformes). Also called favus or ringworm.

Honeyguide: 1) the periodical of the Ornithological Society of Zimbabwe. 2) the vernacular name for a piciform family (Indicatoridae).

hood: 1) a dark-coloured region comprising the head of some bird species, for example the Black-headed Gull (*Larus ridibundus*). 2) the leather cap a falconer puts over the head of a falcon.

hoodwink: a new but unconfirmed distributional avian rarity.

hooklets: tiny hooks on barbules holding the barbs together so that the feather forms a smooth, unbroken vane.

hooting: vocalization of, e.g. owls.

Hopkins' Law: a rule saying that there is a delay of 4-5 days at the start of breeding for each degree of latitude or 125m of elevation.

hopper: used to describe a migrating bird that may stop at one or more sites to feed and recharge its fat reserves; *cf.* jumper.

horizontal classification: a classification grouping species from a similar geological period (horizontal with respect to a phylogenetic tree), rather than those sharing a common lineage; *cf.* vertical classification.

horizontal evolution: evolutionary changes occurring among geographically distributed populations, increasing geographic variation and potentially leading to speciation and macroevolution; *cf.* vertical dimension of evolution.

horizontal transmission: transfer of genes across lineages, as occurs, e.g. among viruses and bacteria, as opposed to inherited, or vertical transmission; *cf.* lateral transfer, lateral transmission.

horizontally transmitted parasites: parasites transmitted between non-related individuals; *cf.* vertically transmitted parasites.

hormone: usually a peptide or a steroid, secreted from the endocrine system and transported by the blood to other tissues in which it elicits a specific physiological response.

Hornero, El: the periodical of la Asociación Ornitólogica del Plata, Argentina.

horsehair fungus: a material in the form of fine, long, black strands similar to horse tail hairs but breakable. Often used in nest construction, e.g. by pittas (Pittidae).

host: the victim of a parasite, a brood parasite, or disease.

host-generalist parasite: a brood parasite that lays eggs in many host species' nests without apparent preference; *cf.* host-specific parasites.

host-intolerant parasite: a brood parasite whose offspring kill or eject a host's eggs or young, e.g. the Common Cuckoo (*Cuculus canorus*); *cf.* host-tolerant parasite.

host mimicry: the case in which egg and/or nestling characteristics of a parasitized host species are mimicked by those of the species parasitizing it.

host-specific parasites: an avian brood parasite that lays eggs only in one or a few closely related host species; *cf.* host generalist parasite.

host-tolerant parasite: a brood parasite that tolerates the host's offspring, e.g. the Great Spotted Cuckoo (*Clamator glandarius*), although many of the latter die of starvation due to competition from the former.

hover gleaning: a foraging technique involving hovering to take insects from a substrate, e.g. a leaf, twig, or bark.

hovering: flight without horizontal or vertical movement. Hummingbirds are especially well adapted to hovering flight; *cf.* windhovering.

hox gene: short for 'homeobox', a group of genes that regulates development (morphogenesis) whereby, e.g. each cell is 'told' which part of the body it is in and thus how it will develop.

H-P system, the: the standard plumage sequence and moult terminology in USA, introduced by Humphrey and Parkes (1959). With the European term in brackets, the plumages are: natal down (natal down), juvenal (juvenile), first basic (first winter), first alternate (first nuptial), basic (winter). Similarly for moults: prejuvenal (postnatal), first prebasic (postjuvenile), first prealternate (first prenuptial), second prebasic (first postnuptial), second prealternate (prenuptial). For some birds, such as gulls (Laridae) and *Aquila* eagles, the terms continue to the fourth plumage and moult.

HSP70: a stress protein.

Hudsonian Zone: one of North America's six life zones, occurring between arctic tundra and coniferous forest.

Humboldt Current: the name of the cold current flowing northwards along the west coast of South America to Punta Parina, Peru, where it turns west and out to sea.

Humboldt's Rule: a rule formulated in 1850 by Alexander von Humboldt according to which the mean temperature decreases by c. one degree Fahrenheit for each degree of latitude when moving away from the equator.

humeral: pertaining to the shoulder region.

humeral patagium: pl. humeral patagia, Am. a membrane of skin on a bird's wing that is supported by tendons and muscles and spans a joint in the wing. Used exclusively for the anterior membrane of the wingbones, stretched between the humerus and radius/ulna. Also called patagium membrane or metapatagium; *cf.* propatagium, postpatagium.

humeral tract: the feather tract covering the shoulder region and the base of the wing. Also called scapulohumeral; *cf.* pterylosis.

humerus: the upper arm (upper wing) bone; *cf.* brachium.

hummer: common nickname for hummingbird, at least in North America.

hummock grass: grasses of the genera *Triodia* and *Plectrachne*, which form spiny, rounded hummocks (spinifex).

humoral: of immunity mediated by antibodies, as opposed to B-cells; *cf.* T-cell, cell-mediated immune defense, spleen.

humoral mechanism: effects brought about not by nerve fibres, but chemically by the ductless glands.

humors: an optical component of the vertebrate eye; *cf.* cornea, lens.

Humphrey-Parkes nomenclature: (**H-P system, the**): a terminology introduced by Humphrey and Parkes (1959) used for plumages and moults. With the European term in brackets, the plumages are: natal down (natal down), juvenal (juvenile), first basic (first winter), first alternate (first nuptial), basic (winter). Similarly for moults: prejuvenal (postnatal), first prebasic (postjuvenile), first prealternate (first prenuptial), second prebasic (first postnuptial), second prealternate (prenuptial). For some birds such as large gulls (Laridae) and *Aquila* eagles the terms continue to the fourth plumage and moult.

hunger track: a narrow, often translucent transverse band found in the feathers of birds, e.g. common in crows, as a result of physical stress, e.g. handling. It is the result of abnormally formed or missing barbules that weaken feathers, making breakage more likely. Most commonly called fault bar, but also **hunger streak, hunger fault, hunger trace**, starvation mark, subordinate bar, feather mark, and by veterinarians stress bands. When formed as spots called fault spot or fault holes.

hybrid: a cross between two forms, e.g. species or subspecies. Latin *hybrida*; *cf.* interspecific hybrid, **hybridisation**, or **hybridization**.

hybridisation parapatry: a situation in which parapatric populations are prevented from sharing an area because they mate with each other but generate progeny that are infertile or have reduced fertility; *cf.* competition parapatry, ecological parapatry.

hybridogenic speciation: speciation through hybridization that leads to the development of a stabilised hybrid population such as the Italian Sparrow (*Passer hispaniolensis italiae*), a population that arose from hybridization between the House Sparrow (*P. domesticus*) and the Spanish Sparrow (*P. hispaniolensis*). Under certain circumstances such a hybrid population may become a separate species.

hybrid zone: an area in which two populations meet and where some hybridization occurs.

hydrology: the study of water.

hydrophilic: having a strong affinity for water.

hydroxyapatite: a calcium phosphate mineral.

Hymenoptera: the insect order of bees, wasps, and ants.

hyoid apparatus: all bones of the tongue, the forward-directed tongue bone (entoglossal) and the backward-directed, paired bones (hyoid horns) in the tongue supporting the floor of the mouth behind and between the lower mandible and greatly elongated in woodpeckers (Picidae) and hummingbirds (Trochilidae); *cf.* basihyal, basibranchial, ceratobranchial, epibranchial.

hyoid horns: the backward-directed, paired bones of the tongue: basihyal, basibranchial, ceratobranchial, epibranchial.

hyperphagia: over-eating to deposit fat for migration.

hypersensitive: abnormally sensitive.

hyperstriatum: a structure just beneath the cortex in the brain, a centre for learning and intelligence.

hyperthermia: when an animal has a body temperature above normal, the opposite of hypothermia.

hypertrophy: excessive growth of something, as opposed to atrophy.

hypocapnia: low levels of carbon dioxide in the blood, e.g. through hyperventilation.

hypocleidium: the laterally-compressed process where the clavicles are fused together to form the furcula; *cf.* wishbone merrythought, shoulder girdle.

hypodermis: the deeper layers of the skin, below the outermost layer (the epidermis).

hypoglottis: the under surface of the tongue.

hypophysis: a two-lobed gland situated below the hypothalamus in the brain; it produces several important hormones, including prolactin and gonadotropic hormones that regulate the endocrine system of the body and govern reproductive behaviour, moult, and migration. Also called the pituitary gland; *cf.* hypothalamus.

hypoptilum: a normally small and often down-like feather that grows from the base of the main feather shaft in many birds, although often vestigial. A well-developed hypoptilum, which is considered a primitive trait, is found in cassowaries (Casuariidae), ducks, geese, and swans (Anatidae), gallinaceous birds (Phasianidae), and trogons (Trogonidae), among other families, but it is absent or greatly reduced in passerines (except in Acanthisittidae); in some birds such as the Emu (*Dromaius novaehollandiae*) the hypoptilum is of almost equal size to the main feather. Also called afterfeather or aftershaft; *cf.* hyporachis.

hyporachis: the shaft of an afterfeather.

Hyposittidae: a family containing only the Nuthatch-Vanga (*Hypositta corallirostris*), now usually included in the vanga family Vangidae.

hypotarsus: a muscle at the joint between the tibiotarsus and tarsometatarsus.

hypothalamus: part of the lower forebrain that secretes hormones controlling the nervous system and stimulating gonad growth, moult, and migration. Connected to it is the pituitary gland; *cf.* epithalamus, thalamus, diencephalon.

hypothermia: a condition in which the body temperature has fallen below the normal level by more than a few degrees. The cause may be insufficient heat production (starvation) or poor insulation, e.g. owing to oil contamination of the plumage; hypothermia may also be a normal condition, at least in hummingbirds (Trochilidae) which become torpid at night and, more irregularly, in some swifts (Apodidae) and nightjars (Caprimulgidae). Also termed facultative hypothermic response. Some authors include torpor and rest-phase or controlled hypothermia in hypothermia because the distinction remains controversial; *cf.* hyperthermia, rest-phase hypothermia, shallow hypothermia, hibernation, torpor.

hypothermic torpor: the dormant state of a warm-blooded animal that has reduced its body temperature below normal in order to conserve energy, e.g. during a period of food shortage; *cf.* rest-phase hypothermia, shallow hypothermia, hibernation, torpor.

hypothesis: a proposed explanation of phenomena in the natural world from which may be generated testable predictions. The term is often used also of fairly simple statements that may be tested statistically; *cf.* theory.

hypothetico-deductive method: in scientific research the formulation of hypotheses from which testable predictions are deduced.

hypothetical species: a new species only described on the basis of field notes and photographs, i.e. without a study skin.

hypotype: a specimen used to extend knowledge about an already described taxon; *not* equivalent to a holotype, but rather extending an understanding of a taxon by adding novel types to the known reference types of the taxon.

hypoxia: oxygen deficiency.

Hz: abbr. for Herz, unit equivalent to cycles per second and used in connection with various kinds of wave motion (sound, radio, etc.); *cf.* kilohertz.

I

IBA: abbr. for 'important bird area'. A concept introduced by ICBP and IWRB in connection with a programme aiming at identifying and protecting important bird sites

Iberia: the Iberian Peninsula, containing Spain and Portugal.

Iberomesornis: an Early Cretaceous fossil enantiornithine, or 'opposite' bird with a modern alula, from Spain.

ibid: Latin *ibidem* = in the same place.

Ibis: periodical of the British Ornithologists' Union (abbr. BOU), founded in 1858. Also a common name for most members of the family Threskiornithidae.

ICBP: abbr. for International Council for Bird Preservation, an organisation formed in 1922; renamed BirdLife International in 1990.

ichnology: the study of tracks.

ichthyophagous: fish-eating; also called piscivorous.

Ichthyornis: famous genus of fossil birds in the superorder Neognathae, representing a group of poorly known gull-like species from the Late Cretaceous of North America.

ichthyosaur: a marine reptile from the Mesozoic era.

iconotype: a photograph, drawing, or digital image of a type specimen.

icterid: any member of the New World family Icteridae, which includes oropendolas, caciques, American orioles, American blackbirds, grackles, cow-

birds, and the Bobolink (*Dolichonyx oryzivorus*).

i.e.: Latin *id est* meaning that is.

ileum: pl. ilia, lower part of the small intestine.

ilio caudatus: muscle attached to the pelvis.

ilio femoralis: a muscle attached to the thigh bone (femur) and ilium.

ilio fibularis: a muscle along the front of the thigh bone (femur).

ilio tibialis: a group of muscles anterior on the thigh bone (femur). Also called **iliotibialis extensor**; *cf.* semitendinosus.

ilium: pl. ilia, in vertebrates with four limbs (tetrapods), the dorsal part of the pelvis including the fused vertebrae (synsacrum); *cf.* pelvic girdle, pubis, and ischium.

image-fighting: a term for a bird attacking its mirror reflection, e.g. in a window or water surface.

imago: pl. imagines, an adult and sexually mature insect.

imitative learning: learning by imitating another bird.

immaculate: an egg with a plain shell colour lacking markings.

immature: sub-adult, generally used to mean older than juvenile, although there is no biological threshold separating the two terms. Many authors use this term for the period from when a bird is no longer under parental care until adulthood (sexual maturity).

immigrant: a bird that immigrates from another area, often to a previously unoccupied area.

immigration: individuals moving into an area from elsewhere; as opposed to emigration.

immune system: the defense system of the body; *cf.* spleen, bursa Fabricii, and thymus.

immunogen: any substance that generates an immune response; *cf.* antigen.

immunological distance: a quantitative measure or estimate of the difference between two antigens determined by immunological techniques.

immunoglobulin: a broad group of proteins that includes antibodies and that occur in body fluids.

immunosuppression: of the ability to mount an immune response.

impervious: impermeable, relating to the closed nostrils of birds such as gannets, boobies (Sulidae), and cormorants (Phalacrocoracidae); *cf.* pervious.

imprinting: a form of learning in very young birds, e.g. a newly born chick learns its own parents and their behaviour during the first days of life during its critical learning period. The first animal or animated object to which a chick is exposed during imprinting will result in the chick imprinting on this individual or object, regardless of whether it is the chick's parent; *cf.* filial imprinting, sexual imprinting.

inattentive period: a term for an incubating bird during the time it is away from its nest, e.g. to feed. As opposed to attentive period.

inbreeding: mating between close relatives, leading to reduced genetic variability (homozygosity) in the offspring; *cf.* outbreeding, genetic bottleneck.

incertae cedis (**or** *sedis*): abbr. *inc. ced.* Latin meaning 'taxonomic position uncertain'.

inch: unit of length, equal to 25.4 mm.

incipient species: a population on the way to evolving into a separate species.

income breeder: a migratory bird that may acquires all the necessary resources to reproduce on the breeding ground, opposite a capital breeder.

incubation patch: a patch on the belly of an adult bird that becomes naked and vascularized before egg laying, and usually edematous during incubation, against which the eggs are warmed during incubation. May be paired or single, and is absent in species that do not incubate (e.g. brood parasites, megapodes) and even in some species that do. Also inaccurately termed brood patch (brooding being a secondary purpose it sometimes serves).

incubation period: 1) the interval between laying the last egg of a clutch and the hatching of the last egg. Many birds have asynchronous hatching (e.g. pelicans, cormorants, herons, storks, eagles, hawks, cranes, parrots, and owls) beginning incubation with the laying of the first egg. 2) the period between infection and the appearance of symptoms of an infectious disease.

incubation pouch: a featherless cavity on *Aptenodytes* penguins (Spheniscidae) where the egg is held for incubation.

incumbent: of a foot in which the first toe (hallux) is pointed backwards and toes 2-4 forwards, all at the same level

incursion: a rarely used term for invasion (irruption).

independent contrasts: a method for analysing data that uses phylogeny to identify a set of mutually independent comparisons between pairs of species, pairs of nodes, or a node and a species.

independent samples: in statistics, samples or datasets in which the selection of one set of samples does not affect selection of the other samples.

independent variable: the input to a mathematical function; also used of the controlled variable in statistical regression analysis.

indeterminate layer: a bird that continues to lay eggs to replace those removed from the nest.

index: a term occasionally used for the second digit of the hand next to the thumb.

index count: a method using a count or mapping of landbirds as an index to relative abundance. It tallies bird records during one or more surveys of points, transects, or defined areas; *cf.* empirical modelling technique.

Indian subregion: the part of the Oriental Region comprising the Indian subcontinent south of the Himalayas together with Sri Lanka.

indicator species: a species that, by its presence, absence, or abundance tells something important about the quality of the habitat and thus serves as a tool in monitoring the state of the environment in an area. Also called biological indicator.

indigenous: a bird native to the area in question, in contrast to an introduced species.

indirect calorimetry: measuring the energy content of a specific food item indirectly, e.g. by the amount of oxygen consumed in its metabolism, as opposed to directly measuring it through burning it in a calorimeter; *cf.* direct calorimetry.

indirect competition: competitive relationship in which individuals compete indirectly for a resource, e.g. when a nocturnal frugivore such as a bat consumes fruit that is then not available for a diurnal frugivore such as a bird (or vice versa); *cf.* direct competition.

indirect head-scratching: head-scratching by passing the foot over the wing,

in contrast to direct head-scratching by passing it under the wing.

indirect life cycle: pertaining to a parasite that spends part of its life outside the host, either as a free-living stage or in an intermediate host.

indirect selection: the emergence by natural selection of traits that do not promote, and often harm the reproduction of the bearer, but nevertheless increase the bearer's inclusive fitness because the traits promote the reproduction of close relatives, sharing a large proportion of the bearer's genes. Kin selection is hypothesized to explain many cases of apparently altruistic behaviour. Also known as kin selection; *cf.* group selection.

individual distance: the minimum distance at which a bird will tolerate conspecifics except mate and offspring; *cf.* contact species, pecking distance.

Indo-Malayan subregion: a subdivision of the Oriental Region including tropical and subtropical parts of southeast Asia from the Malay Peninsula south of the Isthmus of Kra with nearby islands and eastward to between Sulawesi and the northern Moluccas southwards between Sula and Obi islands, thence west of Buro and then southeast to between Babar and Tanimbar, bounded by Weber's Line.

indumentum: rare term for bird plumage, also used in botany for hairs on plants.

infanticide: the killing of young conspecifics.

infectious bronchitis: a virus disease causing respiratory distress, sneezing, and rattling. In laying birds it can cause a drop in egg production or misshaped eggs of low quality. Some strains of the virus may cause severe kidney damage.

infectious laryngotracheitis: a viral infection of the respiratory tract (trachea - windpipe) in chickens, pheasants, and peafowl.

infectus synovitis: a viral infection in chickens and turkeys. Signs: depression, ruffled feathers, lameness, and a swollen and green liver.

influenza A: an RNA virus causing disease in birds and mammals; waterbirds (e.g. ducks, geese, and shorebirds) are typical hosts, but the virus can emerge into atypical hosts such as landbirds (e.g. chickens) and mammals (e.g. pigs, seals, mink) and become more virulent. Pathogenicity is defined based on an influenza strain's effects in poultry (chickens), and highly pathogenic (HP) strains can cause severe economic damage in the poultry industry. Strains are named based on their hemagglutinin (H) and neuraminidase (N) subtypes. Epidemic and pandemic human influenza episodes have frequently stemmed from avian influenzas that have apparently undergone subsequent mutations in another mammalian host.

infra-: prefix meaning below, on the underparts, smaller.

infraclass: taxonomic level between subclass and parvclass with the suffix -aves.

infraorder: taxonomic level between suborder and parvorder with the suffix -ides.

infrasound: low-frequency sound below 20 Hz, i.e. below the hearing range of humans; cf. ultrasonic sound.

infundibulum: the funnel-shaped and open upper end of the oviduct, where the egg (ovum) enters and is fertilized. Also called ostium; cf. magnum, isthmus, uterus.

infusorian: a microscopic organism (*Protozoan*) in the historic, now obsolete group Infusoria, found in stagnant water and infused organic laboratory cultures.

ingestion: the swallowing of solid food, **ingestive**, adj. **ingest** = to eat.

ingluvies: a thin-walled extension of the upper food canal (oesophagus) in some birds, where food is stored before being passed on to the gizzard; more commonly called crop.

ingroup: the taxon under study; cf. outgroup.

injury-feigning: a form of distraction behaviour found in many species, especially ground-nesting birds, in which the bird acts sick and unable to fly until the predator is diverted away from its nest or chicks; also called broken-wing display or trick, crippled bird act, or deflection display; cf. diversionary display.

in litt.: Latin *in litteris* = in correspondence with.

innate: pertaining to instinctive or genetically transmitted traits, especially behavioural ones.

innate behaviour: a behaviour that is genetically based and that consequently occurs independently of learning; instinctive.

innate releasing mechanism: a call, a posture, movement, or a scent that functions as a stimulus releasing a response. Also referred to as releasing mechanism.

inner ear: see: semicircular canals, cochlea, columella auris; cf. middle ear.

in-out bathing: bathing by repeatedly jumping in and out of water, e.g. a babbler (Timaliidae); cf. flight bathing, plunge-bathing, rain-bathing, stand-in bathing, stand-out bathing and swim-bathing.

inquiline: an animal living in the nest of a bird or other animal without harming the host, opposite to a parasite.

insecticide: a toxic chemical used against pest insects.

insectivore: bird or other animal feeding on insects and/or other land arthropods; adj. **insectivorous**; *cf.* entomophagous.

insemination window: the short period from when an egg is laid to the time the next ovum has arrived in the infundibulum, where fertilization can occur.

Insessores: old name for the perching birds (Passeriformes) together with various other groups.

insight learning: solving a problem by evaluation.

in situ: Latin meaning on the place, in the original place.

insolation: exposure to the radiation from the sun.

instinct: innate behaviour independent of learning.

instinct bird: a species whose migratory timing is inflexible, hence easy to predict; also termed calendar bird.

instinctual behaviour: innate behaviour, a behaviour that is genetically based and that consequently occurs independently of learning; instinctive.

Instituti Ornithologici Hungarici: a Hungarian ornithological organization that has published *Aquila* since 1894.

Institut Royal des Sciences Naturelles de Belgique: abbr: IRSNB. A Belgian ornithological organization that has published *Le Gerfaut* since 1919.

instrumental song: mechanical (non-vocal) sound having a similar function as normal bird song, e.g. advertisement of territorial ownership or attraction of a mate. Examples are sound produced by the vibration of the outer tail feathers as by many snipe (*Gallinago*), and the drumming of woodpeckers (Picidae).

insulin: a hormone produced by the islets of Langerhans in the pancreas and controlling blood sugar levels; *cf.* glucagon.

integument: external part of an animal, in birds including plumage, skin,

scutes, claws, spurs, muscle, and sensory nerves in the skin and the oil glands. Also called **integumentary system**. Latin *integumentum* = cover.

integumentary structure: a term for external appendages; e.g. wattles, combs, gular sacs, wing, and leg spurs, etc.

intention movements: Two types of movements, those that are not completed or that prepare the individual for a subsequent action; both can indicate what a bird will do next, e.g. a shorebird sleeping on one leg on a beach may begin to lower its second leg or raise its head as it perceives possible danger but retracts both once the conscious mind realizes the danger is not present; or the same bird may execute leg and wing stretches when it awakes prior to flying away; *cf.* displacement behaviour.

inter-: prefix from Latin *inter* meaning between.

inter alia: Latin = among other things.

interatrial septum: the wall separating the atria of the heart; *cf.* interventricular septum.

interference: 1) when one bird defends a resource, e.g. an apple tree with fruits against other birds, reducing its own food-intake rate. 2) optical phenomenon in which light waves interact with each other and which, for example, gives rise to iridescent colours in feathers; *cf.* diffraction.

interference competition: competitive interaction in which the use of a resource by one population or species limits the availability of that resource to another species or population. Such competition can be indirect, e.g. nocturnal versus diurnal frugivores or nectivores, or direct, e.g. individuals of different species fighting for a nest hole; *cf.* exploitation competition, direct competition, indirect competition.

intergeneric: between genera; *cf.* intrageneric.

interglacial: a warm period between two glacials, during which ice sheets shrink and more or less disappear. The present interglacial is called the Quaternary.

intergradation: the merging of two species or habitats with one another, or interbreeding of two populations, usually subspecies of the same species, producing offspring with intermediate plumage; *cf.* hybrid.

intergrades: unstable intermediate taxon as a result of interbreeding in a zone where two species or subspecies meet. Often interpreted as evidence that the two forms are not reproductively isolated and therefore should not be recognised as two species.

intermediate goal area: a site along the migratory route where the birds stop for a period, to feed and, sometimes, to complete their moult; *cf.* stopovevrsite.

intermediate host: a host species that only carries a parasite for a short period during that parasite's immature stage and is different from the final host species of the parasite.

intermedius: Latin = intermediate.

intermittent flight: a type of flight in which flapping is interspersed with pauses during which the flight path is continued ballistically (bounding flight), or during which the bird glides (undulating flight).

intermittent migration: an intermediate explorative migratory movement, especially known in young herons (Ardeidae), Lapwings (*Vanellus vanellus*), and Starlings (*Sturnus vulgaris*); *cf.* cannonball effect.

internal: inside; inner regions; from the Latin *internus*, opposite to external.

internal clock: common term for endogenous diel (the 24hrs period) and annual physiological cycles that enable animals, including birds, to engage in appropriate behaviour or physiological acts (e.g. sleep, moult, migration) at various times of the day or year, and which experimentally have been shown to operate in the absence of external cues.

internal pulp caps: a series of downward-projecting, cup-like structures inside the lower part of a feather shaft (calamus).

internal respiration: the oxidative processes within the cells; *cf.* external respiration.

International Code of Zoological Nomenclature: The internationally adopted set of rules governing zoological nomenclature, first published in 1905 and often abbr. the Code.

International Commission on Zoological Nomenclature: a permanent commission that makes recommendations for changes in zoological nomenclature. Their proposals are thereafter presented at the International Congress of Zoology for adoption; after 1972 the authority was transferred to the International Union of Biological Sciences. Its first Code, the Stricklandian Code, was adopted as early as 1842.

International Council for Bird Preservation: abbr.: ICBP, founded in 1922 in Cambridge, UK. Produces Red Data Books about birds having conservation importance. Now a global alliance of conservation organisations working together for the world's birds and people under the name BirdLife International.

International System of Units, the: (abbr. SI from the French language name *Système International d'Unités*) is the modern form of the metric system. It is the world's most widely used system of units, both in everyday commerce and in science.

International Waterfowl and Wetlands Research Bureau: abbr. IWRB. Slimbridge, UK. Founded in 1954. Now an adviser in ornithological cases such as policy planning, nature conservation, environmental monitoring, etc. Formerly called **International Wildfowl Research Bureau**.

International Union for the Conservation of Nature and Natural Resources: abbr. IUCN. Founded in 1948 in Morges, Switzerland. Produces Red Data Books – listings of threatened and endangered species – although those on birds are now produced by BirdLife International.

International Union of Biological Sciences: a union that since1972 makes recommendations for changes in zoological nomenclature (the Code).

internus: Latin = internal.

interorbital septum: the thin plate separating the two eye sockets (orbits) in the skull of a bird.

intersex: an individual showing characteristics intermediate between those of normal males and females of its species, but that is of one sex only; *cf*. hermaphrodite, gynandromorph.

intersexual selection: competition in mate choice in which one sex (typically males) displays ornamental plumage (i.e. a secondary sexual character), thus giving the other sex the opportunity to choose a mate with superior ornaments. These are often costly to produce or wear and thus may provide a visual measure of the wearer's fitness; *cf*. intrasexual selection.

interspecific: between species; *cf*. intraspecific.

interspecific competition: competition for limited resources between species; *cf*. intraspecific competition.

interspecific hybrid: a hybrid between two different species; *cf*. intraspecific hybrid.

interspecific releaser: a social signal by one species that is responded to by one or more other species; e.g. the alarm calls of some songbird species that are understood by other species that take flight in response.

intertarsal joint: the joint between the tarsometatarsus and tibiotarsus, usually called the heel despite the fact that it is not exactly homologuous to the mammalian heel.

intertidal: between the tides.

intertidal zone: the seaside zone between the high-water and low-water lines.

interventricular septum: the wall separating the ventricula of the heart; *cf*. interatrial septum.

intestinum: Latin, for intestine. It consists of the small intestine and the large intestine; *cf*. duodenum, jejunum, ileum, caeca, colon, rectum, digestive system.

intra-: prefix meaning within.

intrageneric: within a genus; *cf*. intergeneric.

intrasexual selection: competition within one sex for access to individuals of the opposite sex, often expressed in larger body size in the competing sex; *cf*. intersexual selection.

intraspecific: within the species; *cf*. interspecific.

intraspecific brood parasitism: brood parasitism in which parasite and host are of the same species; *cf*. interspecific brood parasitism.

intraspecific competition: competition within a species for a reserve that is in limited supply; *cf*. interspecific competition.

intraspecific hybrid: a term occasionally used for crosses between subspecies of the same species; *cf*. interspecific hybrid.

intrinsic: within an individual, group, or system.

intrinsic muscles: muscles inserting on the syrinx; *cf*. extrinsic muscles.

intrinsic rate of increase: the potential growth rate of a population in an unlimited environment.

introgression, introgressive hybridization: the appearance of characters of one taxon in another taxon as a result of interbreeding; used of phenotypic or genetic characteristics.

intromittent organ: the avian male sexual organ, uncommon in birds but present in waterfowl, ordinarily coiled within the cloaca. Also called phallus.

invalid name: a name that is not valid under the International Code of Zoological Nomenclature, called a *nomen invalidum*.

invasion species: a species occurring in large numbers outside its normal range at irregular intervals, so-called invasions; most invasion species are specialised on fluctuating foods such as fruit, seeds, or small rodents, especially at boreal/subarctic latitudes. Examples are Asian Pallas's Sandgrouse (*Syrrhaptes paradoxus*), Snowy Owl (*Nyctea scandiaca*), Waxwing (*Bombycilla garrulus*), and Brambling (*Fringilla montifringilla*). Also called eruptive or irruptive species; *cf.* gradation-bird.

inverse density dependence: a phenomenon occurring when a mortality factor, such as raptor predation, acts more strongly at low densities than at high ones; *cf.* delayed density dependence.

inverse migration: a phenomenon among migrating birds in which an individual migrates in the opposite direction of the species' normal migratory route; *cf.* abmigration.

invertebrate: animals without a vertebral column; *cf.* vertebrate.

in vitro: Latin meaning 'in glass', referring to biological experiments carried out outside the living organism, opposite of *in vivo*.

in vivo: term applied to studies occurring within the living organism, opposite of *in vitro*.

involuntary muscle: muscle whose action is not under conscious control, as opposed to voluntary muscles.

ipsilateral: affecting the same side; may be used, e.g. of the action of the song nuclei of the brain, which control the muscles in the same side of the syrinx, unlike many other nerve pathways that are crossed.

Irian fauna: the fauna occurring below 1,200m above sea level on the island of New Guinea.

iridescence: structural colours, glossy or metallic, that change with the angle of light, produced by refraction of light and not by pigment; gives metallic coloration in feathers as seen in glossy starlings (Sturnidae), hummingbirds (Trochilidae), sunbirds (Nectariniidae), and many others; **iridescent**; *cf.* non-iridescent coloration.

iris: pl. irides, the coloured tissue surrounding the pupil of the eye. Often simply called eye.

Irish Birds: Journal published by Irish Wildbird Conservancy since 1977.

irreversible: that cannot be reversed or made undone.

irruptive species: a species occurring in large numbers outside its normal range at irregular intervals, so-called invasions; most irruptive species are specialised on fluctuating foods such as fruit, seeds or small rodents, especially at boreal/subarctic latitudes. Examples are Asian Pallas's Sandgrouse (*Syrrhaptes paradoxus*), Snowy Owl (*Nyctea scandiaca*), Waxwing (*Bombycilla garrulus*), and Brambling (*Fringilla montifringilla*). Also called eruptive or invasion species; *cf.* gradation-bird.

IRSNB: abbr. for Institut Royal des Sciences Naturelles de Belgique. Ar ornithological organization publishing *Le Gerfaut* since 1919.

ischium: part of the pelvic girdle, paired plate-like bones situated parallel to and above the pubis; the hole is called the **ischiadic foramen**; *cf.* ilium, acetabulum.

islet: a small island, usually under 10 ha.

islet of Langerhans: tiny groups of endocrine cells scattered throughout the pancreas; they produce insulin and glucagon that regulate blood sugar levels.

iso-: prefix from the Greek *isos* meaning equal.

isobar: a line joining points of equal pressure, for example on a map; *cf.* isotherm.

isochronal line: a line on a map delineating where phenological events occur at the same time, e.g. arrival of a migratory bird species, the appearance of leaves, etc.

isodactylous: with all digits of equal size.

isohyet: a line on a map joining points of equal mean annual rainfall.

isolate: a population or group of populations that is separated from other populations.

isolating mechanism: any intrinsic or extrinsic barrier that prevents interbreeding between populations, e.g. different courtship behaviour or gametic incompatibilities; *cf.* reproductive isolation.

isolation species concept: species concept stating that 'groups of actually or potentially interbreeding natural populations which are reproductively isolated from other such groups' form species entities (Mayr 1963); also called the biological species concept; *cf.* recognition species concept, cohesion species concept, phylogenetic species concept.

isometric: having equal dimensions or measurements.

isophane: a function of latitude, longitude, and elevation used in the study of geographic variation within species.

isophene: 1) a line on a map showing where a character of a polymorphic species has the same phenotype, or lines that connect points of equal expression of a clinally varying character. 2) a line on a map connecting points having the same timing of a phenological event such as the arrival of a migratory bird, the appearance of leaves, etc.; *cf.* isochronal line.

isophyte: a line on a map showing places with the same vegetation height.

isospecies: a species without close relatives.

isosporous: having asexually produced spores of but one kind.

isotherm: a line joining points of equal temperature on a map; *cf.* isobar.

isthmus: 1) the middle section of the oviduct where the two egg membranes are added; *cf.* infundibulum, magnum, uterus. 2) a narrow section of land connecting two larger landmasses and bounded on both sides by water.

itch mite: an ectoparasite of the family Sarcoptidae, feeding on the skin, scutes, and feathers and causing infections and feather mange; *cf.* nasal mites, red mites, feather mites.

iteroparity: an organism that has more than one reproductive cycle during its lifetime. Adj. **iteroparous**.

itinerant breeder: a bird that breeds in two or more different geographical areas within the same year, such as e.g. some European Quail (*Coturnix coturnix*), the Sedge Wren (*Cistothorus platensis*), and Dickcissel (*Spiza americana*) in North America and the Eared Dove (*Zenaida auriculata*) in Brazil.

IUCN: International Union for the Conservation of Nature and Natural Resources, founded in 1948 in Morges, Switzerland. Produces Red Data Books – listings of threatened and endangered species – although those on birds are now produced by ICBP.

IWRB: International Waterfowl and Wetlands Research Bureau, now Wetlands International.

ixodid tick: an ectoparasitic mite of the family Ixodidae; ticks are vectors of many diseases, including rickettsia (*Borrelia burgdorferi*).

Jaarbericht der Club van Nederland-sche Vogelkundigen: periodical published by the Nederlandse Ornithologische Unie: abbr. NOU. Published 1917-1928, now called *Limosa*.

jack: a falconry term for a male Merlin (*Falco columbarius*).

jackknife: in statistics a parametric technique that enables reduced bias in estimating the population value for a statistic and also provides a standard error for the estimate. The method involves repeatedly computing the statistic from the full sample minus one individual, and for each computation leaving out a different individual.

jaeger: Am. term for three skua species, family Stercorariidae.

jaw: a rarely used term for the bill.

jejunum: the long middle portion of the small intestine.

jerkin: a falconry term for a male Gyrfalcon (*Falco rusticolus*).

jess: a falconer term for the leather straps placed round a raptor's legs.

jizz: a combination of characters or the overall impression that a bird gives: size, colour, form, posture, and movements, which together help to identify a bird in the field.

joint-nesting: a term for collective breeding, e.g. when more than one female lays eggs in the same nest and all take part in the breeding duties,

e.g. Groove-billed Ani (*Crotophaga sulcirostris*).

joule: abbr. J, the International System of Units (SI) of energy. As a rough guide, one joule is the absolute minimum amount of energy required (on the surface of Earth) to lift a one kilogram object up to a height of 10 centimetres.

Journal für Ornithologie: the periodical for the Deutsche Ornithologen-Gesellschaft: abbr. DO-G. Published since 1853. Since 2004 called *Journal of Ornithology* and appearing only in English.

Journal of Avian Biology: published by the Scandinavian Ornithologists' Union from 1995, formerly called *Ornis Scandinavica* 1970-1994.

Journal of the Bombay Natural History Society: covers all Indian animals with many important ornithological papers. In English.

jugal bone: a paired thin bone between the base of the upper mandible and the quadrate bone. Also called **jugal arch** and **jugal bar**.

jugging: the sleeping place of Partridges (*Perdix perdix*) (jug = to nestle together); when they are calling it is also called jugging.

jugular: pertaining to the neck, from Latin *jugulum* = neck.

jugular vein: blood vessel bringing blood from the head back to the heart; *cf.* carotid artery.

jugulum: the lower part of the throat.

jump dispersal: movement of a bird across inhospitable areas to colonise another place, for example to an oceanic island.

jumper: a migrant that accumulates sufficient fat reserves prior to migration for its entire journey; *cf.* hopper.

junctura: something that connects two things, Latin *junction*, joint.

junior synonym: in taxonomy, the youngest or most recently introduced of one or more nomenclatural synonyms, the first being the senior synonym. Also called younger synonym.

Jurassic: a period of the Mesozoic era, from 208 to 147 mya; subdivided into Early J (208-179 mya), Middle J (178-158 mya), and Late J (157-147 mya).

juvenal: Am. for a bird in its juvenal plumage (prior to moult into the first basic plumage), or a bird in its first plumage after the downy plumage in the pullus stage. Largely equivalent to juvenile.

juvenile: Eur. term for a young bird in its first non-downy plumage, usually of a somewhat looser texture than subsequent plumages and partly moulted in the first autumn. We propose the term changed worldwide to a young bird that is out of the nest and able to care for itself. Note, many authors use the terms immature and juvenile as synonyms, meaning any fledged bird that has not yet attained adulthood; *cf.* immature.

K

K: 1) standard symbol for carrying capacity in logistic and other models: the maximum number of individuals of a species that can live in a given area on a sustained basis. 2) also the standard abbreviation for amino acid lysine, but K is here not italicized.

karyotype: a description of the number and structure of the chromosomes in the cell nucleus of an organism.

katabolites or catabolites: waste products of metabolism, carried away by the circulatory system; **katabolism** (or catabolism) is the breaking down of chemical compounds, in organisms generally for release of energy; *cf.* anabolites.

kb: kilobase; one thousand base pairs of DNA sequence.

ked fly: member of the family Hippoboscidae, flattened ectoparasitic flies with a leathery surface and well developed claws, mostly wingless at least after having settled on a host. Also called birdfly, feather-fly, flat-fly, hippoboscid fly, louse-fly, spider-fly, and tick-fly; *cf.* ectoparasites.

keel: the carina of the breastbone or sternum, the site of attachment of the large pectoral flight muscles.

Kendall's tau or **Kendall's rank correlation coefficient:** a statistic used in non-parametric correlation analysis.

keratin: protein making up the major part of horny structures such as feathers, bill and claw, and of the outermost layer of skin.

kettle: a migrating group of birds moving together and usually soaring within thermals, most often applied to birds of prey.

key factor analysis: statistical method for identifying the most important factors influencing the system under study.

keystone species: in ecology and conservation, a species whose presence is vital to many other species in the ecosystem; *cf.* umbrella taxon.

kHz: abbr. kilohertz, a measurement of the frequency of sound or other wave phenomena; one thousand hertz, i.e. one thousand cycles per second; *cf.* hertz.

kidney: paired organ, situated at the back of the abdominal cavity; removes metabolic waste products from the blood.

Kikuth's disease: an avicultural term for avian pox infecting canaries (*Serinus* spp.).

kilobase (kb): one thousand base pairs of DNA sequence.

kilohertz: abbr. **kHz**, a measurement of the frequency of a sound or other wave phenomena; one thousand hertz, i.e. one thousand cycles per second; *cf.* hertz.

kilojoule: abbr. kJ, one thousand joules, the SI unit of energy.

kilometre: Am. kilometer, abbr. km, one thousand metres (meters) corresponding to c. 0.62 statute miles.

kinematics: the description and study of motion of bodies, with no reference to its causes (which are the subject of dynamics).

kinesis: movement, in birds for example the movement of the upper mandible relative to the skull, which is very pronounced in parrots (Psittacidae) and other fruit-eating birds; adj. **kinetic**; *cf.* nasofrontal hinge, mesokinesis, rhynchokinesis.

kingdom: the highest taxonomic rank; one widely accepted system classifies all organisms in five kingdoms, Animalia (multicellular animals), Plantae (multicellular plants except algae), Fungi (fungi), Protista (unicellular eukaryotes plus multicellular algae), and Monera (prokaryotes or bacteria). However, the archaebacteria differ fundamentally from other bacteria, so it is becoming usual to split the Monera into two kingdoms, Archaea and Eubacteriae; *cf.* genus, family, order, class, phylum.

kin selection: the emergence by natural selection of traits that do not promote and often harm the reproduction of the bearer, but nevertheless increase the bearer's inclusive fitness because the traits promote the reproduction of close relatives, most often the offspring of siblings or parents, sharing a large proportion of the bearer's genes. Kin selection is hypothesized to explain many cases of apparently altruistic behaviour. Also known as indirect selection; *cf.* group selection.

kleptoparasitism: stealing food from an individual of another species, as commonly occurs in jaegers or skuas (Stercorariidae).

kleptoptily: of attacking other flying birds and forcibly ripping feathers from them, applied to its nest as insulating material. Seen in, e.g. the Fork-tailed Palm Swift (*Tachornis squamata*).

km: abbr. of kilometre, Am. kilometer, one thousand metres (meters) corresponding to c. 0.62 statute miles.

knemidocoptic mange: a honeycomb-like deposit on head, legs, and feet on victims of a common skin disorder, caused by a spider-like mite called scaly face mite; *cf.* tassel foot.

knob: a fleshy fold of skin at the base of the bill in some pigeons (Columbidae).

koilin layer: the internal hard surface of the muscular stomach or gizzard, especially pronounced in seed-eating birds. Also called cuticula gastrica or gastric cuticle.

Kolmogorov-Smirnov test: a nonparametric statistical test that tests for whether two underlying one-dimensional probability distributions differ, or whether an underlying probability distribution differs from a hypothesized distribution, in either case based on finite samples.

krill: marine crustaceans of the order Euphausiacea; most species are pelagic filter feeders, some living in great swarms and constituting the chief food of many other animals, especially in Antarctic and sub-Antarctic waters.

kronism: Am. cronism, the eating of dead or moribund nestlings by their parents; adj. **kronistica**.

***K*-selected species**: species with a high survival rate and a low reproductive rate (small clutch, delayed sexual maturity); among the most extreme cases are oceanic birds such as albatrosses and other petrels (Diomedeidae and Procellariidae); *cf. r*-selection.

***K*-selection**: natural selection favouring traits characteristic of *K*-selected species; *cf. r*-selection.

K-T extinction: the mass extinction that occurred 65 mya at the Cretaceous-Tertiary (K-T) boundary when, e.g. most dinosaurs were wiped out, presumably caused by a large meteor colliding with Earth.

kurtosis: in statistics, the measure of how much a distribution departs from the normal.

L

labia: most commonly, lips, but in birds a paired structure with a slit in the middle found in the syrinx vibrating the air and perhaps producing sounds; *cf.* pessulus.

Labrador current: a cold current flowing south along the east coast of arctic Canada.

lachrymal gland: Am. **lacrimal gland,** one of two tear glands in birds, the other being the so-called Harderian gland.

lacrimal bones: paired bone plates between bill and brain case and near the tear glands, fused in most bird families but separate in some, e.g. turacos (Musophagidae). Also called prefrontals.

lactoflavin: an old term for vitamin B_2. An orange-yellow crystalline compound, $C_{17}H_{20}N_4O_6$, the principal growth-promoting factor in the vitamin B complex, naturally occurring in milk, leafy vegetables, fresh meat, and egg yolks. Also called riboflavin.

lacustrine: pertaining to lakes.

lagena: a blind tubular projection, in birds and other higher vertebrates extended and wound up into the cochlea of the inner ear.

lagoon: a salt water 'lake' separated more or less completely from the sea by a sandbank, a coral reef, or the like.

lakeshore: the shore of a freshwater lake; *cf.* beach and seashore.

Lamarckian evolution: the (hypothetical) inheritance of traits acquired during the lifetime of individuals.

Lamarckism: Lamarck's theory of evolution based on the inheritance of acquired traits.

lamella: pl. lamellae, the numerous small plates or comb-like 'teeth' on the inner edge of the bill, used for filter-feeding in, e.g. surface-feeding ducks (Anatidae) and flamingos (Phoenicopteridae).

lamellar corpuscles: nerve endings at the base of filoplumes that are sensitive to changes in pressure and vibrations. Also called Pacinian bodies.

laminar flow: smoothly flowing fluid; e.g. air over the airfoil of the wing.

laminiplantar: a tarsometatarsus having an undivided horny sheath on the posterior surface but scutellation on the anterior surface. Also called scutellate-booted; *cf.* reticulate, scutellate-reticulate, booted.

lanceolate: lance- or spear-shaped, pertaining to the shape of feathers.

land-bridge islands: islands connecting two continents or other large land masses, for example the Aleutian Islands between Alaska and Russia.

landscape ecology: the study of ecology and ecological factors at broader, e.g. multi-community scales across a landscape, often including humans as an important component; *cf.* ecogeography.

La Niña: climatic phenomenon characterized by unusually cold ocean temperatures in the equatorial Pacific, as compared to El Niño, which is characterized by unusually warm ocean temperatures in the equatorial Pacific; *cf.* El Niño,

lankesterellosis: a protozoan infection, common in the House Sparrow (*Passer domesticus*) and with a distension of the liver as a main symptom.

lanneret: a falconry term for a male Lanner Falcon (*Falco biarmicus*).

laparotomy: a surgical procedure involving an incision through the abdominal wall to investigate, e.g. the gonads to determine sex or degree of development.

lappet: a wattle, usually at the base of the bill or a hanging lobe-like structure.

lapsus calami: Latin meaning a slip of the pen, i.e. an error.

larder: the short-term storage of food on wires or thorns as performed by shrikes (Laniidae). Shrikes are therefore also called butcherbirds, a name also given to the Australian family Cracticidae.

large intestine: the short part of the intestine in most birds between the caecae and the cloaca where water is reabsorbed; *cf.* rectum, colon, small intestine.

larid: a member of the gull family (Laridae).

Larus: the periodical for the Institute of Ornithology of the Yugoslav Academy of Sciences and Art and the genus name for most gulls.

larynx: a dilated region that leads into the upper trachea, the point where the respiratory and digestive tracts diverge. It consist of cartilage called **laryngeal cartilages**; *cf.* glottis.

last male sperm precedence: cases in which the sperm of the last copulating male has a better chance of fertilizing the next egg than sperm from earlier copulations.

latebra: the small mass of white yolk at the centre of a bird's egg.

lateral: situated at the side, e.g. of the body; *cf.* dorsal, ventral.

lateral caudal process: the process on the anterior end of the sternal notch. Also called external lateral xiphoid.

lateral condyle: a rounded process at the terminal end of the tibiotarsus.

lateral coronal stripe: a streak running on the side of the crown to the nape; *cf.* mesial coronal stripe.

Latin America: the part of the Americas where Spanish or Portuguese is the main language.

Latin name: common term for 'scientific name', slightly misleading because both Latin and Greek words are commonly used in the nomenclature.

latiplantar: having the back side of the tarsus flat, as found in oscine passerines, the opposite of acutiplantar.

latissimus: Latin = broadest.

latissimus dorsi: a muscle beneath the scapula.

latitude: one of the coordinates used to indicate a position on the surface of the Earth: the angle between the equatorial plane and an imaginary line from the centre of the Earth to a point on the surface, equivalent to the angular distance from the point to the equator along the meridian; adj. **latitudinally**; *cf.* longitude, altitude.

latus: Latin = side, flank, or broad ample, large, wide.

Laurasia: one of the two major continents existing during the Mesozoic era, broadly comprising the land masses today forming Europe, Asia except India, and North America. Gondwanaland was the second major continent comprising all the southern land masses; in the Triassic period both were united into the super-continent of Pangaea.

law of priority: the principle in zoological nomenclature that the valid name of a taxon is the oldest available name applied to it, with the 10th edition of the Systema Natura from 1 January 1758 as the starting point, provided that it is not invalidated by another long-accepted (e.g. 50 years) name.

Lawrence's Warbler: a hybrid between Blue-winged Warbler (*Vermivora pinus*) and Golden-winged Warbler (*Vermivora chrysoptera*). See also Brewster's Warbler.

LBJ: Am. abbr. for 'little brown job', i.e. an unidentified little drab bird.

LCT: lower critical temperature, the temperature at which a warm-blooded animal begins to increase heat production and oxygen consumption, often accompanied by shivering; *cf.* upper critical temperature.

leading edge: 1) the forward edge of the wing, composed of the lesser coverts, alula, and edge of the outermost primary, which together cut through the air. 2) the narrow web on the outside of a flight-feather.

leading line: a landscape feature along which bird migration is regularly directed, such as a river valley, a coastline, or a mountain range. Also called leitlinie; *cf.* diversion line.

leaf petioles: the shafts of the pinnate leaves of deciduous trees; often used as bird nest material.

leaf skeleton: the lacy remains of leaves retrieved from leaf litter. Often used in nests.

leaf tossing: a foraging behaviour of many ground-living birds, e.g. pittas (Pittidae) and thrushes (Turdidae), who toss leaves aside with the bill or foot to reveal hidden food.

leaf warbler: common name for any member of the genus *Phylloscopus* (Sylvidae).

leapfrog: a distributional situation in which two populations of similar appearance occupy disjointed ranges between which there is one or more populations of the same species that look different.

leap-frog migration: a situation in which a migratory population passes over (or through) the breeding and wintering ranges of another population of the same or closely related species to reach its own breeding or wintering range, such that the breeding and wintering ranges of the leaper latitudinally (or elevationally) encompass the breeding and wintering ranges of the population that is 'leaped'.

least squares method: a curve-fitting method in statistics based on the minimization of the sum of squared deviations of the observations from a curve modelled to fit these observed data.

leatherjacket: crane-fly larva. The larvae of some species, living in soil and destroying plant roots, are common garden pests; they are also important food for some bird species, e.g. the Starling (*Sturnus vulgaris*).

lectins: proteins that specifically bind to (and crosslink) carbohydrates.

lectotype: in taxonomy a type specimen chosen among a syntype series by a researcher in the absence of the type designated by the author (holotype); *cf.* holotype, syntype, paratype, neotype, protype, pseudotype, topotype.

Le Gerfaut: periodical published since 1919 by the Institute Royal des Sciences Naturelles de Belgique (IRSNB).

leg: a hindlimb of a bird; *cf.* calcaneus, cnemial crest, femur, fibula, hallux, lateral condyle, patella, phalanx, tarsometatarsus, tibiotarsus.

leg flag: a coloured ring with a broad flange used to mark individuals in population studies of larger birds.

leg-ging: the thigh.

leitlinie: word adopted from German, meaning leading line: a landscape feature along which bird migration is regularly directed, such as a river valley, a coastline, or a mountain range. Also called leading line; *cf.* diversion line.

lek: 1) a site where a group of males engage in courtship display to attract females, also called arena or booming ground. 2) a group of lekking or displaying males.

lekking: group courtship display by promiscuous males of certain polygynous species to attract females: performing courtship display and/or song at a communal area. Known, e.g. in the Ruff (*Philomachus pugnax*), birds of paradise (Paradisaeidae), and manakins (Pipridae); *cf.* exploded lek.

lek-promiscuity: a reproductive system in which females briefly visit lekking promiscuous males for the propose of fertilization. Also called **lek-polygyny, lek-mating systems, lek-reproductive strategies;** *cf.* lek, lekking, exploded leks.

lekking polybrachygamy: a mating system in which individual males may mate with more than one female each season without prolonged social bonding with them.

lens: a transparent structure near the front of the eye through which light is focused onto the retina; *cf.* ciliary body.

Lepidoptera: the insect order of butterflies and moths.

lesion: term for a damaged area of tissue, external or internal, resulting in discolouring, swelling, or lack of function.

Lesser Antilles: a group of islands in the West Indies comprising the Leeward Islands, Windward Islands, Virgin Islands, and some small islands north of Venezuela; *cf.* Greater Antilles.

lesser coverts: the smallest coverts nearest the front of the wing. Also spelled with a hyphen. Also called lesser wing coverts.

Lesser Sunda Islands: a chain of islands including Bali, Sumbawa, Flores, Moyo, Sumba, Timor, and Komodo island, all now collectively called Nusa Tenggara; *cf.* Greater Sunda Islands.

lesser wing coverts: the smallest wing coverts nearest the carpal joint. In American usage it often refers only to the two-three rows directly over the median coverts, and the rest are called marginal coverts or marginal wing coverts; *cf.* greater wing coverts.

leucism: absence of dark pigment resulting in a reduction in the intensity of all pigments, which weakens the feather structure, but with normal iris pigmentation, also called dilutium or dilute albino. Leucism also sometimes used for various forms of schizochroism. Adj. **leucistic**. Note: often called partial albinism, but that is not appropriate.

leucocyte: a white blood cell. Also also spelled **leukocyte;** *cf.* erythrocyte, thrombocyte.

leucocytozoonosis: a disease caused by blood protozoa transmitted by blood-sucking flies and causing cysts in the heart, gizzard, or skeletal muscles, fatal for ducks and geese (Anatidae); **leucocytozoon.**

LH: abbr. of luteinizing hormone, produced by the pituitary gland to stimulate growth and development of the gonads; *cf.* FSH.

Library of Natural Sounds: a collection of bird songs and calls at Cornell University's Laboratory of Ornithology, archiving more than 160,000 recordings. Now called Macaulay Library. A list of equipment and advice on how to use it can be found on their web site: www.birds.cornell.edu/LNS/

lien: Latin = spleen.

life history strategy: the major feature of the life cycle of an organism, es pecially those related to reproduction and survival, such as growth rate, longevity, number of offspring, etc. Used as a lineage-based concept rather than one of variation among individuals of the same lineage.

life table: a comprehensive tabulation of mortality data of a population or cohort, with respect to age.

life list: list of all bird species seen by a person; such lists are mainly being kept by 'twitchers', i.e. birders concerned with number of species seen.

lifer: a (rare) bird species observed for the first time in the wild by a birder.

lifetime recruitment: the number of offspring known to have survived at least to breeding age produced by a single bird during its lifetime.

life zone: 1) a region with a characteristic flora and fauna. 2) the characteristic types of vegetation that occur along a latitudinal or elevational gradient; the temperature and humidity of an area rather than its vegetation, opposite biome.

lift-to-drag ratio: the lift force divided by the drag force on a flying animal or object.

ligament: tissue that joins bones to each other, also called gristle; *cf.* tendon.

likelihood: probability of a particular hypothesis given observed data; largely the same as probability. In systematics, maximum likelihood optimizes the parameters of a model to obtain the best possible fit to a set of observations; *cf.* maximum likelihood.

lily-trotters: another name for jacanas, family Jacanidae.

limberneck: a symptom of severe cases of botulism in birds, accompanied by flaccid paralysis of the neck.

lime, bird: a very sticky substance, e.g. made from holly bark, that has been used to catch wild birds by causing them to stick to a perch.

Limosa: journal published by the Nederlandse Ornithologische Unie (NOU) since 1937, as a continuation of *Jaarbericht der Club van Nederlandsche Vogelkundigen* (1917-1928) and *Orgaan der Club van Nederlandsche Vogelkundigen* (1928-1936). Also the genus name for four species of godwits.

Lincoln Index: a population estimate based on a capture-recapture experiment.

lineage: a group of organisms linked by common descent, whether at population, species, genus, or higher taxonomic levels.

linear regression: in statistics, the calculation of the linear relationship best fitting a set of corresponding observations of two variables, one independent (controlled) and one dependent; or a similar calculation with several independent variables.

linear relationship: relationship between two variables through a first order expression: $y = mx + b$, in which y is the dependent variable, x is the independent variable, m is the slope of the line that describes their relationship, and b is the y intercept. May be generalized to any number of independent variables, in which case the straight line becomes a plane in a multidimensional space.

line transect: a census of bird populations taken by counting detections of individuals along a line, usually in which only birds within a certain distance from the line are counted; also called strip census or strip transect; *cf.* belt transect.

lingua: Latin = tongue.

lining of the wing: a collective term for underwing coverts.

linkage: the association of two or more genes on the same chromosome such that they do not assort independently but rather exhibit linked expression(s);

the tendency of two or more genes to be inherited together due to their linkage on the same chromosome.

Linnaean classification: the classification system founded by the Swede Carl von Linné using species, genus, family, order, class, phylum, and kingdom.

Linnaeus: (1707-1778), Latinized version of (Carl von) Linné, author of the Systema Naturae, of which the 10th edition (1758) forms the starting point of binomial nomenclature. Linnaeus named many species, and his name in such cases is usually abbreviated to L. or Linn.

Linnaean Society of New York: a scientific society founded in 1878, later with its famous offshoot the Bronx County Bird Club.

Linnean Society of London: a scientific society founded in 1788, promoting the study of biology.

lipid index: measure of a bird's fat load or fat reserve.

lipochrome: a fat-soluble pigment belonging to the carotenoids, having yellow, orange, or red colour (rarely blue or green); *cf.* melanin.

lipogenesis: the formation of fat in the body.

lipolysis: enzymatic break-down of fats.

lipomatosis: disease involving extensive deposits of fat in a tumour, **lipomas**.

lister: a birdwatcher who lists all new species seen. Also called tick-hunter, ticker, twitcher, or birder, although the latter may also simply mean 'birdwatcher'.

listeriosis: disease caused by a bacterial infection, causing infection of the bloodstream (septicaemia). Also spelled **listerellosis**.

litter: dead leaves and other decomposing plant residues on the forest floor.

littoral: of the shore of a body of water, but also used to refer to various depths near the shore and to the intertidal zone of a seashore.

liver: a large internal organ, in birds composed of two lobes; one of several functions is to remove potentially harmful (toxic) substances from the blood; also stores fats and sugars.

live trap: a trap that captures animals alive and unharmed.

llano: a flat, treeless plain or steppe-like habitat in South America.

loafing platform: a platform on water where waterfowl rest.

lobe: a rounded protuberance, for example the swimming lobes on the toes of grebes, coots, and some other waterbirds; adj. **lobate**.

lobus: Latin = lobe.

local nomad: a resident species or population that wanders locally, better defined as **local wanderer**.

loc. cit.: abbr. of the Latin *loco citato* = in the place cited, may be used instead of a proper reference where a reference was used previously in the same paragraph.

locus: pl. **loci** 1) the position of a gene on a chromosome, usually stated in terms of its relation to other genes on the same chromosome. 2) used generically in population genetics and systematics to refer to different markers or segments of DNA, e.g. mtDNA, being nonrecombining, is inherited as a single locus, whereas allozyme and microsatellite studies typically involve multiple putative loci, each of which may have two alleles in an individual. Data from multiple loci are considered more robust in recovering lineage histories than data from a single locus. 3) Latin *locus*, pl. *loci* meaning the place.

locust-bird: one of the different bird species in Africa that feeds on locust (grasshopper) swarms.

logistic regression: similar to standard regression but with the dependent variable being dichotomous.

loin: the part of the body on both sides of the spine between the false ribs and the hip bones.

long-distance migrant: a bird that moves great distances, often between continents, in its biannual migrations; *cf.* short-distance migrant, elevational migrant.

longevity: how long a bird does or can live.

longissimus: Latin = longest.

logotype: a new animal described only in writing without any voucher specimen.

longitude: the angular distance east or west between a standard meridian (today always the meridian through the Greenwich observatory) and the meridian of the place in question; adj. **longitudinal**; *cf.* latitude, altitude.

long-wings: a falconry term meaning falcons; *cf.* short-wings, round-wings.

loomery: British term for a breeding colony of guillemots (genus *Uria*).

loon: Am. for diver, family Gaviidae.

loop migration: used of migrating species or populations whose spring and autumn migratory pathways are different, causing a circular or elliptical route when the movements are considered over an entire annual cycle, also called ellipse migration such as, e.g. Red-backed Shrike (*Lanius collurio*), Sand Martin (*Riparia riparia*), or Ruddy Turnstones (*Arenaria interpres*) in the north Pacific.

loops of Henle: loops in the kidney forming a counter-current system, mainly involved with reabsorption of water and salt, hence with water conservation and osmotic equilibrium; much shorter in birds than in mammals, which may be seen in light of the fact that birds excrete nitrogen as insoluble uric acid, which in itself allows for a very good water economy compared with mammals (which excrete nitrogen as a urea solution).

lores: the area between the eye and base of the upper mandible, **loral region**.

louping ill: disease caused by a tick-borne virus often found in Red Grouse (*Lagopus lagopus*).

louse: pl.lice, any member of the order Phthiraptera of wingless, dorso-ventrally flattened insects ectoparasitic on warm-blooded vertebrates, feeding on the surface layers of the skin or on skin or feather debris. Normally relatively harmless.

louse fly: member of the family Hippoboscidae, flattened ectoparasitic flies with a leathery surface and well-developed claws, mostly wingless at least after having settled on a host. Also called birdfly, feather-fly, flat-fly, hippoboscid fly, ked-fly, spider-fly, or tick-fly; *cf.* ectoparasites.

Lower Austral Zone: one of six life zones in North America.

lower beak: the lower section of the bill, also called lower mandible; *cf.* upper mandible, maxilla.

lower critical temperature: abbr. LCT, the temperature at which a warm-blooded animal begins to increase heat production and oxygen consumption, often accompanied by shivering; *cf.* upper critical temperature.

lower jaw bones: the five fused bones on each half that together comprise the lower mandible in birds.

lower leg: the tarsometatarsus or 'tarsus' for short, a bone consisting of fused tarsals and metatarsals that together with the toes comprise the avian foot. Also called shank.

lower mandible: the lower section of the bill; *cf.* upper mandible.

lower risk: a conservation category formulated by IUCN and used by BirdLife International for species that do not satisfy the criteria of 'critically endangered', 'endangered', or 'vulnerable', but which must be monitored to get more information on their status; *cf.* data deficient, not evaluated.

lower umbilicus: a hole at the lower end of the hollow and transparent base of the feather shaft (calamus); *cf.* upper umbilicus.

loxodrome: a curve on the surface of the Earth, drawn by keeping a constant compass course. On a Mercator projection loxodromes are plotted as straight lines; *cf.* orthodrome.

LRS: abbr. lifetime reproductive success.

lucidus: Latin = bright, clear.

lumbar: pertaining to the lower back region.

lumbosacral enlargement: a swelling of the spinal cord in the synsacrum.

lumbosacral plexus: the nerve fibres running from the synsacrum to the pelvis and leg muscles; *cf.* brachial plexus.

lumbosacrum: rare term for an element of the pelvis of birds formed by the fusion of the thoracic, lumbar, sacral, and caudal-vertebrae. Usually called synsacrum.

lumper: a taxonomist prone to joining taxa into one species or genus, in contrast to a splitter who emphasises differences rather than similarities.

lung: the respiratory organ of land vertebrates.

lure: 1) an instrument to imitate birdcalls. 2) a falconry term for a 'dummy', such as a pheasant or grouse wing with some meat fastened to it. 3) a device with an attached hook, used to catch fish.

lutein: a carotenoid pigment found in yellow feathers, egg yolk, and fat.

luteinizing hormone: a gonadotrophic hormone controlling breeding physiology in both sexes. Abbr. LH; *cf.* follicle stimulating hormone.

lutino: a change to yellow in the plumage, captive parrots sometimes loose their dark pigment and become yellow.

Lyme disease: disease caused by *Borrelia burgdorferi*, a spirally twisted bacterium (spirochaete) transmitted by ticks and giving rise to influenza-like symptoms.

lymph: a colourless fluid containing water, salts, and suspended fats; *cf.* lymph nodes, lymphatic system.

lymph nodes: nodes along lymphatic channels where particles such as bacteria and virus are removed and lymphocytes added (recirculated) before the lymph reaches the blood. Well developed in mammals but rare in birds.

lymphatic system: network of fine vessels in the body carrying foreign bodies, with connections to the venous blood circulatory system; *cf.* lymph nodes.

lymphocyte: a type of white blood cell, part of the immune system.

lymphoid leucosis: lymph cancer, a virus of the leukosis-sarcoma complex. Occurs mainly in laying hens between 4 and 10 months of age. Tumors in the bursa of Fabricius will spread to many other internal organs, especially the liver, spleen, and kidney.

lymphoid tissue: is found in the walls of the intestine, including the caeca, and in the bursa of Fabricius, spleen, and thymus where it encounters foreign antigens and participates in immune reactions.

lyrates: the two very elongate tail feathers of the Superb Lyrebird (*Menura novaehollandiae*).

lysine: one of the 20 amino acids of which proteins are made.

M

m: abbr. of metre, the SI unit of length equal to about 39.4 inches.

Macaronesian region: zoogeographic region comprising the islands off West Africa: Cape Verde Islands, Canary Islands, and Madeira.

Macaulay Library: a collection of bird songs and calls at Cornell University's Laboratory of Ornithology, archiving more than 160,000 recordings. Formerly called Library of Natural Sounds. A list of equipment and advice on how to use it can be found on the web site: www.birds.cornell.edu/LNS/

macchia: a vegetation type in the Mediterranean region, consisting of evergreen scrub and small trees with thick, leathery, leaves. Also called maquis. Its equivalent in North America is called chaparral, in South America matorral.

macro-: prefix from the Greek *makros* meaning long, large, or great.

macroclimate: the climate over a large area or general climate in its usual sense; *cf.* microclimate.

macroecology: the study of organisms and their relationships to the environment at larger spatial scales in order to study things such as the diversity of living taxa and the distribution, abundance, and latitudinal gradients of species richness.

macroevolution: evolutionary events across larger time scales, i.e. over geological time; e.g. the origins of higher taxonomic categories, major radiations, etc.; *cf.* microevolution.

macrofauna: larger animals of an area, often including insects and worms (macroscopic animals) of an area; *cf.* microfauna.

macrogenesis: the sudden origin of new types by saltation.

macrolecithal: large-yolked (used of eggs).

macronutrients: nutrients required in quantity for proper growth, i.e. proteins and lipids; *cf.* carbohydrates.

macrosmatic: having a well developed olfactory sense; the opposite of microsmatic.

Madagascar subregion: the faunal region formed by Madagascar and its surrounding islands, north to the Seychelles. By some authors regarded as a subregion of the Ethiopian region. Also called Malagasy subregion.

magnetic compass: a navigational tool possessed by some birds that uses the earth's magnetic north and south poles, which are situated close to the geographical poles; *cf.* olfactory, star, sun compass, and vector orientation.

magnetoreceptor: a sensory cell able to detect magnetic fields such as the geomagnetic field; migratory birds are assumed to possess magnetoreceptors of some kind, possibly in the brain, but they have yet to be found; **magnetoreception**.

magnum: the section of the oviduct where the egg-white (albumen) is added; *cf.* infundibulum, isthmus, uterus.

Mahgreb, the: Morocco, Algeria and Tunisia.

maintenance activity: common term for feather maintenance: bathing, sunning, anting, and preening (including oiling and powdering of the plumage); *cf.* comfort behaviour.

major digit: the much-flattened finger in the hand between the carpometacarpus and terminal digit (digit 2); *cf.* alular digit, minor digit.

major hen: the predominate breeding female in some bird species in which females are far more common than males, e.g. Ostriches (*Struthio camelus*), in which the sex ratio is 1:4, and where some females, called 'minor' hens, lay eggs in the nest of a 'major' hen.

mala: Latin = jaw.

Malagasy subregion: the faunal region formed by Madagascar and its surrounding islands, north to the Seychelles. By some authors regarded as a subregion of the Ethiopian region. Also called Madagascar subregion.

malar region: the side of the cheek; many birds have a malar stripe below this region.

malar stripe: a dark streak from the base of the bill down the side of the jaws to the side of the throat; *cf.* moustachial stripe, sub-moustachial stripe. (Am. mustachial).

Malayan subregion: Indo-Malayan subregion of the Oriental region.

Malay Archipelago: Indonesia, Borneo, Sulawesi, and the Moluccas, but excluding New Guinea.

male deception polygyny: mating system in which males mate with multiple females through deception, i.e. polygyny made possible because the second and subsequent females are unaware that the male is already mated; thought to be the mechanism behind polygyny in, e.g. the Pied Flycatcher (*Ficedula hypoleuca*).

male guarding behaviour: when a male persistently escorts a female during her fertile period to prevent other males from copulating with her; the same as paternity assurance behaviour; *cf.* mate guarding.

malignant tumour: cancer; *cf.* benign tumour.

Malimbus: journal of the West African Ornithological Society, Nigeria. Also the genus name of ten *Malimbus* species in the family Ploceidae.

mallee or **mallee scrub**: a semi-arid Australian scrubland dominated by multi-stemmed *Eucalyptus* species; *cf.* Malleefowl (*Leipoa ocellata*), family Megapodiidae.

Mallophaga: feather lice, formerly treated as a suborder or family (Mallophagidae) of the insect order Phthiraptera, but apparently an artificial assemblage of species belonging to different suborders; feather lice live on mammals or birds and eat hair or feathers, and some species suck blood. Vectors of a number of avian diseases.

Maluku: an island group between Sulawesi and New Guinea, also called Moluccas Islands.

mandibles: the two parts of the bill, called upper mandible and lower mandible, although by some authors this term in the singular is restricted to the lower part, and the upper mandible is termed maxilla in correspondence with common use in vertebrate anatomy.

mandibular rami: the two halves of the lower mandible, separated by the soft tissue at the base and united distally at the gonys.

mangrove: tidal plant community in the tropics or subtropics dominated by woody vegetation (trees or scrub), generally of *Rhizopora* species, which commonly have tangles of aerial roots.

Mann-Whitney *U*-**test**: non-parametric statistical test to determine whether the ranked values from two random, independent samples could have come from populations with the same distributions; *cf.* median test.

mantid: any member of the family Mantidae, c. 1,800 species of predatory insects of which a well known species is the praying mantis (*Mantis religiosa*).

mantle: the upper part of the back.

manual: in ornithology synonymous with primary.

manus: Latin *manus* = hand. The primary feathers are attached to several of the bones making up the manus.

map-based navigation: in bird navigation the ability to determine spatial position from empirical data consistent with a map and compass model, in which position or home is given as a compass direction.

mapping census: a census that maps specific locations, often down to the level of bird territory boundaries.

MAPS: abbr. of Monitoring Avian Productivity and Survivorship programme, coordinated by the Institute for Bird Populations. Important elements are the intensive use of point-counts during breeding seasons and mist-netting and ringing at other periods.

maquis: a vegetation type in the Mediterranean region, consisting of evergreen scrub and small trees with thick, leathery, leaves. Also called macchia. Its equivalent in North America is called chaparral, in South America matorral.

marbled: pattern, e.g. of an egg with a lined and streaked (marbled) surface, or a marbled feather plumage, e.g. the Marbled Godwit (*Limosa fedoa*).

Marek's disease: A herpes virus. Occurs mainly in chickens under 16 weeks of age and produces leg and/or wing paralysis, high mortality, and tumors on visceral organs.

marginal coverts: Am. term for the foremost parts of the lesser wing coverts.

Mariana Trench: located in the Pacific Ocean, just east of the 14 Mariana Islands near Japan. It is the deepest part of the Earth's oceans and the deepest location of the Earth.

marine bird: seabird.

marisma: Spanish, meaning a marshy habitat.

marking: an old term for bird ringing (Am. banding), now extended to mean all techniques used to mark birds, e.g. ringing, neck collars, wing clips, radio tracking, web tags, or plumage dyeing.

Markov process: a random process in which the probability that a system will be in a certain state depends only on the system's state at the previous unit of time, used in, e.g. **Markov no-memory property**.

Mascarene Islands: an island group including Réunion, Mauritius, and Rodriguez in the Indian Ocean.

marsh: an area of waterlogged soil with rich herbaceous vegetation of, e.g. grass, sedge, and cotton grass; *cf.* swamp, fen, bog, wetland.

mask: a dark or black area around the eyes.

mass: the property usually meant by the word 'weight', and of which the SI unit is the kilogram (kg); the weight of a body is a force (the force of gravity acting on the body), measured in Newtons (N), which is proportional to the mass.

mass resting area: a place where many migrating birds congregate to fuel and rest, one of the most impressive is the mouth of the Copper River delta in southern Alaska where 20 million waders and water birds stop over during their northward migration.

mast: large seeds used as food source, e.g. beech nuts, acorns, and other large seeds that fall to the ground when ripe.

mate desertion: desertion of mate and offspring by one mate of a pair, leaving the other parent with a choice between rearing the brood alone or abandoning it; occurs particularly often in the Penduline Tit (*Remiz pendulinus*), in which the deserter might be of either sex. Also called offspring desertion or brood desertion.

mate guarding: the close following of the female by her mate during the female's fertile period, presumably to prevent her being fertilized by other males.

maternity: motherhood; *cf* paternity.

mate switching: occurs when an established pair bond is broken by one sex and a new bond with a different mate established.

mating: another word for pairing or copulation.

mating system: the mating strategy adopted by a taxon, such as seasonal monogamy, polygyny, etc.

matorral: a vegetation type in South America, consisting of evergreen scrub and small trees with thick, leathery leaves. Its equivalent in North America is called chaparral and macchia in the Mediterranean.

mature: capable of reproduction.

maxilla: the upper mandible or beak; *cf.* jugal bone, quadratojugals, mandibles, premaxilla.

maxillary bones: paired, fused bones forming the anterior palate in the bill of some birds.

maxillopalatine: pertaining to the upper jaw and palatal bones.

maximus: Latin = greatest or most; largest.

maximum likelihood: statistical techniques for choosing a model and its parameters to provide the most probable description of observed data.

maximum parsimony: in cladistic systematics, the reconstruction of a cladogram (phylogenetic tree) in a way that minimizes the number of character state changes required to explain the distribution of these characters among the operational taxonomic units, resulting in the simplest possible tree given the data.

maximum wing length: the wing length measured after flattening and straightening the primaries along a ruler, to give a maximum measurement. Also called wing arc; *cf.* chord.

maypole bower: a variable type of bower constructed of sticks, orchid stems, or ferns by bowerbirds of the genera *Amblyornis, Archboldia*, and *Prionodura*; *cf.* avenue bower.

Mayr, Ernst: (1904-2005), a famous ornithologist, naturalist, historian, and biological philosopher.

meadow: a low and well watered grassland, as for example near rivers.

mealworm: larva of a beetle *Tenebrio molitor*, much used as bird food in aviculture.

mean: the average of a set of numbers, calculated using a specific formula; the most common is the arithmetic mean, whereas other means (geometric mean, harmonic mean) have special applications.

meatus: the external acoustic canal.

mechanical sounds: non-vocal sounds, e.g. White Storks (*Ciconia ciconia*) bill clappering, snipe (*Gallinago* spp.) producing a sound with the tail in aerial display, or woodpeckers (Picidae) drumming wood with their bill.

mechanoreception: detection of mechanical stimulations such as the pressure of something against the body surface, sound waves, barometric pressure, etc.

medial: toward the midline of the body.

medialis: Latin = medial.

median: middle, on the midline of the body.

median coverts: the coverts between lesser and greater wing coverts. Also seen spelled with a hyphen.

median test: a statistical test that performs the same function as the Mann-Whitney U-test and can be extended to compare central values of three or more samples.

medianus: Latin = median, middle.

median wing coverts: the middle row of wing coverts on the upper and under wing, covering the base of the secondaries; *cf.* greater and lesser wing coverts.

Mediterranean shrub: a woody shrub found along the California coast. One of the nine major communities (biomes) in North America, characterized by a Mediterranean climate and a vegetation of woody shrubs with evergreen leaves. Also called chaparral; *cf.* macchia.

medius: Latin = middle.

medulla: 1) central part of an organ or tissue, interior to the cortex. 2) the part of the kidney where water is reabsorbed and urine is produced. 3) also means marrow, or 4) the firm and opaque tissue of the tapering shaft of a feather (rachis).

medulla oblongata: the hind-most part of the brain, linking the brain with the spinal cord.

medullary: pertaining to the medulla.

mega-: prefix meaning great, large, greater than usual.

megafauna: all terrestrial vertebrates inhabiting a region.

megaspecies: a polytypic species consisting of megasubspecies; *cf.* mesospecies.

megasubspecies: a subspecies that is approaching species status with a narrow hybrid zone with other subspecies; *cf.* mesosubspecies.

megasuperspecies: a group of species derived from the same ancestor that replace each other geographically and are too distinct morphologically to be regarded as forming a single species. Also called superspecies or second order superspecies; *cf.* subspecies, species.

meio-: prefix from Greek *meion* meaning less.

meiosis: reduction division, the process involving two cell divisions by which the number of chromosomes is reduced to half the number found in somatic cells during formation of gametes (gametogenesis); *cf.* mitosis.

Melanesia: a west Pacific island region, containing the Admiralty Is., the Bismarck Is., Solomon Is., Fiji, Vanuatu, New Caledonia, and the intervening islands, all east and south of New Guinea; *cf.* Micronesia, Polynesia.

melania: Latin = blackness, black spots.

melanin: the most common pigment in feathers, synthesized from amino acids and giving black and brown colours (eumelanin), but also, for example, the brick-red coloration in the Red Junglefowl (*Gallus gallus;* a mixture of eumelanin and phaeomelanin), the yellow in the plumage of the Western Tanager (*Piranga ludoviciana* phaeomelanin), and the green in the head of the male Mallard (*Anas platyrhynchos*) a mixture of eumelanin and phaeomelanin). Melanin also occurs in the skin, the horny covering of the bill, the scales of the feet, and some internal organs. It is insoluble in water and makes feathers more resistant to wear; *cf.* carotenoids, lipochromes, porphyrins, melanocytes.

melanism: an increase in the black pigment in feathers, causing a darkening when compared to other individuals or populations, such as seen in association with Gloger's Rule, although alternatively sometimes considered an aberrant condition of individuals. Adj. **melanistic**; *cf.* albinism.

melanoblast: a mobile pigment cell situated in the inner dermis and producing melanin.

melanocyte: a specialized cell synthesizing melanin.

melatonin: a hormone secreted by the pineal gland, its function is unclear but is thought to regulate secretion of gonadotrophin-releasing hormones.

Meliphagoidea: an Australasian superfamily comprising the fairy wrens (Maluridae), honeyeaters and Australian chats (Meliphagidae), and Australian warblers, pardalotes, and thornbills (Acanthizidae).

melogram: similar to a sonogram but with the intensity in decibels given more precisely. A graphic representation of a vocalization, usually with indication of time on the horizontal axis and frequency of pitches on the vertical axis. The apparatus used is called a **melograph**.

melotope: a term used to express the adaptation of vocalizations to the habitat, e.g. a Reed Warbler (*Acrocephalus scirpaceus*) has a loud voice to overcome the noise of wind through rushes.

membrane: a thin sheet of tissue, e.g. the nictitating membrane of the avian eye.

membranous labyrinth: the inner 'sac' of the ear; *cf.* endolymph.

memory cell: a long-lived cell having the ability to store information about an antigen encountered in the past, and the immune response against it.

Mendel's laws: The basic rules of genetic inheritance in diploid species, worked out by Gregor Johann Mendel (1822-1882) in 1865 but largely overlooked until 1900. Inheritance according to these laws is called **Mendelian**.

meninges: the membranes covering the brain; its inner layer is the pia mater, the outer layer the dura mater.

mental map: the mental image that a migrating bird presumably has of its route, gained from experience or inheritance. Also called cognitive map.

mentum: Latin = chin.

Menuroidea: an Australasian superfamily containing the Australian treecreepers (Climacteridae), lyrebirds and scrubbirds (Menuridae), and bowerbirds (Ptilonorhynchidae).

Mercator: 1) Gerardus Mercator (Gerhard Kremer, 1512-1594), a Flemish mathematician and geographer, famous for his cartography. 2) a curve on the surface of the Earth, drawn by keeping a constant compass course (loxodromes) and shown as straight lines.

meristic character: a countable character; *cf.* qualitative, quantitative.

Merkel's corpuscles: elaborate sensory nerve fibres or tactile corpuscles found in the skin; *cf.* Grandry's corpuscles, Herbst's corpuscles.

meroandry: having only one testis, adj meroandric.

merrythought: the furcula, a bone formed by the two fused clavicles acting as a spring during flight and thereby storing some of the energy in the downstroke to be reused in the upstroke; also called wishbone.

mesencephalon: the midbrain, the central part of the brain stem including the cerebellum, optic lobes, and chiasma, among other things controlling vision, locomotion, and reproduction.

mesenteric vein: a vein between the loops of the intestine, near the tail.

mesial: term meaning medial, central or toward the middle; e.g. used in anatomy.

mesial coronal stripe: a streak on the centre of the crown running from the front to the nape.

Mesitornithiformes: an order comprising only one family, the mesites (Mesitornithidae) with three species now included in the order Gruiformes by most authorities.

neso-: prefix from the Greek *mesos* meaning middle, intermediate.

mesobronchus: the extension of the bronchi in the lungs; *cf.* parabronchi.

mesoderm: the third germ layer of cells in an early embryo, the others being ectoderm and endoderm; mesodermal derivatives include muscles, heart, and kidney.

mesoduodenum: a two-layered fold in the pancreas.

mesokinesis: mobility of the upper bill at its connection with the forehead with the main hinge within the dermal skull roof of the brain case. Also called nasofrontal hinge; *cf.* rhynchokinesis, prokinesis.

mesoptile: the second generation of nestling downy plumage, occurring in penguins (Spheniscidae) and owls (Strigiformes); the first plumage in such cases being termed protoptile; *cf.* neossoptile, teleoptile.

mesospecies: a polytypic species none of whose subspecies are approaching species status, in contrast to a megaspecies.

mesosubspecies: a subspecies that is not approaching species status, opposite megasubspecies.

mesotrophic: applied to a fresh water body containing an intermediate amount of plant nutrients; *cf.* eutrophic, oligotrophic.

Mesozoic: an era 245 to 66 mya, subdivided into the Triassic, Jurassic, and Cretaceous periods; *cf.* Cenozoic, Palaeozoic.

mesquite: woody shrubs or small trees of the genus *Prosopis* and occasionally generally applied to arid scrubland habitats in the southwestern United States and Mexico dominated by these species.

meta-: prefix from Greek *meta* meaning after, between, change, or among.

metabolic rate: the rate of heat production in an organism, usually expressed in kcal per day; *cf.* basal metabolic rate, standard metabolic rate.

metabolism: all the chemical processes that take place in the body; *cf.* basal metabolism.

metacarpal primaries: the proximal primaries attached to the metacarpal bones; *cf.* digital primaries.

metacarpals: the three fused bones in the hand of a bird, forming the carpometacarpus to which some primaries are attached. Also called palm bones; *cf.* phalanges.

metamorphosis: change; in zoology especially applied to the transformation of a larva into an adult insect (imago).

metapatagium: a membranous flap of skin between body and elbow joint on the posterior part of the humerus. Also called patagium; *cf.* propatagium, humeral patagium.

metapopulation: a population comprised of a number of subpopulations that, although in the main separate, interbreed to some extent through the dispersal of individuals.

metasternum: the posterior border of the breast bone (sternum); *cf.* fenestra.

metatarsal: any of the small bones joining ankle and toes, which in birds are fused with the distal tarsus.

metatarsus: a shortened form of tarsometatarsus, the (bones of the) part of the foot between ankle and toes.

Metazoa: the multicellular animals, i.e. the same as kingdom Animalia in classifications recognizing more than two kingdoms.

metencephalon: the cerebellum part of the hindbrain, important for balance and coordination of movements, but having many other functions as well.

metre: Am. meter, the SI unit of length equal to c. 39.4 inches; abbr. m.

Mettnau-Reit-Illmitz: a standardized ringing scheme used in Germany and Russia.

mew: a name given to gulls in imitation of their calls (onomatopoeic), also the American name Mew Gull for the Common Gull (*Larus canus*).

Mexican subregion: a subdivision of the Neotropical region.

micro-: prefix from Greek *micros* meaning small or short.

microbe: microscopic organisms, including pathogenic bacteria.

microclimate: the climate of a restricted area or microhabitat, e.g. between two stones, among grass, within the nest of a bird, below snow, etc; *cf.* macroclimate.

microecology: small-scale study of the interrelationship between a single species and its environment, in contrast to macroecology.

microevolution: evolution on a small scale, including changes in gene frequencies in a population; *cf.* macroevolution.

microfauna: a fauna generally consisting of microscopical animals of an area; *cf.* macrofauna.

microflora: a flora consisting of microscopical 'plants' of an area, usually meaning fungi, algae, and bacteria rather than members of the kingdom Plantae.

microhabitat: a small-scale habitat.

micron: old name for a micrometer (ìm, a millionth of a meter).

Micronesia: an area of the west Pacific, including the Palau Islands, the Mariana and Caroline islands, and the Marshall and Gilbert islands; *cf.* Melanesia, Polynesia.

Micropodiformes: an outdated order for swifts (Apodiformes) and hummingbirds (Trochilidae).

microrace: a taxon that differs only slightly in morphology from its closest relatives.

microsmatic: having a poorly developed olfactory sense; the opposite of macrosmatic.

microsome: a small chromosome.

midbrain: the central part of the brain stem including the cerebellum and optic lobes, controlling among other things vision, locomotion, and reproduction. Also called mesencephalon; *cf.* forebrain.

middle ear: the air-filled cavity housing the ear drum and the auditory ossicles; the auris media.

mid-stratum: pl. mid-strata, the middle part of the vertical structure of vegetation, e.g. the mid-level of a forest, also called mid-story.

migration: seasonal movements between areas, usually used in a go-and return context between a breeding and a non-breeding area; in genetic often used in lieu of effective dispersal; *cf.* dispersal.

migration corridor: a pathway along which migrating birds concentrate also called a flyway.

migration program: the inherited information that guides birds on their migrations; *cf.* internal clock, circannual rhythm, migratory restlessness vector navigation.

Migratory Bird Convention: an agreement of 1916 between USA and Canada to protect species migrating across national boundaries; *cf.* Bonn Convention.

Migratory Bird Treaty Act: a law in USA passed in 1918 that effectively protected all migratory birds in the country for the first time.

migratory divide: of some species with breeding contact zones, e.g. from North Europe wintering in Africa the population in west Europe migrates west around the Mediterranean and the population from East Europe migrates east around the Mediterranean.

migratory fattening: of migrating birds at stopover sites gaining fat reserves for the rest of their travelling to breeding grounds or winter ranges; e.g. the Red Knot (*Calidris canutus*) gains up to a 100 percent increase in body mass by eating horseshoe crab (*Limulus polyphemus*) eggs during spring stopover in Delaware Bay, USA; *cf.* hyperphagia.

migratory overshooting: when a migratory bird overshoots its normal range or destination (i.e. flies too far).

migratory restlessness: behaviour of captive birds at seasons when they would normally be migrating, manifesting itself in unrest: an increased rate of to-and-fro hopping, wing fluttering, and wing flicking. Researchers studying bird migration take advantage of this unrest because it is usually directed in the normal migration direction. Also called premigratory restlessness or zugunruhe.

migratory urge: the innate urge in migratory birds to make relatively long distance movements at given periods of the year. Formerly called migration instinct.

millennium: a period of 1,000 years.

millinery trade: in connection with birds, the commercial trade of past centuries in feathers and prepared bird skins for decorating women's hats; this trade nearly led to the extermination of some hummingbird species and greatly reduced populations of some egrets.

millipede: any member of Diplopoda, a class of arthropods having a high number of body segments, each carrying two pairs of legs; some species roll into a ball when threatened.

milt: 1) fish sperm. 2) a rare name for the spleen.

mimesis: imitation; in connection with birds, camouflage and concealment gained by virtue of cryptic plumage coloration and adopted postures/ movements.

mimicry: some form of imitation, especially the protective similarity of a harmless species to a dangerous species brought about by evolution (Batesian mimicry). Different poisonous or otherwise dangerous species may also resemble each other (Müllerian mimicry). The similarity of a brood parasite's eggs to those of the host species, and imitating the songs of other species are other kinds of mimicry; *cf.* hawk mimicry, host mimicry, mouth mimicry, vocal mimicry.

minimum viable population: the minimum number of individuals that will assure the survival of a population for the foreseeable future.

minor digit: the digit or phalange attached on the inside of the major digit; *cf.* alular digit.

minor hen: applied to, e.g. Ostriches (*Struthio camelus*), which can have a reproductive sex ratio of 1.4 females to every male, for a female that is not the leading female but is one that lays her eggs in the nest of the leading female or 'major' hen.

Miocene: epoch in the Tertiary period, from 23.5 to 5.0 mya.

miombo: a type of central African deciduous forest dominated by leguminous trees of the genera *Isoberlinia* and *Brachystegia*.

mirror: an uncommon term for the white spots near the tip of the primaries of gulls (Laridae) or the glossy patch of the secondaries of the wing of a duck (Anatidae); these are also termed 'windows' or 'specula' respectively.

Mississippi flyway: a major route for birds migrating along the Mississippi Valley, North America; *cf.* Atlantic, Pacific, and Central flyway.

mist net: a fine net used to capture birds, usually black and difficult to see against a dark background of vegetation.

mite: any of the chelicerate arthropods which, together with the ixocic ticks, make up the order Acarina. Many mites are parasitic, feeding upon bird feathers and skin, e.g. itch mites, nasal mites, and red mites, others are free-living in terrestrial or aquatic habitats.; *cf.* tick.

mitochondrion: pl. mitochondria, organelle occurring in several copies in most eukaryote organisms involved in energy metabolism. Mitochondria contain some DNA of their own.

mitochondrial DNA: abbr. mtDNA, DNA residing in mitochondria instead of the cell nucleus and containing genes for some of the enzymes that are active in the organelle. Since sperm contributes no mitochondria to the embryo in birds and mammals, mtDNA is inherited maternally and is nonrecombinant, making it a useful and popular source of data for determining relationships among lineages and populations, a fact that simplifies analysis of relationships between closely related species or between different populations of the same species for example human.

mitosis: the nuclear division of a cell that produces two daughter cells each with a double set of chromosomes; *cf.* meiosis.

mixed flock: a flock containing more than one species; such flocks occur commonly in birds during migration and often throughout the year in, for example, tropical forests.

mnemonic device: a method employed to remember something, such as a bird species' song, by linking it to something easily remembered, such as by translating it to human speech.

moa: any member of the extinct family Dinornithidae (Struthioniformes) from New Zealand, comprising about 22 flightless species from the Pleistocene or earlier; representatives were still present when Polynesians (Maories) colonized New Zealand, the last species disappearing shortly before or after the arrival of Europeans. Some species were very large, the biggest moa standing 3m tall.

mobbing: noisy and sometimes aggressive behaviour of individuals (often of different species) toward potential predators, making the predator's presence conspicuous so that it often decides to move away. Mobbing behaviour of older birds may also teach young birds to avoid the predators in the future. Cats, snakes, raptors, and owls all commonly elicit mobbing behaviour in small birds, and many colonial nesters such as gulls and terns can be very tenacious in mobbing aerial and terrestrial animals (including humans) perceived as possible predators.

mode: the value occurring most often in a sample.

Modern Synthesis: term for the important and dynamic period (c. 1936-1947) in biology during which Darwin's theory of evolution was reconciled with genetics; also termed evolutionary synthesis, new synthesis, or neo-Darwinian theory.

modus operandi: pl. *modi operandi*. Latin = working method. The way a thing operates or the way in which a person performs a task or action.

modus vivendi: pl. *modi vivendi*, Latin = a way of living. A practical arrangement between conflicting parties until a matter is settled.

molecular genetic information: data derived from the molecular properties of DNA, RNA, or their protein products, e.g. DNA or RNA sequences, allozymes, restriction fragment length polymorphisms (RFLPs), single nucleotide polymorphisms (SNPs), microsatellites, amplified fragment length polymorphisms (AFLPs), etc.

Moluccas Islands: an island group between Sulawesi and New Guinea, now called Maluku.

Mollusca: phylum of more than 80,000 species of mostly soft-bodied marine animals with, or less often, without an external shell.

molt: Am. for moult, the growth of new feathers, usually through a process of regular renewal, i.e. the term covers both the loss of old feathers and the growth of new ones, it takes place in annual cycles that normally do not interfere with breeding and migration; *cf.* post-breeding moult, post-juvenile moult, partial moult, complete moult, fright moult, adventitious moult.

moniliasis: a fungal disease (mycotic) caused by an infection of the digestive tract, found in geese (*Anser*), pheasants (Phasianidae), pigeons (Columbidae), and parrots (Psittacidae). Also called thrush infection or sour crop.

monistic: a single factor explanation.

monkey bread tree: a general term for eight species of trees in the genus *Adansonia* growing in Africa, Madagascar, and Australia; known for their hugely swollen trunks; also called baobab.

mono-: prefix from Greek *monos* meaning one or single.

monobrachygamic: refers to a female mating only with one male in any one breeding season.

monochromatic: 1) having only one colour plumage or morph, opposite to dichromatic. 2) when applied to the sexes it means that male and female look alike. Often called monomorphic.

monocotyledons: plants with a single seed leaf, in contrast to the two seed leaves of dicotyledons.

monocular vision: one-eyed vision, such as that occurring in birds with one eye on each side of the head and thus with little or no field of vision in which the view from both eyes overlaps, the predominate type of vision among birds, especially good for viewing close objects; *cf.* binocular vision.

monocyte: a type of white blood cell, the primary function of which is to eliminate bacteria and other parasites.

monogamy: a pairing system in which one male and one female stay together and cooperate in breeding for at least one breeding cycle; the opposite is polygamy of two forms (polygyny and polyandry). More than 90% of all bird species are monogamous, although DNA fingerprinting shows that many apparently monogamous females have some of their offspring sired by a male other than their partner; this is called social monogamy. Adj. **monogamous**; *cf.* male deception, permanent pair bond, polygyny, polyandry, polygamous, polygynandry, polygyny, promiscuous.

monolectic: an animal that gathers pollen from a single plant species, opposite to polylectic.

monomorphic: applied to the sexes when males and females are indistinguishable (phenotypically essentially identical), although more accurately this is termed monochromatic, because sexual size dimorphism is usually present; **monomorph**, n. **monomorphism**; also called monochromatism.

monophagous: 1) feeding only on one type of food as does, e.g. the Snail Kite (*Rostrhamus sociabilis*); *cf.* euryphagous, stenophagous. 2) specialized on a single host species.

monophyly: when a group of animals comprises all descendants of the latest common ancestor, adj. **monophyletic**.

monophyletic group: a group of taxa containing all extant descendants of their most resent common ancestor; *cf.* paraphyletic, polyphyletic.

monospecific: of a genus with only one species.

monotely: in plants breeding once and then dying, as opposed to perennation, surviving to reproduce for more than a single year; called semelparity in animals.

monotypic: having no taxonomic subdivisions; a genus with only one species or a species without subspecies.

monoxenous: a parasite living on a single host species during its whole life span.

monsoon forest: forest in an area where moist winds blow during one half of the year and dry winds during the other half; monsoon forest trees are deciduous, losing their leaves in the dry season.

Montgomery's Rule: states that levels of subspecific differentiation among migrant species are, on average, lower than among non-migrants.

moor: an upland heath without trees and with acid soil.

moribund: in a dying state.

morph: any of two or more normal plumage variants in a polymorphic species, e.g. the Arctic Skua (*Stercorarius parasiticus*). Commonly called 'phase'. The term is not applicable to variation that occurs along the lines of sex, age, season, habitat, or locality.

morphology: 1) the branch of biology dealing with form and structure of animals or plants; also used synonymously with anatomy, i.e. the internal structure. 2) the structure and form of an organism, especially the external characteristics; adj. **morphological**.

morphological species concept: the definition of species solely on the basis of external features such as form, size, plumage colours, etc.; *cf.* taxonomy, systematics, phylogeny, convergence.

morphometrics: morphological analyses using measurements such as, e.g. wing, bill, tail, and tarsus lengths, body mass, etc.

mortality rate: the proportion of individuals in a population or cohort that die during a time period, calculated in many models as an instantaneous rate but frequently used for annual mortality. Also called death rate; *cf.* recruitment rate.

morula: the product of the first rounds of cell division of a fertilized egg.

mosaic map navigation: of goal orientation in navigating birds, based on learned spatial relationships among landscape forms and their relationships to home.

motor neurons: neurons that convey nerve impulses from the central nervous system to muscles and organs; *cf* sensory neurons.

mound builder: a megapode (Megapodiidae).

mound nest: some megapodes (Megapodiidae) build large mounds of decomposing plant material in which the heat from plant decomposition incubates the eggs.

moult: Am. molt, the growth of new feathers, usually through a process of regular renewal, i.e. the term covers both the loss of old feathers and the growth of new ones, it takes place in annual cycles that normally do not interfere with breeding and migration; *cf.* post-breeding moult, post-juvenile moult, partial moult, complete moult, fright moult, adventitious moult.

moult migration: annual migration from the breeding area to a specific moulting area before subsequent migration to the wintering area; occurs in some geese and ducks (Anatidae).

moult score: any method used to quantify the progression of a regularly scheduled moult; a widely applied scheme expresses primary moult on a scale of individual feather growth from 0 (e.g. still in sheath) to 5 (growth complete).

mounting: when the male steps or flies onto the back of the female during copulation; *cf.* reverse mounting.

moustachial stripe: a contrasting mark extending from the bill back towards and above the malar region, seen in many birds, for example the Bearded Tit (*Panurus biarmicus*). Am. mustachial; *cf.* malar stripe, submoustachial stripe.

mouth mimicry: imitation in connection with the mouth, referring to cases in which nestling brood parasites have evolved colour patterns on the palate or tongue closely resembling the specific patterns present in the mouth of the host's chicks; *cf.* mimicry, hawk mimicry, vocal mimicry.

MS: abbr. for manuscript, from the Latin *manuscripta*, pl. **MSS** = manuscripts.

mtDNA: mitochondrial DNA, DNA residing in mitochondria instead of the cell nucleus and containing genes for some of the enzymes that are active in the organelle. Because sperm contributes no mitochondria to the embryo in birds and mammals, mtDNA is nonrecombinant and inherited as a single locus solely from the mother, facts making this a popular molecular marker for systematics and population genetics studies determining relationships among lineages and populations.

mucosal lining: 1) the inner wall of part of the small intestine (ileum). 2) the outer layer of the hard surface of the muscular gizzard; *cf.* koilin layer.

mucous membrane: any epithelial layer secreting mucus, e.g. the lining of the nasal cavity (which traps dust and warms the air), the reproductive tract, and the gut.

mudnesters: 1) a common name for the Australian corcoracids comprising the White-winged Chough (*Corcorax melanorhamphos*) and the Apostlebird (*Struthidea cinerea*). 2) members of the magpie-larks (*Grallina* spp.) from Australia in the monarch family (Monarchidae).

mudnest builders: 1) members of the magpie-larks (*Grallina* spp.) from Australia in the monarch family (Monarchidae). 2) a common name for the Australian corcoracids comprising the White-winged Chough (*Corcorax melanorhamphos*) and the Apostlebird (*Struthidea cinerea*).

mule: a term used by aviculturists for a hybrid, named after the sterile cross of a horse and a donkey.

mulga or **mulga scrub**: a semi-arid Australian scrubland that includes mulga (*Acacia aneura*) and thus the source of the name of the Mulga Parrot (*Psephotus varius*), family Psittacidae.

Müllerian duct: the oviduct.

Müllerian mimicry: the presence of similar, often striking, colour patterns in two or more poisonous or otherwise noxious species; the colour patterns facilitate the emergence of avoidance behaviour in predators, which is probably reinforced by several species sharing the same 'warning' colours. Not known in birds; *cf.* mimesis, Batesian mimicry, hawk mimicry, host mimicry, mouth mimicry, and vocal mimicry.

multi-: prefix from Latin *multus* meaning many.

multibird nest: a nest with more than two attendant birds.

multi-brooded: of a bird species laying more than one clutch a year, as opposed to those laying only a single clutch (single-brooded).

multiple logistic regression (MLR): in statistics, a variant of multiple regression in which one or more of the independent variables is categorical (and others continuous).

multiple regression: in statistics, the computation of the function (often linear) of a given type of two or more independent variables that best fits a sample (set of observations); *cf.* linear regression, regression.

multivariate analysis: statistical analyses examining the relationship of a single dependent variable to two or more independent variables.

multivariate analysis of variance: abbr.; MANOVA. A statistical analysis of variance for experiments in which more than one dependent variable has been measured for two or more sample groups; *cf.* univariate.

muscicapid: any member of the Old World flycatcher family (Muscicapidae).

musculi pennati: the small muscles at the base of feathers that can raise or flatten the feathers, e.g. for thermoregulation.

musculus complexus: a muscle on the upper part of the hind neck that helps a chick break its shell.

museum beetles: beetles of the family Dermestidae, whose larvae consume dead, dried animal tissues; although they can be a problem to museum collections because they will eat skin and feathers of preserved bird specimens, they are routinely used to clean flesh from skeletons (under great safeguards from escape). Also called dermestid beetles.

museum skin: a stuffed bird or mammal prepared in a stereotypic, space-saving way for museum storage and study (e.g. birds lying on their backs with wings closed, mammals on their bellies with limbs pointed straight forwards and backwards), with cotton eyes and an attached label with associated data. Also called cabinet skin or study skin.

muskeg: a badly drained wetland with scattered trees in subarctic and without trees in arctic North America; *cf.* taiga.

musket: a falconry term for a male Sparrowhawk (*Accipiter nisus*).

Musophagiformes: order comprising 23 species of turacos and plantain-eaters (Musophagidae). The Hoatzin (*Opisthocomus hoazin*) is sometimes placed in this order.

mustachial stripe: Am., a contrasting mark extending from the bill back towards and above the malar region, seen in many birds, for example the Bearded Tit *Panurus biarmicus*). (Eur. moustachial; *cf.* malar stripe, submoustachial stripe.

mutant: an organism showing an atypical phenotype attributable to a mutation.

mutation: in its narrowest sense, a genetic change, e.g. the replacement of a single base in DNA (A, G, C, or T) with a different base (with a corresponding change in the paired base); such changes can be neutral (e.g. synonymous, or occurring in 'junk' DNA), or non-neutral, in the latter case implying that a different amino acid is incorporated in the gene product (protein), potentially altering protein function. Mutation may also be caused by insertions or deletions of bases, duplication of genes, etc. In rare cases the change may be advantageous so that the mutation will be favoured by natural selection; *cf.* genetic drift, natural selection, sexual selection.

mutualism: a symbiosis in which both organisms benefit; *cf.* commensalism.

mutual preening: the preening of one bird by another, usually of the same species. Also called mutual preening or allopreening.

Myanmar: the new name for Burma.

myco-: prefix from Greek *mykes* meaning fungus.

mycology: the study of fungi.

mycoplasmosis: a chronic respiratory bacterial infection by *Mycoplasma gallisepticum* common in poultry, raptors, and parrots.

mycoplasmal conjunctivitis: an eye infection recently found in the House Finch (*Carpodacus mexicanus*).

mycosis: a disease caused by a fungal infection.

myelin: a substance in the nerve sheath, important for the functioning of the nerve fibres; *cf.* sensory neurons, motor neurons.

myiasis wound: a wound of a living bird in which maggots are present.

myo-: prefix from Greek *mys* meaning muscle.

myoglobin: protein that binds and stores oxygen in muscles.

myology: the study of muscles.

myopia: nearsightedness, such as occurs, e.g. in penguins (Spheniscidae) due to their adaptation to underwater vision.

Myr: abbr. of megayear (one million years).

myrmecophagous: feeding on ants.

N

NABU: Society for the Protection of Birds in Germany, formerly called BfV, founded in 1889.

nail: an enhanced, harder, and often translucent part of the beak at the tip of the upper mandible, looking like a nail in many species (e.g. some ducks, Anatidae) and forming a hook as in albatrosses (Diomedeidae), petrels (Procellariidae), and frigatebirds (Fregatidae).

nalospi: a measurement of distance between the anterior edge of the nostrils to the anterior tip of the bill.

nanometer: a unit of length, 10^{-9} m.

NAO index: reflects the relative air pressure difference between Iceland and the Azores and has been found to correlate with variation in local climate over large areas. Also called North Atlantic Oscillation.

nape: the place on the head between the crown and the hind neck, also called nuchal.

narial feathers: long bristle-like feathers at the base of the upper mandible and covering the nostrils, such as in crows (Corvidae).

naris: pl. nares, the external nostrils, also rarely used for the internal openings in the roof of the mouth.

naricorn: a nostril sheath that prevents salty drops from the salt glands entering the eyes. Found in the tubenares (Procellariiformes).

narrow-front migration: a term for species that during migration concentrate in rather narrow places, e.g. Gibraltar in Spain and Bosporus in Turkey; *cf.* broad-front migration.

nasals: a paired skull bone between the premaxillae and the hinge.

nasal canthus: the anterior corner of the eye in which the eyelids come together; *cf.* temporal canthus.

nasal mites: ectoparasites of the family Rhynonyssidae, living in the avian nasal cavities and causing infections; *cf.* itch mites, red mites, feather mites.

nasal operculum: a flap-like structure at the upper rim of the nostril, found in pheasants (Galliformes), pigeons and doves (Columbidae), and many hummingbirds (Trochilidae).

nasal septum: a bony wall separating the two nasal cavities. It can be perforated or without any openings (imperforate).

nasal tuft: an erect tuft of bristles near the nostrils.

naso-frontal hinge: the junction between the culmen and the skull, quite flexible in some birds, e.g. parrots (Psittaciformes). Also called craniofacial hinge or frontonasal or nasofrontal hinge; *cf.* kinesis.

natal: pertaining to newly-hatched young.

natal dispersal: dispersal away from the place of birth, usually in the sense 'from place of birth to place of first breeding' even if this takes place months or years after birth; *cf.* breeding dispersal.

natal down: the first down, later pushed out of the follicles by the growing juvenal feathers, often remaining attached at the end of the new feathers for some period. Also termed neossoptiles; *cf.* body down.

natal dispersal: movement between the place of birth and of first breeding.

natality: birth rate, term for the reproductive capacity of a female, i.e. the number of eggs she can lay and hatch in a season or throughout her life.

natal philopatry: the return of adults to the area where they were raised; *cf.* breeding site fidelity.

National Association of Audubon Societies for the Preservation of Birds: until 1941 the name of the National Audubon Society, founded in 1905 in New York, and one of the largest non-profit conservation organisations in the world.

National Trust: the largest conservation organisation in the UK, founded in 1895. Its purpose is to buy lands of scientific importance.

Natural Environment Research Council: government body based in London and promoting research on the natural environment. Founded in 1965.

naturalisation: the process by which an animal becomes adapted to a new area with a different climate; *cf.* allochthonous, acclimatisation.

naturalized species: a species that, after having been introduced by man, has established a breeding population, such as the Ring-necked Pheasant (*Phasianus colchicus*), or the House Sparrow (*Passer domesticus*) nearly worldwide, and the European Starling (*Sturnus vulgaris*) in North America, Australia, and New Zealand.

natural selection: the mechanism of Darwinian evolution through which some individuals survive and reproduce more successfully than others, causing the frequency of their genes to increase in the population and the genes of others to decrease, or, in other words, the fittest or best-suited survive and pass on their genes to the next generation. The three theories against natural selection in the nineteenth century were: orthogenesis, saltationism, and Lamarckism; *cf.* founder effect, genetic drift, sexual selection.

Nature Conservancy Council: UK government agency established in 1949 in London with the purpose of buying land and creating nature reserves. In 1991 divided into English Nature, Scottish Natural Heritage, and the Countryside Council for Wales.

nature reserve: an area that is protected to some extent and usually managed according to a plan to maintain the habitat(s) in some desired state. The ownership of a nature reserve can be public or private, and access may be public or restricted.

Naturschutzbund Deutschland: a German conservation organisation formerly called Deutsche Bund für Vogelschutz. Situated in Bonn.

Nearctic region: a zoogeographical region composed of North America (including Greenland) south to the tropical parts of Mexico; also called the **Nearctic realm**; *cf.* the Neotropical, Palearctic, Ethiopian, Oriental, and Australasian regions.

nebbing: another name for billing; a form of 'kissing' or greeting ceremony between the members of a mated pair of birds, in which they touch or clasp bills.

nec: Latin meaning not (of), nor (of).

neck collar: 1) a band placed around a bird's neck as an individual marker that can be read from some distance. 2) a device put around the neck of nestlings to prevent the passage of food to the stomach and so provide a sample meal for study.

necklace: a band across the breast or around the neck, e.g. in Necklaced Pitta (*Pitta arcuata*).

necrophoric behaviour: of parent birds removing their dead offspring from the nest.

necropsy: post-mortem examination. Also called autopsy.

necrosis: death of cells or tissues, e.g. caused by damage.

nectar: sweet-tasting liquid secreted by the nectaries of flowers to attract insects and nectivorous birds.

nectivore: an animal that feeds on nectar, adj. **nectivorous**; also sometimes **nectarivore**.

Nederlandse Ornithologische Unie: abbr. NOU. The Ornithological Society in the Netherlands. Has published *Ardea* since 1912 and *Limosa* since 1937, formerly *Jaarbericht der Club van Nederlandsche Vogelkundigen* (1917-1928) and *Orgaan der Club van Nederlandsche Vogelkundigen* (1928-1936).

nekton: macroscopic marine or freshwater organisms that move independently of water currents, including fishes and marine mammals.

nematode: any member of the phylum Nematoda, the roundworms.

neo-: prefix from greek *neos* = new or young.

Neoaves: the infraclass that includes all neognathous birds except Galloanserae.

neo-Darwinism: scientific theory of evolution combining classic Darwinism (centered around natural selection of inherited characters and the theory of common descent) and genetics, systematics, and paleontology; the result of the so called New or Modern Synthesis; *cf.* evolutionary synthesis.

neo-endemic: an endemic species that evolved relatively recently; *cf.* palaeo-endemic.

Neogene: Miocene and Pliocene epochs combined.

Neognathae: a superorder of birds introduced by A. Wetmore whose members have the paired vomer bones in the middle of the roof of the palate reduced, comprising some fossil and all recent birds except the paleognathous penguins (Sphenisciformes), ratites (Struthioniformes), and tinamous (Tinamiformes), adj. **neognathous**; *cf.* palaeognathae.

neo-Lamarckism: a later version of an early theory of evolution, incorporating the now abandoned idea of inheritance of acquired characters.

Neolithic: of the later (advanced) New Stone Age; *cf.* Paleolhitic.

neomorph: a mutation causing a novel phenotype.

neonate: a newly born animal.

neontology: the study of geologically recent animals, as opposed to palaeontology.

neophilic: attracted to novel situations.

neophobic: literally a fear of novelty, exhibited in bird behaviour by, for example, individuals or species that show little opportunism in food foraging or in the retention of a narrow set of behaviours, habitat exploitation, etc. despite opportunities to expand.

neoplasm: new and local cell growth that is not normal, e.g. a tumor, or a swelling not directly caused by inflammation.

neoptile: natal downy plumage, the feathers of which are, subsequently pushed out by the next generation of feathers, also seen spelled neosoptile; *cf.* protoptiles, mesoptiles, teleoptile.

neopulmo: a small additional network of parabronchi to the lungs. Different in size in bird families and absent in penguins (Spheniscidae) and emus (Dromaiidae); *cf.* paleopulmo.

Neornithes: modern birds, a taxon comprising all living and some fossil birds.

neossoptile: syn. of neoptile, natal downy plumage, the feathers of which are subsequently pushed out by the next generation of feathers; *cf.* protoptile, mesoptile, teleoptile.

neostriatum: part of the corpus striatum in the forebrain.

neosympatry: a term for a population that has recently evolved ecological separation, allowing it to occur sympatrically with a closely related taxon (e.g. sister species).

neoteny: arrested development, the appearance in adults of traits that were originally embryonic or juvenile characters, adj. **neotenic**. Also called paedomorphosis; *cf.* progenesis, plesiomorphy.

Neotropical region: the zoogeographical region comprising all of the Americas south of subtropical Mexico, including the West Indies; *cf.* the Nearctic, Palearctic, Ethiopian, Oriental, and Australasian regions.

neotype: in taxonomy a specimen chosen to replace a lost or destroyed holotype or lectotype; *cf.* paratype, syntype, protype, pseudotype.

nephric: pertaining to the kidney, **nephros**.

nephritis: inflammation of the kidneys. Also called nephrosis.

nephron: a part of the kidney involved in excretion.

nephrosis: inflammation of the kidneys. Also called nephritis.

neritic zone: the marine zone overlying the continental shelves, the zone farther from land being the oceanic zone.

nerve: a bundle of nerve fibres with accompanying connective tissue. It is capable of generating, receiving, and conducting electric nerve impulses. Also called neurone; *cf.* dendrites, axon, synapse.

nerve fiber: the process of a neuron (dendrite or axon), along which nerve impulses run.

nerve knot: an accumulation of neurones in the peripheral nervous system. Also called ganglion.

nervous system: all of the nerve cells in an animal, e.g. brain, spinal cord, and peripheral nerves, responsible for all a bird sees, smells, tastes, hears, thinks, feels, and does, comprising a system that communicates by electrochemical impulses and that quickly responds to external and internal stimili, analyses information, stores it in the brain, and acts when the system gives commands to the body; *cf.* central nervous system, peripheral nervous system, autonomic nervous system.

nest: the place where a bird lays its eggs. The most common type is a cup nest, but see also: adherent nest, platform nest, pensile cup nest, pendulous nest, retort nest, or, the most primitive, a scrape nest; *cf.* mound nest.

nest burrow: a burrow, often excavated, used for nesting.

nestling period: the period from hatching to leaving the nest; if applied to a brood usually meaning the period during which at least one nestling is present in the nest.

nest record scheme: an extensive project in which nest records are collected by a large number of volunteers, pioneered by the British Trust for Ornithology and subsequently implemented by other organisations.

nest-relief display: an elaborate display in some bird species in which both sexes take care of eggs or nestlings, the parents performing it as one takes over incubation or brooding from its mate, e.g. penguins (Spheniscidae), albatrosses (Diomedeidae), and boobies (Sulidae).

nest sanitation: keeping the nest clean, e.g. by removing food remains and excrement; *cf.* faecal sac.

net energy gain: the efficiency of food uptake, the energy assimilated from the food minus the energy spent in collecting and digesting it. Also called ecological efficiency.

net primary productivity: the rate at which solar energy is converted into tissue by primary producers, e.g. plants.

neural: pertaining to the nervous system.

neural arch: an arch on the dorsal surface of the vertebrae through which the spinal cord runs. Also called **neural canal**.

neural tube: the beginning of the spinal cord of the vertebrate embryo.

neuroendocrine hormone hormone released by endocrine tissue of neural origin, e.g. epinephrine, released by the adrenal medulla, the secretory cells of which are sympathetic ganglion cells.

neuroglia: protective cells supporting the nerve axons.

neurohypophysis: the neural part of the pituitary gland.

neuron: syn. of nerve cell.

neurotoxin: a poison that acts on the nervous system.

neuter: the state of being sexually undeveloped or castrated; also used as a noun of a neuter individual.

Newcastle disease: disease of the central nervous system, also afflicting the digestive and respiratory tracts, caused by a virus (paramyxovirus) transmitted primarily through contaminated food or water. Very contagious and found in most bird families, though especially Galliformes; also called fowl plague.

New Synthesis: the result of the scientific revolution of the 1930s and 1940s that combined classic Darwin-ian principles of evolution with the findings of genetics, systematics, and paleontology. Also called Modern Synthesis or Evolutionary Synthesis.

New World: North and South America; *cf.* Old World.

New Zealand Bird Notes: journal published by the Ornithological Society of New Zealand 1941-1942, now *Notornis,* published since 1950.

nibble-preening: term for preening with the bill.

niche: a conceptualization of the role of a species and the multidimensional ecological space it occupies in an ecosystem. Although each species is generally considered to occupy unique, if overlapping niches, complexities can include temporal, age/sex, and geographic shifts within species. Also called ecological niche.

niche shifting: 1) when a species occupies different niches in different communities depending on which groups of competing species it coexists with. 2) a species that changes its niche between seasons, e.g. the Eastern Kingbird (*Tyrannus tyrannus*), which is insectivorous during the breeding season in temperate North America and frugivorous while migrating and wintering in the Neotropics.

nictitating membrane: a transluscent membrane that acts as a third eyelid, being drawn across the eye from front to back to cover it.

nidicolous: referring to a nestling hatched naked and helpless in all perching birds, also called altricias. As opposed to precocious or nidifuge; *cf.* psilopaedic, ptilopaedic.

nidicoly: when a bird builds its nest in a structure built by another species, e.g. the Eurasian Tree Sparrow (*Passer montanus*) nesting in the nest of a Stork (*Ciconia ciconia*).

nidification: a term for nest building, and manner of nesting; often now used to include all aspects of nesting (i.e. the nidification of a species).

nidifuge: a chick born in a fairly advanced state, with downy plumage and able to see and move around, usually leaving the nest shortly after hatching and often capable of feeding itself. Also called precocial; adj. **nidifugous**; *cf.* sub-precocial, super-precocial, altricial, nidicole.

niger: Latin = black, dark.

nine-primaried: of certain oscines, having nine visible primaries in contrast to most passerine birds that have ten functional primaries, or with primary 10 concealed by primary covert 9; the nine-primaried families Emberizidae, Cardinalidae, Parulidae, Thraupidae, and Icteridae may form a natural group.

n. n.: Latin = *nomen nudum* = naked name, a name published without sufficient descriptive information or definition to satisfy criteria required by the International Code of Zoological Nomenclature and thereby invalid.

n. nov.: Latin = *nomen novum* = new name.

noctivation: short-term nocturnal hibernation, as in hummingbirds during intense cold.

nocturnal: active at night.

nocturnal birds of prey: old term for owls.

nocturnal homoithermy: the maintaining of a constant body temperature, typically above the ambient one, at night.

node: 1) a phylogenetic branching point. 2) the swollen junction of cells in a downy barbule often formed with up to four triangular plates, which makes down three-dimensional; *cf.* villi.

nomadic species: a species whose members do not breed within a particular area to which they return each sea-

son, but instead settle whenever and wherever food is plentiful and so may breed in widely separated areas during their lifetime. Best known among birds in certain seedeaters such as Budgerigars (*Melopsittacus undulatus)* and in predators specializing upon rodents with highly fluctuating populations.

nomadism: the phenomenon of being nomadic.

nomen: Latin = name. *nominis.*

nomenclature: the system and use of applying scientific names to taxa; often used interchangeably with taxonomy, adj. **nomenclatural**; *cf.* binominal (trinominal) nomenclature.

nomen conservandum: abbr. nom. cons. or nom. conserv., a scientific name that is conserved in spite of the existence of an older, in principle more valid name, because the older name has been little used.

nomen dubium: abbr. *nom. dub.*, Latin = dubious name, name in doubt.

nomen invalidum: Latin, meaning a name that is not valid under the International Code of Zoological Nomenclature.

nomen neglectum: Latin meaning a valid but neglected name.

nomen novum: abbr. *nom. nov.,* Latin = new name.

nomen nudum: Latin = naked name; a name published without sufficient descriptive information or definition to satisfy criteria required by the International Code of Zoological Nomenclature and thereby invalid.

nomen oblitum: abbr. *nom. oblit.,* Latin = a forgotten name not used for a period of at least 50 years, and so invalidated by the International Code of Zoological Nomenclature.

nomen protectum: protected name, a name that has been given precedence over its unused senior synonym (which is then a *nomen oblitum*).

nomen rejectum: a published scientific name that is rejected for some reason.

nominalistic species concept: defines a species as the arbitrary man-made abstraction of individuals under a species name; *cf.* biological species concept, evolutionary species concept, nominalistic species concept, phylogenetic species concept, typological species concept.

nominate form: the subspecies of a polytypic species upon which the species description was originally based and thus for which the species and subspecies names are identical, e.g. *Falco peregrinus peregrinus* (Peregrine Falcon subsp. *peregrinus*), often abbreviated to *Falco p. peregrinus*.

non: Latin meaning not.

non-compass orientation: a navigation behaviour of birds that is not goal oriented. Oriented movement based on environmental stimuli that do not provide compass direction, e.g. topographic features.

non-eumelanic schizochroism: abnormal plumage lacking black or grey pigmentation.

non-iridescent coloration: a structurally-based feather coloration causing a metallic effect, especially in blues and greens, but without any changes in colour when the light angle is changed. It arises because of tiny pockets (vacuoles) in the feathers, which scatter incoming light; *cf.* iridescence.

non-obligate brood parasite: a bird species that occasionally lays eggs in the nests of other birds, but normally breeds non-parasitically, for example the Black-billed Cuckoo (*Coccyzus erythropthalmus*) and the Yellow-billed Cuckoo (*Coccyzus americanus*); *cf.* obligate brood parasite.

nominalist: one who denies the existence of species in nature, viewing the concept of species as a human abstraction.

non-oscine: syn. of suboscine, a suborder within the order Passeriformes, a perching bird having simple syringes with mostly two to four pairs of extrinsic syringeal muscles. Most bird families within Passeriformes in South America belong to this group, e.g. woodcreepers (Dendrocolaptidae), ovenbirds (Furnariidae), antbirds (Formicariidae), and tyrant flycatchers (Tyrannidae).

Norsk Ornitologisk Forening: Norwegian ornithological society abbr. NOF. Has published *Fauna norvegica, Ser. C, Cinclus* since 1979; formerly *Cinclus* (1978 only).

North Atlantic Oscillation: abbr. NAO, a large scale climate phenomenon influencing the climate in the North Atlantic region.

Northern Marine region: a faunal region encompassing all waters north of 35°N. Most characteristic here are the alcids (murres, guillemots, puffins, and auklets, family Alcidae); *cf.* Tropical Marine region, Southern Marina region.

North Pacific bridge: the land bridge connecting Russia and Alaska during the last ice age, better known as the Bering land bridge.

Nos Oiseaux: periodical for the Swiss organisation Societé Romande pour l'Etude et la Protection des Oiseaux, published since 1947 in French.

nostril: the external breathing aperture on the upper mandible, also called nare.

notarium: the segment of fused dorsal vertebrae that occur in some bird families, such as in the grebes (Podicipedidae), cranes (Gruidae), and pigeons (Columbidae). Also called os dorsale.

notch: a V-shaped indentation on the edge of a feather, e.g. found on outer primaries of many raptors. Also called emarginate.

not evaluated: a category used by BirdLife International for a taxon not yet assessed against set criteria for its status; *cf.* data deficient.

Notornis: periodical of the Ornithological Society of New Zealand, published since 1950.

nova species: abbr. *nov. sp.* or *n. sp.* Latin = new species; more frequently encountered as *sp. nov.*, or *species nova*.

n. sp.: pl. **n. spp.**, abbr. for nova species.

novice: a female bird lacking nesting experience, a term commonly used in reference to wild ducks.

nuchal: of the nape (e.g. nuchal crest). Latin *nucha*.

nuchal collar: a band or ring across the hind neck.

nuchal line: the superior line or tiny wall on the posterior skull that circles the supraoccipital bone.

nuclear DNA: DNA in the nucleus of a cell, as opposed to mitochondrial DNA, arising as a random mixture, half from each parent, brought together when a sperm fertilizes an egg. The exception to this random mixing of nuclear DNA occurs with the sex chromosomes. Female birds produce two types of eggs, those with a W chromosome, which, on fertilization will produce daughters, and those with a Z chromosome, which when fertilized will produce sons (all sperm have Z chromosomes). Thus, in birds females are the heterogametic sex (unlike mammals, in which males are heterogametic), and W chromosomes only get passed on from mother to daughter; *cf.* DNA-DNA hybridization, mitochondrial DNA.

nuclear gene sequence: DNA sequence data from a nuclear gene.

nucleotides: a chemical compound that consists of a heterocyclic base, a sug-

ar, and one or more phosphate groups. The four nucleotide bases that comprise DNA are adenine (A), guanine (G), cytosine (C), and thymine (T).

nucleotide sequence analysis: analysis of the nucleotide sequence of a nucleic acid, typically a gene or other fragment of DNA.

nucleus: pl. nuclei, 1) a cellular organelle, containing the chromosomes. 2) a cluster of nerve cell bodies in the central nervous system; *cf.* ganglion.

nucleus of Pander: in an egg a flat cone in which the narrow column from the centre of the yolk (latebra) to the germinal spot broadens, containing the germinal disc.

null hypothesis: (H_0) the hypothesis that no association or difference exists between groups being examined a basic starting point in making statistical tests. If the probability of the null being true is very small (e.g. < 0.05), it is usually rejected in favour of the alternative hypothesis (e.g. that an association or difference exists given the observations or measurements).

numerical response: change in the size of a population due to some stimulus, e.g. a raptor or other predator due to a change in the number of its prey or to numbers of game bird because of augmentation feeding.

numerical taxonomy: a taxonomic method, once popular in entomology, in which a large number of phenotypic characters were measured or scored and given equal weight, most often used to determine relationships among confusing groups; also called phenetic taxonomy; *cf.* cladistic taxonomy, evolutionary systematics.

Numidian bird: name given to domesticated guineafowl (*Numida meleagris*) by the early Greeks and surviv ing as the scientific name of the family, Numididae.

nunatak: an ice-free bedrock knob that rises above the surrounding glaciated or snow-covered area.

nuptial: pertaining to breeding.

nuptial plumage/moult: old term for breeding plumage/moult, also called alternate moult.

nursery group: a day nursery for mobile chicks from different broods, with or without any adults in attendance, known in many species such as Eider (*Somateria mollissima*), boobies (Sulidae), or penguins (Spheniscidae). Also called crèche, crèching behaviour.

Nusa Tenggara: a chain of islands including Bali, Sumbawa, Flores, Moyo, Sumba, Timor, and Komodo Islands; also called Lesser Sunda Islands; *cf.* Greater Sunda Islands.

Nuttall Ornithological Club: created in the early 1870s as the first ornithological club in America. One of its member was Theodore Roosevelt.

nutrient: a substance that upon ingestion provides essential elements for the maintenance of life.

nutritional independence: situation in which young do not depend on parents to provide food.

O

ob-: prefix from Latin *ob* = against, the other way round, signifying.

obesity: abnormal fatness.

obligate annual migration: condition in which a whole population migrates each year; *cf.* obligate partial migration, facultative partial migrants, partial migration, irruptive species.

obligate (brood) parasite: a parasite such as, e.g. the Common Cuckoo (*Cuculus canorus*), that cannot breed in the absence of a host; *cf.* non-obligate parasite, brood parasite, facultative parasite, nest parasite, temporary parasite.

obligate learning: the learning that young obtain by observing their parents, such as predator avoidance and seeking the right food; *cf.* facultative learning.

obligate partial migration: condition in which parts of the population migrates regularly every year; *cf.* partial migration and facultative partial migration, irruptive species.

obligatory mutualism: when two interacting species have become dependent upon each other.

obliquus abdominus externus: a broad abdominal muscle.

obliterative shading: colour patterns found in most birds that have paler underparts than upperparts, a camouflage strategy that reduces the shadow effect, causing an apparent loss of three-dimensionality and thus making birds less visible; more commonly called countershading.

obsolete: applied to a character exhibiting reduction or loss to the point of being rudimentary or nearly lacking.

obstruction currents: local current effects caused by, e.g. wind striking obstacles such as cliffs or high waves; *cf.* soaring, static soaring, dynamic soaring flight.

obturator foramen: a small round hole in the pelvis at which the pubis ends, close to the socket of the femur.

Occam's Razor: general principle in science and elsewhere, stating that if more than one hypothesis is available to explain a phenomenon, the simplest of them is to be preferred. Used as a basic criterion in phylogenetic reconstructions, in which the preferable phylogeny of a group of species is the one requiring the smallest number of changes. Also called parsimony.

occipital: referring to the back or base of the skull; *cf.* foramen magnum.

occipital condyle: a bony knob at the back of the skull that connects with the first vertebra (the atlas); unpaired in birds, paired in mammals.

occipital spot: a spot on the plumage of the nape, e.g. found in some raptors (Accipitridae) and cuckoos (Cuculidae).

occiput: Latin: *occipitium* = the back of the head or the rear part of the crown.

oceanic: occurring in a sea at depths that exceed 200m; *cf.* pelagic.

oceanic zone: the deep sea, all seas except continental shelf waters; *cf.* neritic zone.

oceanodromous: animals that migrate only within oceans; *cf.* potamodromous.

ocellus: pl. ocelli, in birds an eye-like spot, e.g. those found on the upper tail coverts of the peacock (*Pavo cristatus*) and Ocellated Turkey (*Agriocharis ocellata*).

ocreate: anterior scutes on a tarsus composed of a single long scale, also termed booted; *cf.* endaspidean, exaspidean, holaspidean, pycnaspidean, taxaspidean.

oculomotor muscles: the six eye muscles, being reduced in birds.

oculomotor nerve: the nerve controlling some eye muscles.

oculus: Latin = eye.

Odonata: the insect order comprising dragonflies and damselflies.

Odontognathae: a superorder of fossil toothed seabirds from the Early and Late Cretaceous.

odontoid process: a process on the axis vertebra upon which it rotates.

oecoparasite: a parasite with one or few related host species. Also spelled ecoparasite.

oedema: Am. edema, a condition characterized by the presence of an excessive amount of fluid in the affected part of the body, adj. **oedematous**, also called edematous.

oesophageal fluids: crop milk, pigeon milk, i.e. the secretions from the crop by which pigeons and a few other birds feed their chicks. Am. esophageal.

oesophagus: part of the upper alimentary canal, between the pharynx and the stomach. Am. esophagus.

oestrogen:, a female sexual hormone; *cf.* testosterone. Am. estrogen.

offshore feeder: a bird that hunts for food far out to sea such as albatrosses (Diomedeidae) and gannets (Sulidae). Also called pelagic feeder.

offspring: another name for progeny, young, or brood.

offspring-desertion: when one or both parents desert offspring, also known as brood-deserting.

L'Oiseau et la Revue Française d'Ornithologie: the periodical of la Société Ornithologique de France.

Oiseaux, Nos: periodical of the Swiss organisation Societé Romande pour l'Etude et la Protection des Oiseaux, published since 1947. In French.

oidiomycosis: a disease caused by mycotic infection of the digestive tract, found in grey geese (*Anser*), pheasants (Phasianidae), pigeons (Columbiformes), and parrots (Psittaciformes). Also called candidiasis, moniliasis, sour crop, or thrush infection.

oil glands: the paired or bi-lobed glands at the base of the dorsal surface of the tail of most birds, lacking in the Ostrich (*Struthio camelus*), Emus (Dromaiidae), cassowaries (Casuariidae), some pigeons (Columbidae), parrots (Psittacidae), and woodpeckers (Picidae); secretion from these glands are spread to the bill and plumage in preening, and have antifungal and antibacterial properties and may also have other functions in connection with feather maintenance; possibly contain an ingredient that is converted to vitamin D when exposed to sunlight. Also called preen glands or uropygial glands; *cf.* oil gland papilla, powder down.

oil gland papilla: the duct from the oil glands, often with a circlet of feathers around the opening (of which there may be more than one).

Old World: the eastern hemisphere comprising Europe, Africa, and Asia;

that part of the world known before the discovery of the Americas; *cf.* New World.

olecranon process: a process on the proximate end of the ulna, forming the point of the elbow.

olfactory compass: pigeons (Columbidae) may be capable of olfactory navigation by using olfactory odour cues in the atmosphere; *cf.* magnetic, star, sun compass, and vector orientation.

olfactory epithelium: the limited part of the nasal cavity's epithelium where olfactory receptors are situated, i.e. where the sense of smell is located.

olfactory lobes: part of the anterior forebrain where olfactory input is processed. All birds can presumably smell, but the sense appears to be particularly well developed in kiwis (Apterygidae), tube-nosed seabirds (Procellariiformes), some New World vultures (Cathartidae), and a few other species. Generally, however, birds have a poor sense of smell. Also called **olfactory bulb**.

oligo-: 1) prefix from Greek *oligos* = little, few, or small. 2) also now commonly used alone as a shorthand for oligonucleotide primers used in DNA amplification through the polymerase chain reaction (PCR).

Oligocene: epoch within the Tertiary period of the Cenozoic era, approx. 37-24 million years BP.

oligophagy: the eating of a narrow, or specialised, range of food, e.g. the snail diet of the Snail Kite (*Rostrhamus sociabilis*). Adj. **oligophagous**; *cf.* euryphagous, stenophagous, polyphagous.

oligotrophic: applied to waters that are nutrient-poor with low primary productivity, most often referring to fresh water and often to lakes in which the upper layer does not become oxygen depleted during the growing season; *cf.* eutrophic, mesotrophic.

omni-: prefix meaning all, universally.

omnivore: an animal that is both a carnivore and an herbivore, i.e. eating both animals and plants, adj. **omnivorous**, also called euryphagous.

one-tailed test: a statistical test of an hypothesis that determines the probability of, e.g. a sample mean occurring on only one side of the mean of a distribution to which it is being compared (perhaps a control group), as opposed to a two-sided test, which determines this probability for the value falling on either side of the compared distribution.

onomatopoeic: of words formed in imitation of the sound of the thing meant; some bird names are onomatopoeic, e.g. the Cuckoo (*Cuculus canorus*), Chiff-chaff (*Phylloscopus collybitus*), or Bobwhite (*Colinus virginianus*). Also called onomatopoetic.

ontogenetic allometry: refers to the differential growth rates of different body parts.

ontogeny: development of an individual from fertilization (zygote) to adulthood, **ontogenesis, ontogenetic;** *cf.* epigenetic, phylogeny.

ontological: development of an individual.

oocyte: a female germ cell that produces an egg (ovum) by meiotic division.

oogonium: diploid precursor to female germ cells; *cf.* oocyte.

oology: the scientific study of bird eggs. Also spelled **oölogy**.

oophagous: feeding on eggs.

opera citato: abbr. *op. cit.* Latin = in the work cited. Used to avoid duplicate citations in the same paragraph or letter.

operational sex ratio: the ratio of sexually active males to sexually active, fertile, females.

opercular feathers: ear coverts, the loose feathers covering the external ear opening. Also called auriculars.

operculum: 1) a flap-like membrane above the nostril, partially covering the nasal opening, sometimes swollen as in doves and pigeons (Columbidae). 2) a fleshy flap along the anterior margin of the ear opening in some owls.

Opisthocomiformes: order comprising only the Hoatzin (*Opisthocomus hoazin*).

opportunist feeder: a bird eating a wide variety of available foods, many gulls (Laridae) are typical examples.

opportunistic: adapted to take swift advantage of temporary resources.

opportunistic breeding: breeding immediately in response to suddenly favourable environmental conditions. Species so characterized have juveniles that mature earlier and adults with larger gonads (not totally regressing seasonally), e.g. Common Crossbill (*Loxia curvirostra*), and Zebra Finch (*Taeniopygia guttata*).

opposite birds: a subclass of fossil birds from the Cretaceous, so named because their metatarsal is fused with the tarsometatarsus from the proximal end to the distal end, a direction opposite to that of modern birds. Formally called Enantiornithes.

optic lobe: (mesencephalon), the part of the brain beneath the midbrain that processes visual information.

optic nerve: the nerve running from the retina of the eyes to the optic lobe in the brain, concerned with vision. Also called **optic tract**.

optimal foraging: feeding that maximizes energy gained and minimizes energy spent, e.g. by preferentially hunting prey with a high food value.

oral cavity: the mouth, the beginning of the food channel; site of the tongue, the taste buds, and the openings of the salivary glands.

oral flange: fleshy swellings at a chick's gape, sometimes distinctively coloured.

orbits: the two eye sockets of the skull. Latin *orbita*; *cf.* interorbital septum.

orbital feathers: a ring of tiny feathers around the eyes, called the periophthalmic ring, the eye-ring, or the eye-rim.

order: a group of similar families, a taxonomic level between superorder and suborder. The scientific name of bird orders always ends in '-formes'; *cf.* genus, family, class, phylum, kingdom.

Ordovician: geological period approx. 490-440 million years BP in the Paleozoic era.

Orgaan der Club van Nederlandsche Vogelkundigen: periodical published by the Nederlandse Ornithologische Unie: (abbr. NOU) between 1928-1936.

Oriental region: one of the six major zoogeographic regions, extending from the Himalayas, India to south China (Yunnan, Szechuan, and Hainan), the whole of SE Asia including Sulawesi, Greater and Lesser Sundas, south to Wallace's line, east to Timor, and the Philippines. Also called Oriental realm or by some authors Indo-Malayan region; *cf.* Australasian, Ethiopian, Nearctic, Neotropical, Palearctic region, and Indo-Malayan subregion.

orifice: a body opening, such as the mouth, the ears, or the cloaca; an organ in young birds situated at the last of three compartments of the cloaca, which opens to the vent (proctodeum) at the dorsal cloacal wall, behind which the bursa of Fabricius is located in young birds.

ornamental feathers: secondary sexual characters presumed to have arisen and to be maintained by sexual selection, mainly through mate choice and selection for the most exaggerated male traits. Also called sexual ornaments.

ornamental waterfowl: ducks, geese, and swans kept in captivity for their decorative appeal (e.g. to 'ornament' parks and gardens).

ornis: pl. ornithes, Greek word for bird.

Ornis Fennica: periodical published by Ornitologiska Föreningen, the ornithological society of Finland. Published since 1924.

Ornis Scandinavica: a periodical published by the Scandinavian Ornithologists' Union between 1970-1994. Since continued as *Journal of Avian Biology*.

ornithic: pertaining to birds.

ornithichnite: a term for a fossilised bird footprint.

ornithischian dinosaurs: one of the two major groups of dinosaurs. Their hips resembled hips in modern birds. Also called bird-hipped dinosaurs; *cf.* reptile-hipped dinosaurs.

ornithocopophilous: thriving among bird droppings; a term for the fertilization of lichen by bird faeces being deposited upon the substrate upon which they are growing. Birds may also carry the propagating part of lichen from substrate to substrate on their feet.

ornithodolite: an instrument to measure flight speed.

ornitholite: a term for a fossil bird.

Ornitologiya: the periodical from Moscow University, in Russian with English summaries.

ornithologist: a scientist studying birds; also used of an amateur having a serious interest in ornithology; *cf.* birder, birdwatcher.

Ornithological Society of New Zealand: the society that has published *Notornis* since 1950. Formerly published *New Zealand Bird Notes* (1941-1942) and *Bulletin of the Ornithological Society of New Zealand* (1943-1950).

Ornithologische Beobachter, Der: a periodical published by the Schweizerische Gesellschaft für Vogelkunde und Vogelschutz. Published since 1902.

ornithology: the scientific study of birds.

ornithomancy: prophecy or prediction from observations of the flight of birds, also termed ornithoscopy.

ornithophily: 1) applied to plants pollinated by birds, e.g. hummingbirds (Trochilidae). 2) love of birds; adj. **ornithophilous**.

ornithoscopy: a divination from the cries and flight of birds, also termed ornithomancy.

ornithosis: a sometimes fatal viral disease, especially affecting birds but also in mammals, including humans. People keeping parrots are especially exposed. The symptoms include pneumonia, but the liver and central nervous system can also be attacked. Also called chlamydiosis, parrot fever, or psittacosis.

Ornithurae: modern birds (Euornithes or Neornithes) and extinct relatives (Confuciusornithidae, Enantiornithes); *cf.* Sauriurae.

Ornitologia Neotropical: a scientific periodical for the Neotropical Ornithological Society, published since 1987 and accepting papers in English, French, German, Portuguese, and Spanish.

Ornithological Worldwide Literature: abbr. OWL, an indexed compilation of ornithological citations compiled from the periodic, or scientific periodicals. Can be downloaded at no cost from www.birdlit.org; *cf.* Recent Ornithological Literature, Zoological Record.

Ornitologiska Föreningen: the ornithological society for Finland. Has published: *Ornis Finnica* since 1924.

orographic effect: an effect, usually of climate or air movement, caused by geographic features such as mountains, whereby cloud formation, heavy rains, and rain shadow effects often occur.

ortho-: a prefix from Greek *orthos* meaning right, straight, correct.

orthodrome: a great circle on the surface of the Earth; the shortest distance between two points on the surface is measured along the orthodrome between them. Travelling along an orthodrome (except a meridian or the Equator), the bearing (compass direction) will change continuously; *cf.* loxodrome.

orthogenesis: the idea that evolution takes place along some predetermined line independent of natural selection or other external forces.

Orthoptera: order of insects comprising the crickets and grasshoppers.

Ortstreue: a German term meaning fidelity to home area.

oscillations: 1) from Latin meaning a single movement to and fro. In population biology used of more or less regular population cycles, such as the 3-4 year cycles of lemmings (*Lemmus lemmus*) and voles (*Microtus*); *cf.* cycle, fluctuation. 2) the regular cycle by which air is exchanged between the Pacific basin and the Indian Ocean.

oscillograph: a device that records oscillations (relative loudness) as a continuous graph, called an oscillogram, of corresponding variations in an electric current, as would be generated by a sound recording. Frequency or intensity is usually recorded on the vertical axis and time on the horizontal; *cf.* sonogram.

Oscines: songbirds, one of two suborders of the order Passeriformes, comprising most of the extant passerine birds. Characterized by having more than three pairs of intrinsic syringeal muscles; *cf.* suboscines. Treated by Sibley *et al.* as the suborder Passeri.

os dorsale: the dorsal vertebrae are in some bird families fused, as in the grebes (Podicipedidae), cranes (Gru-

idae), and pigeons (Columbidae). Also called notarium.

osmoregulation: an active process controlling the amount of water and/or salts in the body.

osmosis: the process of diffusion of solvent through a semipermeable membrane by osmotic pressure, e.g. the movement of water across cell membranes.

ossicle: Latin: *ossiculum* = small bone or bony structure.

ossification: the formation of bone tissue.

ossuary: a place for depositing bones, in birds a place for food storage and for breaking bones for consumption, as in Bearded Vultures (*Gypaetus barbatus*), which carry bones to rocky sites where they drop them from the air to fragment or disjoin them.

osteoclasts: cells that reabsorb bone; *cf.* osteoblasts.

osteoid: 1) the uncalcified bone tissue secreted by bone cells. 2) bone-like.

Osteodontornithidae: an extinct family of bone-toothed seabirds living until the Pliocene.

osteology: the study of skeletal anatomy and bones, adj. **osteological**.

osteopathy: the diseases effecting bones and the associated cures.

Österreichische Gesellschaft für Vogelkunde: the ornithological society of Austria, publishing *Egretta* since 1958.

ostium: the entrance to the infundibulum of the oviduct.

Ostrich: periodical published by the South African Ornithological Society (SAOS) since 1930.

otic: pertaining to the ear.

otolith: a small bone or stone in the cochlea of the ear.

outbreeding: crossing with genetically different, not closely related individuals, particularly with members of different populations; *cf.* gene flow.

outgroup: in systematics, a group outside of but usually closely related to the group under study; *cf.* ingroup.

outly patch: a species-poor patch or area, the opposite of a hole patch.

outward migration: movement away from the breeding area; the opposite of return migration.

ovary: the female sex organ, situated over the kidney, consisting of many oocytes. In most birds only the left ovary is developed. Latin *ovarius*.

ovate: another term for ovoid or oval, used to describe the shape of an egg.

overlaid: an egg with large, dominant dark spotting evenly distributed over its entire surface.

overflow activity: 1) behaviour performed as a result of the lack of its typically appropriate triggering stimuli, e.g. in the absence of nest-building materials a thus 'frustrated' bird may nevertheless perform nest-building actions. Also termed vacuum or displacement activity. 2) also applied to streams or rivers flowing over an ice covering, causing new ice to form as well as air pockets as water subsides.

overthrow: of a lake, the enhancement of water with nutrients such as nitrates, phosphates, and fertilizers, resulting in an overproduction of algae that take up so much oxygen that they cause other organisms to die out.

overwing scratching: when a bird brings a foot outside and over a wing to preen or scratch its head or upper body directly, as opposed to underwing or indirect scratching.

ovicide: killing of eggs.

oviduct: the duct through which the egg passes from the ovary to the cloaca. The oviduct is straight in a young bird but becomes sinuous as soon as the first egg has passed through it; *cf.* infundibulum, magnum, isthmus, uterus, vagina.

oviparous: egg-laying, the opposite of viviparous, n. **oviparity**.

ovipositing: the act of laying or depositing an egg.

Oviraptor: genus of theropod dinosaurs belonging to the group Oviraptorosauria, known from the Cretaceous.

ovoid: egg-shaped, also called ovate.

ovotestis: 1) the structure that may appear when the left ovary is destroyed by disease or removed, because tissue may then turn into an ovary or testis or occasionally into a mixed structure combining germ cells of both male and female called an ovotestis. 2) also the reproductive organ of hermaphroditic snails, which produces both sperm and ova.

ovulation: the event when a mature egg leaves the ovary and enters the oviduct, adj. **ovulate**.

ovum: pl. ova, an unfertilised large egg cell, which when small is called a follicle; *cf.* zygote.

owlet: a young owl.

oxidation: the chemical process of breaking down a material through the binding of oxygen, and in organic chemistry through the removal of hydrogen; in birds, the breakdown of food.

P

p.: pl. pp. abbr. of Latin *pagina* = page.

Pacheco's parrot disease: a highly contagious, acute disease of parrots (Psittacidae) caused by a herpesvirus that produces bright yellow amorphous urates with scant faeces, anorexia terminally, and visible icterus. At necropsy, affected birds have an enlarged liver that may be mottled or have other colour changes.

Pacific Coast Avifauna: an irregularly published journal of the Cooper Ornithological Society appearing between 1900-1974.

Pacific flyway: one of four distinct migratory routes or corridors used by waterfowl in North America; *cf.* Atlantic, Mississippi, and Central flyways.

Pacinian bodies: nerve endings at the base of filoplumes that are sensitive to changes in pressure and vibrations. Also called lamellar corpuscles.

paddling: 1) propelling through water by means of thrusting webbed feet backwards, as in a swimming duck. 2) trampling on soft soil to stimulate earthworms to move to the surface.

pad: a term for the thickenings under birds' toes, each separated by furrows, also called digital pads or the heel pad in some nestlings, e.g. in the order Coraciiformes and Piciformes.

paedomorphosis: arrested development. In flightless species growth is reduced and adults retain many late embryonic features, e.g. dodos (Ralphidae). Also called neoteny.

pair bond: the social bond between the members of a mated, monogamous species, lasting for one or more breeding seasons. Also called **pair cohesion**.

paired sample test: a statistical test in which a one-to-one relationship exists between the individual sample values in the two samples compared because, e.g. the values are from the same individual before and after some treatment.

palaeo-: prefix meaning old or ancient. Often spelled **paleo-**.

Palaearctic region: a zoogeographical region comprising the arctic and temperate parts of the Old World: Europe, Africa north of the Sahara, the Middle East and northern Arabia, and Asia north of the Himalayas to the Yangtze River. Also called the Palearctic, the **Palearctic realm**; *cf.* Australasian, Nearctic, Holarctic, Neotropical, Ethiopian, and Oriental region or realm.

palaeo-endemic: 1) an endemic species that has survived in only a small part of its former range; *cf.* neo-endemic. 2) also an old endemic species that arose in the distant past, as opposed to a species arising more recently (neo-endemic).

Palaeocene: epoch within the Tertiary period of the Cenoozoic era, approx. 65-54 million years before present.

Palaeogene: the geological period that combines the Palaeocene, Eocene, and Oligocene epoch, approx. 65-26 million years before present.

paleognathous: pertaining to a bony palate characterized by large and imperfectly fused vomers; found in ratites (Struthioniformes) and tinamous (Tinamiformes) and one of four palatal structures traditionally recognized in avian systematics. Also spelt palaeognathous. Also called dromaeognathous; *cf.* aegithognathous, desmognathous, schizognathous.

palaeontology: the study of fossil animals and plants. Am. paleontology.

Palaeotropical: a term for the tropical parts of the Old World.

palaeoxeric: pertaining to the steppes and deserts of the southern Palearctic.

palaeo-xeromontane: a term for the arid mountain slopes of the southern Palearctic.

Palaeozoic: a geological era lasting approx. 570 to 250 million BP comprising the Cambrian, Ordovician, Silurian, Devonian, Carboniferous, and Permian periods.

palaeozoology: the part of palaeontology concerned with animals.

palate: the roof of the mouth. The bony palate (palatine and maxillary bones) has been used in the classification of birds, adj. **palatal**; *cf.* palaeognathous, neognathous, desmognathous, schizognathous, dromaeognathous, aegithognathous.

palatum: the Latin name for palate.

Palearctic region (or realm): the zoogeographical region comprising the arctic and temperate parts of the Old World, i.e. Europe, Africa north of the Sahara, the Middle East and northern Arabia, and Asia north of the Himalayas to the Yangtze River. Also spelled **Palaearctic**; *cf.* Australasian, Nearctic, Holarctic, Neotropical, Ethiopian, and Oriental region or realm.

Paleocene: epoch within the Tertiary period of the Cenozoic era, approx. 65-58 million years BP. May also be spelled Palaeocene.

paleognathous: pertaining to a bony palate characterized by large and imperfectly fused vomers; found in ratites (Struthioniformes) and tinamous (Tinamiformes), this type is one of four palatal structures traditionally recognized in avian systematics. Also called dromaeognathous; *cf.* desmognathous, schizognathous, aegithognathous.

paleolithic: the early Stone Age; *cf.* Neolithic.

paleontology: Am., the study of fossil animals. Eur. palaeontology.

paleopulmo: the basic bronchial arrangement found only in Emus (Dromaiidae) and penguins (Spheniscidae).

Paleozoic: a geological era lasting approx. 570 to 250 million BP comprising the Cambrian, Ordovician, Silurian, Devonian, Carboniferous, and Permian periods.

pallium: syn. with mantle.

palmar: pertaining to the ventral surface of the hand (manus), applied by some ornithologists to the entire arm (wing).

palmate: 1) having toes connected by webs as in ducks (Anatidae). 2) also means resembling an open hand, *cf.* totipalmate.

palm bones: the three fused bones in the hand of a bird forming the carpometacarpus to which the innermost primaries are attached. Also called metacarpals; *cf.* phalanges.

pampa(s): a type of prairie found in South America.

pamprodactyl: of a bird having all toes pointed forward, or being able to turn them forward; found in most swifts (Apodidae) and mousebirds (Coliidae), adj. **pamprodactylous**; *cf.* anisodactyl, heterodactyl, syndactyl, zygodactyl.

pan-: prefix meaning all, whole, completely.

pancreas: endocrine and exocrine gland situated at the inside of the U-shaped loop of the first part of the small intestine (duodenum); secretes bicarbonate to neutralize stomach acids, proteases, and other enzymes, and the hormones glucagon and insulin, the latter from cells grouped in the so-called islets of Langerhans.

panel: term for an elongated wing patch formed by contrasting feather edge coloration.

Pangaea: supercontinent during the late Paleozoic, comprising virtually all existing land masses; started to break up in the early Mesozoic era. Also spelled **Pangea**; *cf.* Laurasia, Gondwanaland.

panic: the communal alarm behaviour of colonial or amassed birds, e.g. as in terns (*Sterna* spp.), suddenly flying up and circling in silence. Also called dread.

panmictic: of an entire population or species freely or randomly interbreeding.

panmixia: a term for indiscriminate or random interbreeding and the unrestricted gene flow that results; syn. **panmixis**.

Pantanal: huge grassland areas in Brazil, Paraguay, and Bolivia that are seasonally inundated due to heavy rains, becoming marshes and hosting great concentrations of birds.

panting: shallow, rapid breathing serving as a kind of heat regulation, in which the bird opens its bill and thus by the evaporation of saliva reduces its body temperature. Gular fluttering and panting compensate for the absence of sweat glands in birds.

pan-tropical: distributed in tropical areas around the world's tropics. **Pantropica**.

papilla: pl. papillae. 1) a cone-shaped structure in a hollow of the skin from which a feather grows. 2) a coloured warty spot or a caruncle such as those found on the faces of some cormorants (Phalacrocoracidae). 3) the spiny-tipped projections on the sole of, e.g. an Osprey (*Pandion haliaetus*). 4) a brightly coloured knob in the mouth of some nestling birds. 5) the tiny, warty spots on the inside of the oviduct.

papilloma: a skin tumour or a wart.

Papuan: pertaining to the island of New Guinea.

Papuasia: a subregion of Australasia comprising the Moluccas, New Guinea, and northern Melanesia.

para-: prefix derived from Greek *para* = beside, by, along, near, surrounding, beyond.

parabolic reflector: a disk having a parabolic cross section and with a microphone in the centre, it forms what could be termed an acoustic telescope and can be used to record bird sounds.

parabronchi: the major microscopic respiratory units of the lungs, where gas exchange takes place; *cf.* bronchus, secondary bronchi.

parachuter: an animal capable of gliding but not of active flight; syn. glider.

paracolon infection: an acute or chronic egg-transmitted infection, primarily from turkeys, caused by *Salmonella arizonae*. Also called Arizona infection.

paradisaeid: pertaining to the bird of paradise family (Paradisaeidae), adj. **paradisaeinine**.

paraglossale: the tongue bone projecting forward; *cf.* basihyal, urohyal, ceratobranchial, epibranchial.

paralectotype: in taxonomy, each of the specimens in a former syntype series that remains after the designation of a lectotype; *cf.* neotype, syntype.

parallactic localization: fixing the position of objects in the environment by moving the head and thereby the eyes. Common in birds, especially those with little overlap in the visual fields of the two eyes.

parallactic orientation: the use of visual landmarks to orient during migration, also called visual or piloting orientation; *cf.* goal, compass, or directional orientation, or vector navigation.

parallel evolution: independent evolution of similar traits derived from a common ancestral condition in two or more lineages related by descent. Also refers to a paralleling of trait condition through evolutionary time between two non-sister lineages; *cf.* homoplasy, parallelism, convergent evolution.

parallelism: independent evolution of a similar character in two different but related lineages.

parameter: any variable in the system under consideration.

páramo: name for moist vegetation communities above the tree line in the Andes.

paranym: in taxonomy, a case in which two names are so similar that confusion is likely to occur.

parapatric speciation: a process of speciation in which two new forms evolve despite their largely separate ranges being in contact along a shared border.

parapatry: occupying different but adjacent geographical areas, such that there is contact between the ranges along a shared border, adj. **parapatric**; *cf.* ecological parapatry, competition parapatry, hybridisation parapatry, allopatry, sympatry.

paraphyletic: used to characterize a group of organisms having a single evolutionary origin, but not including all descendants of their last common ancestor, in contrast to a monophyletic group, which includes all of the descendants.

parasite: 1) individuals or species that exist at the expense of other (host) individuals or species, which may cause the deaths of the host individuals. 2) microparasites: viruses, bacteria, fungi, protozoa. 3) macroparasites: helminth worms, arthropods. 4) or a bird nest parasite or brood parasite; *cf.* ectoparasite, endoparasites, nest parasitism, parasitoid.

parasitoid: an insect whose larvae feeds on other insects during their development and ultimately kill its host.

paraspecies: populations with the same ancestor but occupying different but adjacent geographical or altitudinal areas (parapatry) with limited interbreeding where they meet; *cf.* semispecies, synspecies, allospecies, superspecies, sympatric species.

parasphenoid: a paired bone of the anterior portion of the brain case.

parasympathetic nerves: one of two categories of autonomic nerves (nerves originating in ganglia outside the central nervous system); parasympathetic ganglia are usually found near the organs they supply; *cf.* sympathetic system.

parathyroid glands: paired endocrine glands just dorsal to the thyroid gland on the ventral base of the neck; produce parathyroid hormone (PTH) a hormone that regulates calcium and phosphorus levels and is important for bone and eggshell formation in females; *cf.* thyroid gland, thymus gland.

paratrepsis: synonymous with distraction behaviour.

paratype: in taxonomy, any specimen in the type series except the holotype or lectotype; *cf.* neotype, syntype, protype, pseudotype, topotype.

paratyphoid infection: a disease caused by the bacteria of the genus *Salmonella*, causing diarrhoea. The bacteria are excreted in the droppings. Liv er and spleen become white or grey-spotted. Also called salmonellosis, bacillary white diarrhoea, infections enteritis, and fowl typhoid.

parietals: paired bones of the skull, fused at their medial border and forming the roof of the posterior part of the brain case.

parrot fever: a sometimes fatal world-wide bacterial disease among birds and mammals. Aviculturists who keep parrots (Psittacidae) are particularly prone to this disease. It is an infection caused by *Chlamydia psittaci* transmitted through the air. The lungs are chiefly affected, causing pneumonia, but the liver and central nervous system can also be attacked. Also called chlamydiosis, psittacosis, or ornithosis.

parsimony: a general principle in science and elsewhere proposing that if more than one hypothesis is available to explain a phenomenon the simplest of them is to be preferred. Used as a basic criterion in phylogenetic reconstructions, in which the preferable phylogeny of a group of species is the one requiring the smallest number of changes. Also called Occam's Razor. Adj. **parsimonious.**

parson's nose: the fleshy knob covering the pygostyle (plowshare bone) that is the fused tail vertebrae. Also called Pope's nose.

parthenogenesis: development of an egg without fertilisation, known in the domestic chicken (*Gallus gallus*) and turkey (*Meleagris gallopavo*) but not in wild birds, adv. **parthenogenetic**; *cf.* thelytoky.

parthenogenetic development: development of a bird egg that, although unfertilised, nevertheless may develop because for some reason its chromosomes have been duplicated; the resulting embryo is necessarily male since only ZZ, but not WW, is vial-

ble. Known in the domestic chicken (*Gallus gallus*) and turkey (*Meleagris gallopavo*) but not in wild birds; *cf.* thelytoky, sex chromosome.

partial albinism: an abnormal case that appears as white patches of feathers, or only a single white feather, in the middle of otherwise normally coloured plumage. Iris is normally coloured. The most frequent type of atypical pigmentation, arising from somatic or germline mutations; *cf.* albino, leucism, melanism

partial migration: a condition among many migrating bird populations or species in which only a part migrates. In Europe the term means that within one species some populations are partially migratory, e.g. as others are sedentary; in America the term is used for cases when some individuals migrate while others remain sedentary; *cf.* obligate partial migration, facultative partial migration, and irruptive migration.

partial moult: moult in which only some of the feathers are renewed, typically so that most flight and tail feathers are retained.

parvclass: taxonomic level between infraclass and superorder with the name ending in -ae.

parvorder: taxonomic level between infraorder and superfamily with the name ending in -ida.

passage migrant: a bird species found regularly in an area on migration but which is not breeding or wintering there. Also used for individuals that are present because they are migrating through an area. Also called transitional migrant.

Passeriformes: the largest order of birds, comprising about 5,700 species (58% of all birds); divided into two suborders, the perhaps paraphyletic Tyranni (suboscines) and the monophyletic Passeres (oscines).

passerine bird: a bird belonging to the order Passeriformes. All other birds are collectively referred to as non-passerines or non-Passeriformes.

passive integrated transponder: abbr. PIT, an electronic device placed, e.g. under the skin of an animal and coded to give a specific answer when prompted by a powered sensor placed close by. Often simply called a transponder.

pasteurella pseudotuberculosis: a bacterial disease producing yellow-white 1-2mm spots on the liver and spleen. Found in pigeons (Columbidae), sparrows (genus *Passer*), and captive passerines. Also called pseudotuberculosis, or yersinia; *cf.* tuberculosis.

pasteurellosis: a disease caused by the bacterium *Pasteurella multocida*; among the symptoms are small blood spots on the skin and necrosis of the liver. Found in many bird families but most often in waterbirds. Syn. fowl cholera, avian cholera.

patagium: pl. patagia, a membrane of skin on a bird's wing supported by tendons and muscles and spanning a joint in the wing. Often applied exclusively to the membrane in front of the wing bones, stretched between the humerus and radius/ulna (the propatagium), but categorically the term includes the postpatagium as well. Adj. **patagial**. Also called **patagium membrane** or metapatagium; *cf.* propatagium, postpatagium, humeral patagium.

patagial tag: used to wing-mark birds. A stainless steel pin, with a data tag attached, is inserted through the patagium (propatagium) or elsewhere in the wing. Also called wing tag.

patch model: a model used to examine the choice a bird has to make between different foraging patches supporting different food resources; *cf.* prey model.

patella: the knee cap, not all birds prossess a patella.

paternity: fatherhood; *cf.* maternity.

paternity assurance behaviour: male mate-guarding behaviour, exhibited when a male constantly escorts his fertile mate in order to prevent other males from copulating with her. Also called male guarding behaviour.

path integration: in bird navigation a goal-directed orientation based on unspecified outward journey information that updates a bird's position relative to its point of departure making more direct return routes possible. Syn. reverse displacement navigation.

pathogen: an agent causing disease. Adj. **pathogenic**.

pathology: the study of disease, especially the structural and functional changes caused by disease.

patristic: descended from the same ancestor; also a rare term in taxonomy used to distinguish between taxa of common ancestry and others of similar appearance due to convergent evolution.

patroclinous: resembling the father more than the mother; also called **patriclinous**.

patronymic name: in biological nomenclature the name of an animal or plant after a person.

payload: fat mass of birds with the highest of fat scores.

PCR: abbr. of polymerase chain reaction: a laboratory technique for replicating DNA fragments in which a mixture containing genomic DNA primers, nucleotides, salts, and polymerase enzyme such as *Taq* is run through multiple thermal cycles causing denaturation, annealing, and replication/extension; millions of identical copies of targeted fragments are typically made in this laboratory process.

pealea phenomenon: the presence of atypical spots or streaks in the plumage of some individual storm petrels (Hydrobatidae) or pittas (Pittidae); *cf*. dusky stripes.

peatswamp forest: a wooded peat bog.

peck dominance: when one individual bird pecks another more than it is pecked by the other.

pecking distance: the minimum distance to which a member of a flocking species will allow a conspecific to approach; in colonially breeding birds normally the distance the bird can reach with its bill without leaving its nest; *cf*. individual distance.

peck-order: when dominant bird A has the ability to peck all other birds, bird B pecks all others except A, and so on. Also called **pecking order**, rank order, social hierarchy.

peck right: the social order among birds, the dominance or social hierarchy. Also called pecking order.

pecten: a comb-like, highly vascular body in the eye of birds necessary for supplying the inner layers of the retina with oxygen and nutrients. Additional functions are possible and more than 30 have been proposed, but most of these have been disproven and none has been demonstrated. Pecten is present in all birds and some 'reptiles'. Also called **pecten oculi**.

pectinate: comb-like, furnished with teeth; for example used to characterize the special preening claw found in certain birds, such as nightjars (Caprimulgidae) and herons (Ardeidae).

pectineal: comb-like.

pectoral: pertaining to the chest or breast region between the sternum and the shoulder. Latin *pectus* = breast.

pectoral band: a coloured band across the breast.

pectoral girdle: the skeletal elements associated with the forelimbs, in birds comprising three pairs of bones, the shoulder blades (scapulae), the coracoids, and the furcula (fused clavicles). Synonymous with the shoulder girdle.

pectoralis muscle (major): the large outer breast muscle, responsible for the downstroke of the wing; *cf*. supracoracoideus.

peeking: when a sleeping bird now and then opens an eye and 'peeks', as an anti-predator strategy.

peep: a general name for several small sandpiper species, genus *Calidris*.

peer and pounce: a term for perching motionless until a prey is seen, then flying out and catching it and returning to a perch to eat it. Also called perch-and-pounce sallying; *cf*. flush and rush.

peer review: the review of a scientific manuscript by appropriately qualified colleagues, an obligatory element in the process preceeding publications in any scientific journal.

pelagic: living in the free water masses of the sea (as opposed to on the bottom); of birds, usually meaning oceanic, off-shore feeding; *cf*. neritic zone, coastal species.

pelagic feeder: a bird that forages far out to sea such as petrels (Procellariiformes) and some boobies (Sulidae). Also called offshore feeder.

Pelecaniformes: the order comprising the three species of tropicbirds (Phaethontidae), five species of frigatebirds (Fregatidae), 10 species of gannets and boobies (Sulidae), 36 species of cormorants (Phalacrocoracidae), two species called Anhinga and Darter (Anhingidae), and seven species of pelicans (Pelecanidae). All species in this order have all four toes connected by webs (totipalmate).

pellet: the regurgitated indigestible parts of the food of, e.g. birds of prey (Accipitridae), owls (Strigidae), gulls

(Laridae), and corvids (Corvidae); also called cast or casting.

pelvis: in vertebrates the part of the skeleton that provides support for the hind legs, consisting of three paired fused bones (ilium, ischium, and pubis) and in birds the synsacrum.

pelvic girdle: the part of the skeleton providing support for the hind legs, consisting of three paired bones (ilium, ischium, and pubis) fused with several vertebrae (that form the synsacrum) into a single unit, the pelvis; *cf.* pectoral girdle.

pen: 1) an enclosure to hold animals. 2) a female Mute Swan (*Cygnus olor*), the male being the 'cob'.

pendulous nest: a nest hanging by its uppermost material, usually from a branch or rock; *cf.* cup nest, platform nest, pensile cup nest, retort nest, scarpe.

penis: the male sex organ or intromittent organ, in birds only present in a few families and species, e.g. the ratites (Struthioniformes), tinamous (Tinamidae), ducks (Anatidae), and buffalo weavers (*Bubalornis* spp.). Also called a phallus.

penna: pl. *pennae*, Latin, an old term for contour feathers.

pennaceous: feather-shaped.

pennaceous structure: the vaned structure of feathers that form the main plumage of birds; as opposed to the plumulaceous structure of down, which lacks a vane; *cf.* contour feathers.

pennulum: delicate distal extensions of a barbule.

pensile cup nest: a nest hung from a branch of a tree and supported by its rim; *cf.* pendulous nest, cup nest, platform nest, retort nest.

pentadactylous: having five fingers.

pentosidine: a fluorescent protein of nonenzymatic glycation that accumulates in the tissues of birds over their life and that may be a reliable indicator of age; *cf.* stable isotope analysis.

pepsin: an enzyme in the proventriculus that digests protein.

peptide: an amide formed from two or more amino acids; *cf.* protein.

per-: prefix meaning through.

per annum: Latin = for each year.

per capita: Latin = for each head.

perception: the mental interpretation of stimuli from the environment.

perennation: breeding in successive years, as opposed to monotely, or breeding in only a single year.

perch-and-pounce sallying: a hunting method in which a bird sits watchfully on a vantage point, from where it flies, pursues, and catches prey, and then returns to a perch to eat it. Also called peer and pounce, or only sallying.

perching bird: a passerine bird. The name comes from the automatic biomechanical closure of the foot when the leg is folded, enabling the bird to easily perch on appropriate small diameter perches.

perching foot: an avian foot with three toes pointing forwards and one back all of approximately similar length as found in, e.g. a crow. Also called anisodactylous; *cf.* isodactylous.

perdicine: a member of, or pertaining to a formerly recognized group of partridges (old family Perdicidae now subfamily Perdinae).

peri-: prefix from Greek *peri* meaning around.

pericardial sac: the membrane surrounding the heart, n. **pericardium**

pericarp: the fleshy part of a fruit, covering the seed(s).

periderm: the outermost epidermous layer on a growing feather, which covers the developing feather; *cf.* pin, porcupine.

perilymph: the fluid in the bony labyrinth in the inner ear; *cf.* endolymph

period: 1) in physiology, a diel (24 hrs.) or circannual (365 d.) cycle or time span. 2) in palaeontology, a geological subdivision, comprised of successive epochs; cf. era, epoch.

periodicity: the phenomenon whereby a process recurs at regular intervals, e.g. diel, circannual.

perioditism: the exhibition of periodicity.1) the rise and fall of population size, which, when occurring regularly, is called cyclic. 2) any cyclic event occurring with regularity, such as photoperiodism, in which an organism responds physiologically to a period of 24 hrs. (a diel) or annual light cycle.

periophthalmic ring: eye-ring or orbital ring.

periorbital patch: naked skin encircling the eye, also called eye ring or facial skin.

periosteum: a thick fibrous membrane, of two layers, covering the surface of bones.

peripatric speciation: the generation of new forms through isolation and subsequent modification in a relatively small population at the periphery of the range of the 'mother's species'.

peripheral nervous system: the part of the nervous system consisting of the cranial and spinal nerves and ganglia; cf. central nervous system, autonomic nervous system.

peritoneum: membranous lining of the abdominal cavity.

permafrost: permanently frozen soil in arctic and alpine areas, where only a few inches of the topmost layer may become thawed each growing season, upon which tundra is the most common habitat type.

permanent pair bond: life-long pair bond found, e.g. in some geese and swans (Anatidae) and raptors (Falconiformes).

Permian period: geological period in the Paleozoic era, from approx. 285-245 million years BP, the last period of the Paleozoic era. The most extensive mass extinction occurred at the end of this period.

peroneus longus: a muscle of the leg (tibiotarsus); cf. gastrocnemius.

perosis: a disease in which the gastrocnemius tendon slips out of the groove over the back of the hock (joint formed by the distal end of the tibiotarsus and the proximal end of the tarsometatarsus), causing the tendon to become loose and as a result, for example, the toes are unable to grip a branch.

per se: Latin meaning as such, in itself, oneself, themselves.

pers. comm.: abbr. personal communication.

pervious: as applied to nostrils (nares); refers to the condition in which the nasal cavities are separated by an incomplete internasal septum, be it bony or cartilaginous; cf. impervious.

pessulus: an internal, dorsoventral piece of cartilage in the lower trachea that splits the air flow in the syrinx of most bird species. Only found in the true songbirds (oscines); cf. labia.

pest bird: a species harmful to human interest, usually because it damages crops, e.g. the Red-billed Quelea (*Quelea quelea*) in Africa and the Red-winged Blackbird (*Agelaius phoeniceus*) of North America, or the Starling (*Sturnus vulgaris*) worldwide. Many different factors cause birds to be pests, e.g. the Feral Pigeon (*Columba domestica*) fouls buildings, the Canada Goose (*Branta canadensis*) in Great Britain fouls public areas, and large roosting flocks of various species can become health hazards and noisy irritants in urban and suburban areas.

pesticide: literally 'pest killer', a poisonous substance used to kill animals or plants detrimental to human interests.

petiole: the stalk of a leaf.

Pezophapidae: the family of the little known, extinct Solitaire from Rodriguez, sometimes included with the Dodo (*Raphus cucullatus*) in the family Raphidae.

pH: measure of alkalinity (inverse measure of acidity), the negative of the logarithm of the concentration of hydrogen ions in a solution. The pH of a neutral solution is 7.0.

PHA: abbr. phytohaemagglutinin, a lectin with various physiological effects, found in plants.

phaenology: study of the temporal aspects of regularly repeated natural phenomena and their relation to weather and climate, e.g. when migrating birds arrive or the onset of their breeding. More often spelled phenology, phenomenology.

phaeomelanin: an insoluble melanin synthesized by birds and visible in feathers as light brown, buff, dull red, orange, and yellow, as distinct from the greyish-blacks produced by true melanins, eumelanins (feathers coloured by both carotenoid and phaeomelanin also occur); *cf.* eumelanin. Also spelled pheomelanin.

phagocyte: white blood cell having the ability to 'eat' bacteria and other solid particles; *cf.* T-cell.

-phagous: suffix meaning feeding on, eating.

phalanx: pl. phalanges, any of the bones in a finger or toe. Digit = finger/toe; dactyl = finger.

phallus: pl. phalli, Greek *phallos* = penis. External sexual organ in the cloaca as found in ratites (Struthioniformes), tinamous (Tinamidae), storks (Ciconiidae), flamingos (Phoenicopteridae), ducks (Anatidae), some gallinaceous birds, stone-curlews (Burhinidae), and buffalo weavers (Bubalornithinae). Also called intromittent organ, or penis.

phaneric: of coloration, being conspicuous; the opposite of cryptic.

pharyngotympanic tube: the Eustachian tube, connecting the middle ear to the pharynx.

pharynx: the throat with the entrance to the gut (upper alimentary canal or esophagus) and the windpipe (trachea); adj. **pharyngeal**.

phase: from Greece *phases* = appearance, in biology sometimes used as a synonym of 'morph'; any of two or more normal plumage variants in a polymorphic species, e.g. the Arctic Skua (*Stercorarius parasiticus*). Such polymorphisms are not related to sex, age, season, habitat, or locality; *cf.* polychromatic, polymorphism.

phasmid: any member of the insect order Phasmatodea, including more than 2,500 species of stick and leaf-mimicking insects in the tropics and subtropics.

phenetic species concept: the concept that a species is a set of organisms that resemble each other, i.e. are phenetically similar; *cf.* biological species concept, ecological species concept, recognition species concept, phylogenic species concept.

phenetic taxonomy: a taxonomic method in which a large number of phenotypic characters are measured or scored and given equal weight, most often used to determine relationships among confusing groups; also called numerical taxonomy; *cf.* cladistic taxonomy, evolutionary systematics.

phenology: study of the temporal aspects of regularly-repeated natural phenomena and their relation to weather and climate, e.g. when migrating birds arrive or the onset of breeding. Also spelled phaenology, **phenomenology**.

phenotype: everything about the body, the appearance, morphology, physiology, and behaviour of an organism as opposed to its genetic 'make-up'; *cf.* genotype.

phenotypic variation: variation in characters between individuals; *cf.* genotypic variation.

pheomelanin: an insoluble melanin synthesized by birds and visible in feathers as light brown, buff, dull red, orange, and yellow, as distinct from the greyish-blacks produced by eumelanins (feathers coloured by both carotenoid and pheomelanin also occur); *cf.* eumelanin. Also spelled phaeomelanin.

philopatry: literally loving the place of one's origin, applied to individuals that return to the same place to breed or winter each year or that do not disperse from their natal site. Also often applied to species that tend not to spread or disperse. Also called site-tenacity. Adj. **philopatric**.

Philornis: a group of flies (Diptera: Muscidae) parasitising birds and may be highly detrimental to host nestlings. Found particularly in the Neotropics. Some species feed on nestling faeces (coprophagous scavengers), others on nestling tissue and fluid (subcutaneous parasites), or are bloodsucking (semi-haematophagous parasites). The bloodsucking *Philornis downsi* is newly recorded to cause high mortality in Darwin's finches.

-philous: suffix meaning to love or to thrive in.

Phoenicopteriformes: order comprising 5 species of flamingos (Phoenicopteridae).

Phoenix: a unique individual bird of fable with gorgeous plumage, which ignited itself on a funeral pyre every cycle of some hundreds of years to subsequently emerge from the ashes with renewed youth to then live through another cycle. A symbol of immortality.

phoresy: the transportation of feather lice from bird to bird, e.g. by a louse-fly.

photo-: prefix from Greek *phos* meaning light.

photokinesis: a change in movement of an organism in response to light, adj. **photokinetic**.

photoperiod: the length of the day during which there is light; the optimum length of day for a given species.

photoperiodism: response of plants (and other organisms) to the relative lengths of day and night; **photoperiodicity**.

photopic vision: vertebrate vision based on cones (the receptors responsible for colour vision); *cf.* scotopic vision.

photorefractory period: the period in photosensitive species (e.g. most temperate-zone migratory birds) during which the hormonal system ceases to respond to long daylight periods and, for example, when postbreeding birds with reduced gonads do not show gonadal regrowth in response to long photoperiods (shorter winter days are required to reset this physiological system).

phyletic: pertaining to a branch of an evolutionary lineage, or a line of direct descent.

phyletic evolution: the gradual change of a single lineage over geological time, as opposed to, e.g. stasis, saltation, or other non-gradual evolutionary changes occurring in a lineage.

phyletic nodes: points of divergence in a cladogram.

phyllosc: a term for a member of the genus *Phylloscopus* or leaf warblers, e.g. the Willow Warbler (*P. trochilus*).

phylogenetic tree: a diagram of branching lines showing lineages and their relationships; *cf.* phylogram, cladogram.

phylogenetic constraint: the limitations on subsequent evolutionary options posed by the current state of a trait and of the entire organism of which it is an integral part on subsequent evolutionary options.

phylogenetic classification: classification based on evolutionary relationships between monophyletic lineages. Also called cladistic classification.

phylogenetic species concept: abbr. PSC, the concept according to which a species is defined as any morphologically, behaviourally, or genetically diagnosable population. In its pure form the concept leaves no room for subspecies, treating all meeting PSC criteria as full species; *cf.* biological species concept, recognition species concept, evolutionary species concept, phenetic species concept, and recognition species concept.

phylogeny: the evolutionary history of a taxon or a group of taxa.

phylogeography: the study of the geographical distribution of genealogical lineages.

phylogram: a phylogenetic tree showing the evolutionary relationships within a group.

phylum: pl. phyla, taxonomic rank in the hierarchical classification of biology (i.e. kingdom, phylum, class, order,…), being the principal category immediately below kingdom and above class, thus comprising a group of related classes; *cf.* genus, family, order, class, kingdom.

physiology: the metabolic functions and bodily processes of living organisms, or the science of studying these.

phytophagous: eating plants; *cf.* herbivorous.

phytoplankton: pelagic photosynthetic algae usually unicellular and microscopic. Phytoplankton occurs within the photic zone of seas and lakes worldwide and is responsible for all primary production in the free water masses, thus practically the sole foundation of aquatic food chains; *cf.* zooplankton.

pia mater: the inner layer of the membrane (the meninges) covering the brain, the outer layer being the dura mater.

Piciformes: an order comprising 120 species of toucans and barbets (Ramphastidae), 17 species of honeyguides (Indicatoridae), 210 species of woodpeckers (Picidae), 18 species of jacamars (Galbulidae), and 33 species of puffbirds (Bucconidae).

picofulvin: a carotenoid found in the feathers of woodpeckers (Picidae) of the genera *Picus* and *Piculus*.

pied: having the plumage patterned in black and white.

pigeon fly: a louse-fly that sucks blood from nestling pigeons.

pigeon milk: a secretion from the crop with which all pigeons (Columbidae), Emperor Penguins (*Aptenodytes fosteri*), and flamingos (*Phoenicopterus* spp.) feed their chicks. Also termed crop milk and oesophageal fluids.

pigmentary colours: colours in bill, legs, skin, and plumage produced by pigmentary colour granules; also called biochromes. There are three pigment types: melanin, carotenoid, and porphyrin.

pila otica: a small pillar of bone on the skull that articulates with the quadrate; also called prooticum.

pileated: having a crest or cap.

pileum: an older name for forehead and crown.

piloting: the use of visual landmarks to orientate during migration, also called visual orient; *cf.* goal, compass, or directional orientation, or vector navigation.

pimple: the first stage of a feather's growth; *cf.* pin.

pin: a growing feather still enclosed in its protective waxy sheath. Also called **pinfeather**; *cf.* porcupine.

pineal gland: a small organ of the forebrain secreting the hormone melatonin which, at least in mammals, appears to be involved in photoregulation of the reproductive cycle.

pinion: 1) poetic word for a wing, sometimes specifically applied to the primary feathers, or a single one of these. 2) also a falconry term for the tip of the wings.

pinioning: to render a bird flightless by amputating one wing at the carpal joint; *cf.* brailing, clipping.

pinyon-juniper woodland: one of the nine North American biomes, situated primarily in the Great Basin and the Colorado River region, consisting of two pinyon pine species and with cedars, junipers, and yuccas often the most common species.

pipping: of a bird egg, showing the first crack in the shell as the chick begins to break itself free with it's egg tooth. Such an egg is said to be pipped. Also called starring or chipping.

piracy: the stealing of food from one bird by another, typically of a different species, e.g. performed by skuas (Stercorariidae) and gulls (Laridae). Also termed kleptoparasitism.

piscivorous: eating fish; n. **piscivore**. Also called ichthyophagous.

pishing: onomatopoeic Am. term for people making 'pishing' sounds with mouth and lips to attract a bird.

PIT: abbr. of passive integrated transponder, an electronic device placed, e.g. under the skin of an animal and coded to give a specific answer when prompted by a powered sensor placed close by. Also called transponder.

pitch: 1) a musical note on a scale. 2) in birding: '**pitch up**' used of a rarity landing in an odd place.

pith: the spongy tissue inside the distal shaft of a feather (rachis).

pitilus: Latin = feather.

pituitary gland: a two-lobed gland (anterior and posterior lobe) below the hypothalamus in the brain producing several important hormones, including prolactin and gonadotropic hormones, that regulate the endo-crine system and govern reproductive behaviour, moult, and migration. Also called the hypophysis; *cf.* hypothalamus.

placode: the start of a new feather begins with a thickening of the epidermis called the placode.

plankton: small marine or freshwater organisms living in the water column and moving passively with the water currents; important food for many animals; in contrast to nekton (aquatic organisms that move independently of currents).

Plantae: the plant kingdom that includes eukaryotic organisms with chlorophyll a and b in their chloroplasts (green algae sometimes excluded), i.e. the mainly terrestrial mosses, ferns, conifers, flowering plants, etc.

plantar: sole of the foot.

plantar tendons: tendons in the sole of the feet that flex the toes.

plasma: the fluid component of the blood.

plasma metabolite profiles: a method for estimating the physiological state using sampled blood to provide information about short-term fuel use and storage during migration.

plasmid: a small piece of self-replicating DNA that occurs in prokaryotic and eukaryotic cells, outside the chromosomal and mitochondrial DNA; its presence is not essential to the cell. In the laboratory used as a vehicle for introducing genes into bacteria.

Plasmodium: genus of unicellular parasites causing malaria in birds and mammals, including humans; has a complicated life cycle involving a secondary host, a mosquito.

plastic song: a term applied to the song of young, inexperienced birds that occupy a territory and start to sing, but whose repertoire can be influenced by the song of neighbours; *cf.* subsong, full song.

plate tectonics: the movement of the lithospheric plates of the Earth in relation to each other, causing slow but profound changes in the topography of the Earth (e.g. Himalayas, Mariana Trench) and in the configuration of continents; *cf.* Gondwanaland, Laurasia, Pangaea.

platform nest: a type of relatively flat nest usually built on the branches of a tree, such as those built by hawks and herons, but can also be floating, such as a rail's nest; *cf.* adherent nest, cup nest, pensile cup nest, retort nest, pendulous nest.

playback: a recorded song or call that is played back from a speaker on a portable device, usually to elicit a response from an individual bird.

pleio-: prefix meaning more.

pleiotropy: when a single gene has more than one apparently unrelated phenotypic effect.

Pleistocene: the geological epoch within the Quaternary period of the Cenozoic era, from approx. 1.8 million years BP to the end of the last glaciation about 10,000 years ago, characterised by extensive climate change ranging from nearly tropical throughout the planet, to c. 21 glacial periods, to similar to today's climate; *cf.* interglacial period.

plesiomorphy: a primitive character state within a group inherited from a common ancestor and conserved in some of the members of the group; carries no information about evolutionary relationships within the group; e.g. the dusky stripes in the feathers of some individuals belonging to the pitta family (Pittidae), adj. **plesiomorphic**; *cf.* apomorphy, homoplasy, symplesiomorphy, synapomorphy, pealea phenomenon, neoteny.

Plesiosaurs: marine reptiles known from the late Triassic until the end of the Cretaceous.

plesiotype: a taxonomic term for a specimen on the basis of which a later author has added descriptive material.

plexus: a network of blood vessels or nerves, e.g. nerve fibres running from the spinal cord to the wings and legs.

Pliocene: epoch within the Tertiary period of the Cenozoic era, approx. 5 - 1.8 million years BP.

ploughshare bone: informal name for: 1) paired bone forming the floor of the nasal cavity, also called vomer and prevomer. 2) the fused distal four to seven caudal vertebrae; also called pygostyle.

plumage: all of the feathers on a bird's body.

plumage sequence: the sequence of plumages during the life of a bird, from natal to juvenal plumage, first winter plumage (= first basic plumage), first breeding plumage (= first alternate plumage), etc.

plume: a greatly elongate feather, usually used in display, such as those found in egrets (*Egretta*).

plumology: the study of feathers.

plumule: a down feather, feather without hooks (barbicels) so that the barbs are free and thus form a loose, puffed feather structure; *cf.* natal down.

plumulaceous: downy, loose-webbed, of feathers lacking a pennaceous vane as opposed to plumaceous.

plunge-bathing: bathing by repeatedly diving into water, as seen in, e.g. kingfishers (Alcedinidae); *cf.* flight-bathing, in-out bathing, rain-bathing, stand-in bathing, stand-out bathing, and swim-bathing.

plunge diving: a foraging method used by some birds that dive underwater to catch prey after detecting it, such as gannets and boobies (Sulidae) and in some kingfishers (Alcedinidae).

plural breeding: communal breeding with more than one female per group; *cf.* singular breeding.

pluvial period: a wet period.

pneumatic: having air cavities, e.g. in the bones.

pneumatic foramen: a hole in the proximal end of the upper wing bone (humerus) leading to the air space within the bone.

pneumatic fossa: a groove near the proximal end of the avian humerus, in which the air chamber of that bone connecting with the bird's air sac system is situated.

pneumatic skeleton: a skeleton having some bones that are hollow and air-filled, as in most birds.

pneumatisation of the skull: the condition and process of a double-layered cranium becoming filled with air between the layers, commonly occurring among, e.g. Passeriformes. Gradual bone maturity of the cranial roof causes it to change from a semi-transparent single layer to a relatively opaque double layer connected and strengthened by numerous supporting pillars; **pneumatized** or **pneumatised**; because the precursor is bone growth, this condition and process is more accurately termed skull ossification; *cf.* window.

pneumonia: inflammation of the lung.

Podicipediformes: the order comprising 22 species of grebes.

Podicipitiformes: an outdated term for the order Podicipediformes.

podotheca: the horny covering of the tarsi and feet of birds, hard in land birds, softer in water birds. Six types have been defined, based on the arrangement of scutes and scales: endaspidean, exaspidean, holaspidean, ocreate, pycnaspidean, and taxaspidean, more common terms are scutellate, reticulate, and booted.

poikilothermic: cold-blooded, in contrast to homoiothermal or endothermic; syn. ectothermic.

point count: a bird census in which the birds seen or heard from a fixed point over a fixed period are counted, with such counts taken from several points along fixed a route. The combination of many point counts, repeated for the same routes over several years, is an important method of measuring changes in relative and absolute abundance of common bird species; *cf.* point transect, strip transect.

point transect: a transect or route along which point counts are made; *cf.* point count, strip transect.

polarization sensitivity: the ability, e.g. to see the position of the sun through a thick clouded sky.

pole trap: a trap atop a pole, with jaws that snap shut upon the leg(s) of a bird alighting on the pole. In the past used primarily to catch raptors, but now prohibited among other things because birds may be seriously injured.

polish swan: a mutant Mute Swan (*Cygnus olor*) that is white instead of grey-brown as a young bird, with pink or grey legs, but with normal dark eyes; a form of leucism.

pollen: powdery male gametophytes discharged from the anthers of a flower.

pollex: the thumb, the alular digit.

pollinator: an animal dispersing the pollen of plants and thus causing the fertilization of seeds.

poly-: prefix derived from Greek *polys* = many.

polyandry: a mating system in which a female mates with several males during a single breeding season; occurs in rheas and cassowaries (Casuariidae), emus (Dromaiidae), kiwis (Apterygidae), some tinamous (Tinamidae), button quails (Turnicidae), jacanas (Jacanidae), Painted Snipe (*Rostratula benghalensis*), some plovers (Charadriidae), phalaropes and some sandpipers (Scolopacidae), and Plains-Wanderer (*Pedionomus torquatus*), adj. **polyandrous**; *cf.* cooperative polyandry, male deception polygyny, polygamy, polygyny, polygynandry, monogamy, promiscuous, lekking polybrachygamy.

polybrachygamy: a mating system in which individual males may mate with more than one female each season without prolonged social bonding with them. Also called lekking polybrachygamy.

polychromatic: 1) having more than one colour. 2) applied to a species characterized by having more than one colour phase, form, or morph, e.g. the white and the dark phases of the Reef Heron (*Egretta sacra*).

polydactylous: having more than the normal number of fingers.

polyembryony: the production of two or more individuals from a single egg, caused by the division of the embryo at an early stage of development.

polygamy: mating system in which males and/or females have more than one sexual partner during a single breeding season, thus comprising polyandry and polygyny as specific variants. Approximately three percent of all birds practice polygamy. Adj. **polygamous**; *cf.* lekking, male deception polygyny, monogamy, polyandry, polygynandry, polygyny, promiscuity, extra-pair copulation.

polygeny: a diagram showing the ancestral relation among species. It shows, for each species, which other species it shares its most recent common ancestor with.

polygonal plates: plates formed as polygons.

polygynandry: a mating system in which both males and females have more than one sexual partner during

a single breeding season; rare in birds, occurring in the Hedge Accentor (*Prunella modularis*); *cf.* lekking, male deception polygyny, monogamy, polyandry, polygyny, promiscuity.

polygyny: a mating system in which a male mates with several females during a single breeding season, either simultaneously or serially; at least two percent of all birds practice polygyny. Adj. **polygynous**; *cf.* lekking, male deception polygyny, monogamy, polyandry, polygamy, polygynandry, promiscuity.

polylectic: visiting and gathering pollen from more than one plant species; *cf.* monolectic.

polymerase chain reaction: abbr. PCR, a laboratory process for replicating DNA fragments in which a mixture containing genomic DNA, primers, nucleotides, salts, and a polymerase enzyme such as *Taq* is run through multiple thermal cycles causing denaturation, annealing, and replication/ extension; millions of identical copies of targeted fragments are typically made in this laboratory process.

polymorphism: applied to species or populations having two or more distinct phenotypic types or morphs, usually differing in colour, size, or form. Common in birds, e.g. the Tawny Owl (*Strix aluco*) in Eurasia or the White Goshawk (*Accipiter novaehollandiae*) in Australia; adj. **polymorphic**; *cf.* dichromatic, dimorphic.

polynya: permanent or seasonally recurrent open-water area in an otherwise ice-covered sea, produced by wind or upwelling warm water; often important for foraging seabirds.

Polynesia: one of three divisions of the Pacific Ocean; includes Cook, French Polynesia, Mangareva, Marquesas, Samoa, Society, Tonga, Tuamotu, Tubual, and other islands. Some authors include New Zealand. Hawaii is now generally regarded as separated from the Pacific Islands subregion.

polyphagous: feeding on more than one kind of food.

polyphenism: the occurrence of more than one phenotype (typically many) in a population but without a genetic basis for the differences.

polyphyletic: in systematics used to characterize a group of organisms having different evolutionary origins, meaning that their last common ancestor is outside of the assemblage considered, in contrast to paraphyletic and monophyletic groups; single traits may likewise be of polyphyletic origin, simply meaning that they arose independently in different groups by parallel or convergent evolution.

polyploid: having more than two haploid sets of chromosomes, n. **polyploidy**.

polyploidy: the occurrence of polyploid cells or organisms; commonly seen in plants, where it may stimulate evolutionary change and the formation of new species.

polyterritorial polygyny: a mating system in which a male simultaneously defends two or more different territories and guards two or more different females during the breeding season.

polytomy: the occurrence of a node in a cladogram or phylogenetic tree having three or more branches, in contrast to the usual two (called a dichotomy). Trees with such nodes are incompletely resolved (branching is always dichotomous, at least in principle).

polytypic: 1) of genera with more than one species, or of species split into two or more subspecies. 2) also of species with two or more distinct forms not considered to be subspecies; *cf.* cline, monotypic, polymorphism.

P1: = first primary (P1 to P10); often written p1.

Pope's nose: the fleshy knob covering the plowshare bone (pygostyle) that is the fused tail vertebrae. Also called parson's nose.

population: group of conspecific individuals that, through interbreeding, constitute a single gene pool; *cf.* deme.

population cycles: series of increases and decreases in the numbers of individuals in a population, common, e.g. in grouse (Tetraonidae).

population density: the number of individuals in an area.

population dynamics: all aspects of population change and turnover, including effects of underlying factors such as environmental change and human activity; *cf. K*-selection, *r*-selection.

population ecology: the study of populations and the factors in the environment influencing their makeup, e.g. age structure, numbers of individuals, mortality rates, etc.

population genetics: the study of genetic variation and related evolutionary processes within and among populations.

population index: a measure reflecting the size or density of a population, useful when following changes in the abundance of a species over a period, even though the population size itself often remains unknown; *cf.* census.

population pressure: the 'force' causing centrifugal movements away from overcrowded areas within the range of a population.

population structure: the composition of a population: the relative number of males, females, juveniles, adults, and or other subgroups.

population viability analysis: abbr. PVA, a model-based projection into the future of a specific population to estimate its risk of extinction under various assumptions about environmental factors and management measures.

porcupine stage: applied to nestlings whose developing feathers are all in the pin stage (still in sheath), e.g. kingfishers (Alcedinidae).

porphyrin: any member of a group of fat-soluble pigments responsible for red, green, and brown colours in the down of many birds, in contour feathers of bustards and owls and in, e.g. cuckoo eggshells. Red porphyrins fade rapidly in sunlight. All various porphyrins share one feature: they fluoresce bright red under ultraviolet light; *cf.* carotenoids, melanin, turacin, uroporphyrin.

porro-prism binoculars: a pair of binoculars in which the prismatic arrangement is displaced, as opposed to roof-prism binoculars where it is arranged in a single row.

portal system: a system of large veins with a network of capillaries at each end, such as the one leading blood from the intestine to the spleen and the pancreas to the liver in vertebrates.

post-: prefix from Latin *post* = after, behind, occurring after.

post-breeding moult: Am. prebasic molt, usually complete moult after breeding, in some species starting before the end of breeding.

postcranial: pertaining to all parts of an animal except the head.

posterior: situated towards the hind part of the body, the opposite of anterior. Also called caudal.

posterior condyle: the rounded process of the quadrate bone at the base of the skull, to which the upper and lower mandibles are attached.

posterolateral process: a backward-pointing process on the breastbone (sternum) just posterior to the small pits where the ribs are attached (costal facets).

post-fledging period: the period from when a young bird leaves the nest to when it becomes independent of its parents.

post glaciation: the time after last Ice Age.

post-hatch brood amalgamation: amalgamation (parts of) two or more broods of a nidifugous bird species, also called adoption or, simply, brood amalgamation (pre-hatch brood amalgamation being synonymous with intraspecific nest parasitism) Common in geese and some other waterbirds.

post-juvenile moult: Am. first prebasic molt, the moult in which the juvenal plumage is shed and the bird attains either the first immature plumage, or the first non-breeding adult plumage.

post-mortem examination: examination of a corpse, especially to determine the cause of death. Also called necropsy, autopsy.

post-natal moult: moulting from nestling into juvenal plumage, also called prejuvenal moult.

postnuptial moult: a complete moult after breeding. Syn. post-breeding moult.

postocular stripe: a line behind the eye, the posterior part of an eye-line.

postorbital: posterior to the eye.

postovulatory follicle: in the ovary, a empty egg sac or follicle; unlike corpora lutea in mammals, postovulatory follicles in birds are resorbed leaving no trace after several months and one cannot determine how many eggs a bird has laid among years. Also called calies.

postpatagium: a band of tendinous tissue that holds the flight feather (remeues) on the posterior margin of the upperwing firmly in place; *cf.* patagium, humeral patagium, meta-patagium, propatagium.

post-roost: a roost that individuals join some time after their having left the main roost at dawn, known in geese; *cf.* pre-roost.

postzygapophyses: projections extending backwards from either side of the arch of a vertebra and forming freely-moveable joints with the prezygapophyses on the vertebra immediately behind; syn. zygapophysis caudalis.

postzygotic: pertaining to embryological stages subsequent to the zygote; *cf.* prezygotic.

potamodromous: animals that migrate only within the ocean (not between fresh and salt water). Also called oceanodromous.

poultry: common term for domestic fowl, including chickens (*Gallus domesticus*), pheasants (Phasianidae), and geese and ducks (Anatidae) that mainly are kept as a source of food.

pounce: to swoop or fall upon something suddenly and seize it, e.g. a bird of prey pouncing on a mouse from the air; *cf.* pounding.

pounding: a woodpecker (Picidae) foraging by hammering on a tree trunk.

powder down: down feathers with barbules that disintegrate into a fine talcum-like powder used in preening and found on the skin of the breast, flanks, and rump, e.g. in tinamous (Tinamidae), herons and bitterns (Ardeidae), toucans (Ramphastidae), some parrots (Psittacidae), Cuckoo-Roller (*Leptosomus discolour*), some cotingas (Cotingidae), and wood swallows (Artamidae). Powder down grows continuously, breaking down into powder at the tips; supposed to protect feathers against fouling and to make them water-resistant.

powered flight: active flight. Also called flapping flight, in contrast to soaring and gliding.

pre-: prefix from Latin *prae* = before, occurring before.

pre-adaptation: cases in which a character, evolved as an adaptation to one thing, turns out to be useful in a different connection.

prealternate molt: Am. for pre-breeding moult, the often only partial moult into the alternate plumage, also known as prenuptial moult.

prebasic molt: Am. for a usually complete post-breeding moult (or the moult from juvenal into immature/adult plumage), including moult of bird species with only one moult per year; *cf.* basic plumage.

pre-breeding moult: Am. prealternate molt, nuptial molt, moult into breeding plumage; generally a partial moult.

Precambrian: geological time preceding the Palaeozoic, i.e. c. 4,600-545 mya.

precocial: of chicks hatching in a fairly advanced stage, covered in down, able to thermoregulate, having open eyes, and often able to walk or run within minutes or hours. Such chicks often leave the nest after a short period (i.e. are nidifugous), and may be able to find food for themselves. Examples include: ratites (Struthioniformes), megapodes (Megapodiidae), ducks (Anatidae), pheasants (Phasianidae), rails (Rallidae), and shorebirds (Charadriiformes). In reality, the variation from undeveloped (altricial) chicks to fully precocial chicks is continuous, and precocial chicks may be subdivided into those that are super-precocial, sub-precocial, and semi-precocial.

precocial breeding: birds breeding at an unusually young age.

precocious flight: early flight capability in chicks capable of flying long before they become fully feathered; widespread in gallinaceous birds.

pre-copulatory display: a behaviour stimulating and synchronizing sexual arousal and receptivity in birds; the male usually displays his plumage and the female lowers her body with quivering wings.

predator: an animal that kills and eats other animals, although animals eating seeds in a manner to destroy their subsequent growth capacity are sometimes called seed predators; *cf.* carnivore, insectivore, omnivore.

predation: the catching, killing, and eating of an animal by another, predatory, one.

predation pressure: the influence of predation upon a population.

preen glands: the paired glands at the base of the tail of most birds; lacking in the Ostrich (*Struthio camelus*), emus (Dromaiidae), cassowaries (Casuariidae), some pigeons (Columbidae), some parrots (Psittacidae), and woodpeckers (Picidae); the secretion has antifungal and antibacterial properties and may also have other functions in connection with feather maintenance; possibly contains an ingredient that is converted to vitamin D when exposed to sunlight. Also called uropygial glands or oil glands; *cf.* powder down.

preening: keeping the feathers in good condition by use of the bill and claws, nibbling or scratching at disengaged or tangled barbs, restoring the interlocking structure, or smearing the feathers with 'oils' from the uropygial gland using the bill. In mammals the term 'grooming' is often used instead.

preferential mating: selection of a mate by either sex based upon some individual characteristic; *cf.* sexual selection.

prefix: the beginning of a compound word; *cf.* suffix.

pre-frontals: a pair of cranial bone forming a plate between bill and skull, fused in most bird families bu separate in, e.g. turacos (Musophagidae). Also called lacrimal bones.

pre-hatch brood amalgation: intraspecific brood parasitism; brood mixing as a result of egg-dumping in the nests of conspecifics, also called intraspecific nest parasitism.

prehistoric period: the period prior to the first historical accounts of a people.

prejuvenal molt: Am. for postnatal o prejuvenal moult.

pre-Linnaean: in taxonomy, meaning that the name in question was published before 1758 (or in the case c plants, before 1753).

premating isolating mechanism: an mechanism that prevents hybridization between two forms by preventing their mating, one example coul be incompatibilities in courtship behaviour between the two forms. Also called prezygotic isolating mechanism

premaxilla: a pair of fused bones at the anterior part of the upper jaw, forming the bony part of the upper mandible, upper beak, or maxilla; *cf.* dentary, rhamphotheca.

pre-migratory restlessness: restlessness shown by captive birds of migrating species during the period when their conspecifics undertake migration normally leading to increased rate of to-and-fro hopping, wing fluttering, and wing flicking. This characteristic is used in captive experiment with migratory birds. Also called migratory restlessness or Zugunruhe.

prenuptial: before breeding.

prenuptial molt: old Am. term for pre breeding moult, usually a partial moult not involving the flight feathers; also known as prealternate molt

preoccupied name: in nomenclature, a name that has been used previously for any form in the animal kingdom

prepennae: a hatchling that has but few traces of natal down in tracts that will later hold feathers; *cf.* preplumula.

preplumula: a hatchling with a thick coat of down; *cf.* prepennae.

pre-roost: a roost for noisy gatherings of Rooks (*Corvus frugilegus*) or Starlings (*Sturnus vulgaris*) some time before flying to their main and larger roost; *cf.* post-roost.

prevomer: a paired bone within the central fissure of the palate. Also called vomer or ploughshare bone.

prey: a killed animal that is the food of a predator.

prey model: a model that examines the cost involved in obtaining food against resulting nutritional returns; *cf.* patch model.

prezygapophyses: projections extending forwards from either side of the arch of a vertebra, making contact with postzygapophyses of the previous vertebra.

prezygotic barrier: the most effective of reproductive isolating mechanisms, which prevent fertilization between members of different species from occurring.

prezygotic isolating mechanism: any mechanism that prevents two forms from hybridizing prior to fertilisation, e.g. incompatibilities in courtship behaviour between the two forms. Also called premating isolating mechanism.

pricked: wounded by gun-shot and unable to fly.

primary: pl. primaries, any of the outer flight feathers attached to the hand; the number varies between 9 and 11 but most often is 10 (grebes, Podicepiidae, have 12). Numbered from the innermost (descendant) and termed P1 to P10 (or the appropriate maximum for the taxon), although some authors do not capitalize this (e.g. p1). Historically they were often numbered from the out-

ermost inward. Also called pinion or **primary remiges**; *cf.* secondaries.

primary consumer: a plant eater or herbivore; *cf.* secondary consumer.

primary coverts: the large coverts that cover the bases of the primaries both on the upper and under wing. Also called greater primary coverts; *cf.* median and lesser wing coverts.

primary extension: the length between the tip of the longest primary to the tip of the longest secondary or tertial in a folded wing; also called primary projection.

primary forest: fully developed (climax) forest of indigenous composition; *cf.* secondary forest.

primary moult-score: abbr. PMS, in moult terminology, a measure of the progression of the primary moult using a scale from 0 to 5 for each primary, where 0 means an unmoulted old feather, 1 a feather in pin (or sheath), 2-4 various intermediate stages, and a fully grown new feather is 5.

primary productivity: the production of biomass in a habitat or ecosystem that is based on photosynthesis, e.g. by plants, algae, etc., usually used in terms of a food source for animals.

primary projection: the length between the tip og the longest primary to the tip of the longest secondary (or tertial) in a folded wing; also called primary extension.

primary sexual characters: characters required for reproduction and parental care, the reproductive organs; *cf.* secondary sexual characters.

primary sex organs: the gonads (testes or ovary); *cf.* secondary or accessory sex organs.

primary sex ratio: the ratio of males to females in newly fertilised eggs; *cf.* secondary sex ratio, tertiary sex ratio.

Primates: order of mammals including tree shrews, lemurs, galagos, tarsiers, monkeys, apes, and humans.

primer: 1) the portion of a cartridge that upon impact provides the spark to ignite the powder and thus fire the projectile(s). 2) a small piece of DNA designed to anneal to a complementary portion of the genome, which, when used in pairs in the polymerase chain reaction (PCR), guides replication of fragments of genomic DNA in volume for study.

primitive character: a character that is similar to that of an ancestral form of the group under consideration.

primus: Latin = first, foremost.

priority of a name: the principle that the valid name of a taxon is the oldest available one applied to it, provided that it is not invalidated by the existence of another long-accepted and widely used name (50 + years), or for some other specific reason.

pro-: prefix from Greek *pro* = before, forward, in front of.

proactive coping style: property prossessed by a fast explorer, an individual that adapts quickly to new environmental changes, as opposed to reactive coping style.

proaposematic: of a warning colouration worn by a potential prey species that warns predators that it is poisonous or bad-tasting; *cf.* pseudoaposematic, synaposematic, aposematic.

probing: a foraging technique in which a bird pokes its bill into a substrate (e.g. mud, sand, a curled leaf, or a crevice) to search for prey.

Procellariiformes: the order of tube-nosed seabirds, comprising 13 species of albatrosses (Diomedeidae), 74 species of shearwaters, petrels, and fulmars (Procellariidae), 21 species of storm petrels (Hydrobatidae), and four species of diving petrels (Pelecanoididae).

proclinate: bent forward, opposite reclinate.

procryptic: of coloration or other characters that facilitate concealment from predators; *cf.* cryptic anticryptic.

proctodeum: the last of three compartments of the cloaca, opening to the vent; *cf.* coprodeum, urodeum.

proepisematic: of colour, appearance or behaviour of use in social recognition interaction; *cf.* antepisematic aposematic, episematic, pseudepisematic.

profundus: Latin = deep.

profundus nerve: large branch of the fifth cranial nerve.

progenesis: the maturation of gametes before completion of body growth.

progenitor: an ancestor or ancestral form.

progesterone: female sex hormone; *cf.* oestrogen, estradiol.

prognathous: having an over-developed lower mandible, adj. **prognathism.**

prokaryotes: eubacteria and archaebacteria; unicellular microorganisms whose small simple cells lack a membrane-bounded nucleus.

prokaryotic: one of the two main types of cells, it is simpler and has no nucleus, found in bacteria and Archaea; *cf.* eukaryotic.

prokinesis: the mobility of the upper mandible at its junction with the skull (or farther out); *cf.* rhynchokinesis.

prolactin: a hormone secreted by the pituitary gland. It plays a role in reproduction, stimulates the bird's appetite, and determines whether the liver synthesizes fat as fuel, e.g. for migration.

promiscuity: a mating system in which both sexes copulate with more than one partner, without the formation of a pair-bond. Found in lekking birds such as the Ruff (*Philomachus pugnax*), the Sage Grouse (*Centrocercus urophasianus*) and some manakins (Pipridae) as well as in other species, comprising some six percent of all birds. Adj. **promiscuous**; *cf.* polygamy, polygyny, polyandry, polygynandry.

pronation: forward rotation; *cf.* supination.

pronator profundus: a muscle arising on the humerus and extending along the underside of the wing beside the proximal ends of the radius and ulna.

prong: a projection on a barbule of a down feather that prevents another crossing barbule from interlocking, improving a three-dimensional network.

pronucleus: the nucleus of a sperm or egg during fertilization.

prooticum: pl. prootica, a small pillar of bone in the skull that articulates with the quadrate; also called pila otica.

propagule: part of an organism produced either sexually or asexually that can give rise to a new individual, e.g. a seed, a plant cutting, etc.

propatagium: a membrane of skin along the anterior margin of the wing, from shoulder to wrist, that forms the leading edge of the wing; *cf.* patagium, metapatagium, humeral patagium.

proprioception: detection of position of limbs and tensions in muscles (muscle sense), mediated by specialized sensory neurons; *cf.* sensory neurons, motor neurons.

prospecting movements: young birds making movements away from the territory into the surrounding landscape to obtain information pertinent to dispersal.

protandry: the earlier arrival of males than of females on breeding areas, the opposite of protogyny.

Protarchaeopteryx: a 120 mya old fossil enantiornithine or 'opposite' bird from China.

proteases: (proteinases, peptidases, or proteolytic enzymes) enzymes that break peptide bonds between amino acids of proteins. The process is called proteolytic cleavage and is a common mechanism of activation or inactivation of enzymes especially involved in blood coagulation or digestion.

proteins: polypeptides, macromolecules composed of strings of amino acids; one of the major classes of biological compounds, the others being carbohydrates, lipids, and nucleic acids.

protein electrophoresis: a laboratory technique that separates proteins by placing them into a matrix (such as agarose gel) and exposing them to an electric field for a period of time; through relative mobility differences, this causes even only subtly different proteins to move at different rates and thus cover different distances through the matrix. Used, e.g. to map variation in protein electro-types in various tissues as a means of developing biochemical characters for systematic analyses and population genetics; *cf.* allozyme, isozyme.

proto-: prefix meaning first or original.

Protoavis: a 225 million year old fossil from Texas, maybe a close relative to birds.

Protocalliphora: a genus of 'bluebottle'-coloured flies, the larvae of which occupy nests and nest cavities and suck the blood of birds, often resulting in the death of nestlings.

protograph: all the original illustrations of a holotype.

protogyny: the earlier arrival of females than of males on breeding areas, the opposite of protandry.

proton: a stable subatomic particle occurring in all atomic nuclei.

protoplasm: the active or living substance of the cell, including the nucleus and cytoplasm.

protoporphyrin: a red-brown pigment, which on eggshall can be camouflage and a shell strengthener.

protoptile: downy feather of a nestling bird, or of the first feather generation in the relatively few cases where nestlings have two generations of downs, e.g. penguins (Spheniscidae) and owls (Strigidae), such second generation feathers are called mesoptile; *cf.* neossoptile, teleoptile.

Protostomia: in taxonomy one of the two great Metazoan sub-kingdoms among others including the Annelida, Mollusca, and Arthropoda, in which an embryo begins to develop its ball of cells into the form of a cup which then closes to form a hole that later becomes the mouth, as opposed to a Deuterostomia, in which it later becomes the anus.

prototype: the primary type.

Protozoa: phylum (or sub-kingdom) of single-celled eukaryotic microorganisms such as amoebae.

protype: in taxonomy the intact specimen used as a replacement for an incomplete holotype; *cf.* holotype, neotype, lectotype, syntype, paratype, pseudotype, topotype.

proventriculus: the glandular stomach anterior to the gizzard, also called fore-stomach, particularly well developed in fish-eating and meat-eating birds. Secretes mucus, acid, and digestive enzymes.

proxi-: prefix from Latin *proximus*, meaning next.

proximal: towards the centre of the body, as opposed to distal.

proximate factor: an environmental stimulus that directly causes a biological response, e.g. daylight length is a proximate factor that can affect growth of gonads, timing of breeding and migrating, etc.; *cf.* ultimate factor.

pruning: the foraging behaviour used to eating plant buds.

prying: term for boring wood using the closed bill to enlarge an opening, as is the foraging method for barbets (Capitoninae), woodpeckers (Picidae), and nuthatches (Sittidae).

pseudepisematic: of deceptive appearance or behaviour; e.g. the deceptive appearance of cuckoo eggs being similar to those of the host species; *cf.* episematic, antepisematic, proepisematic, aposematic.

pseudo-: prefix meaning false.

pseudoaposematic: of protective mimicry, having warning coloration that is bluff; e.g. that of some Indonesian orioles (Oriolidae) that makes them look like more aggressive honeyeaters (Meliphagidae); *cf.* proaposematic, synaposematic.

pseudogynandromorph: a term for a bird that appears to be male in one part and a female in another part of the plumage, but which has (or had) the gonads of only one sex; *cf.* gynandromorph.

pseudoschizorhinal: having a form of opening of the nostrils in many ovenbirds (Furnariidae), in which the posterior opening is rounded and extends far back.

pseudosematic: of a characteristic that is a false warning, e.g. warning signals worn by an animal that is not actually dangerous or inedible.

pseudotype: in taxonomy a term for a type specimen selected in error.

Pseudosuchia: suborder of thecodonts (stem-archosaurs), a poorly known, ill-defined, and paraphyletic 'group' from the Triassic period.

pseudotemporal process: a bony process on the mandible.

pseudo-tuberculosis: a bacterial disease often associated with stress and producing 1-2mm yellow-white spots on the liver and spleen. Also called yersinia or pasteurella pseudotuberculosis; *cf.* tuberculosis.

psilopaedic: of a naked or nearly naked hatchling; the opposite of ptilopaedic; *cf.* altricial, nidicolous, nidifugous, precocial.

Psittaciformes: the order comprising 364 species of cockatoos, lories, macaws, and parrots in the single family Psittacidae.

psittacine: a cockatoo, lorry, macaw, or parrot of the order Psittaciformes.

psittacosis: a sometimes fatal bacterial disease among birds and mammals world-wide. Aviculturists who keep parrots (Psittacidae) are especially prone to this disease. It is an infection caused by *Chlamydia psittaci* transmitted through the air. The lungs are chiefly affected, causing pneumonia, but also the liver and central nervous system can be attacked. Also called chlamydiosis, parrot fever or ornithosis.

p2 value: a measure of last male sperm precedence, estimating the proportion of offspring sired by the second of two males copulating with a single fertile female; not to be confused with P2 = second primary.

Pteroclidiformes: the order comprising only the 16 species of sandgrouse (Pteroclididae or Pteroclidae) but included in Columbiformes by many authors. Sometimes spelled **Pterocliformes**.

pterodactylus: a genus of pterosaurs.

pterosaurs: Pterosauria, order of flying 'reptiles', apparently the sister group of dinosaurs (including birds); the wing was primarily supported by the 4th finger. Known from the late Triassic to the end of the Cretaceous.

pterygoids: paired bones articulating with the quadrates and the palate.

pteryla: pl. pterylae, a feather tract, an area of skin from which contour feathers grow and fan out over all bare areas, separated from other pterylae by areas that are naked (apteria) or covered only by down.

Pteryla alaris: the feather tract from which the flight feathers (remiges) and associated coverts grow. Also called alar tract; *cf*. humeral tract.

Pteryla capitalis: the feather tract that covers all surfaces of the head (often by several discrete subunits); *cf*. pterylography.

Pterylae caudalis: the feather tract that includes the tail, its coverts, and adjacent feathering of the uropygial gland and cloaca.

Pteryla cruralis: the feather tract on the thighs.

Pteryla femoralis: the feather tract on and behind the thigh.

Pteryla humeralis: the feather tract on the base of the wings.

Pteryla spinalis: the feather tract running dorsally from the base of the skull to the base of the tail, also called dorsal tract or spinal tract; *cf*. pterylography.

Pteryla ventralis: the feather tracts on the underparts, exclusive of the femoral tract, also called ventral tract*; cf*. pterylography.

pterylography: the study of pterylosis, or how the contour feathers are arranged in eight major feather tracts.

pterylosis: the distribution of feathers over a bird's body.

ptilochronology: the daily growth rate of flight feathers studied by the use of growth bars in order to assess a bird's nutritional state; can be used, e.g. in assessing variation in daily nutrition during feather growth, or long-term changes in habitat quality.

Ptilogonatidae: once given to the passerine family consisting of the three silky flycatchers and the Phainopepla (*Phainopepla nitens*), now usually included as the subfamily Ptilogonatinae in the family Bombycillidae.

ptilopaedic: of a down-clad hatchling; *cf*. psilopaedic, altricial, nidicolous, nidifugous, precocial.

ptilopody: the condition of having feathers on legs and toes.

ptilosis: synonym of plumage and feathering.

pubis: pl. pubes, the anterior ventral part of the pelvis in tetrapods. An often thin, needle-like bone that originates close to the socket of the thigh (femur). Latin *pubes*; *cf.* pelvic girdle, ilium, ischium.

puffinosis: a viral disease causing lesions in the feet and sometimes around the eyes, known in shearwaters (Procellariidae), gulls (Laridae), and oystercatchers (Haematopodidae); mainly affects and kills young birds.

pullet: a young female domestic fowl (*Gallus gallus*), laying relatively small and often infertile eggs.

pullus: pl. *pulli*, Latin = nestling. A chick or nestling before it is fledged.

pulmonary circulation: the circulation of blood to the lungs for exchange of oxygen and carbon dioxide. The path of blood through the right side of the heart and the lungs is the **pulmonary circuit** and is separated from the systemic circulation carrying blood to and from the rest of the body. This system prevents from being oxygenated and deoxygenated blood is mixed.

pulpa: Latin = pulp, also termed papilla. Cone-shaped structures deep within the skin from where feathers are developed.

punctuated equilibrium: in evolution, patterns with long periods of stasis interrupted by periods of rapid change and speciation.

puncture ejection: the removal of the eggs of brood parasites by puncturing them with the bill and removing them from the nest, also called spiking.

pupa: pl. pupae, in insects, the final stage of development between larva and adult, usually immobile and encased within a skin, cocoon, or cell, within which dramatic anatomical changes take place.

pupil: the black opening in the middle of the iris of the eye.

Purkinje fibres: cells specialized for the conduction of impulses.

pus: fluid from festering wounds formed by dead or dying cells and bacteria.

pycnaspidean: of a tarsus, anteriorly covered by large scutes, posteriorly by small scales, also called taxaspidian; *cf.* endaspidean, exaspidean, holaspidean, ocreate.

Pygopodes: an outdated name for an order comprising the Gaviiformes and Podicipediformes and, in very old works, the Alcidae.

pygostyle: the fused distal four to seven caudal vertebrae; also called plowshare bone, uropygium, or tailbone. Absent in most ratites (Struthioniformes) and tinamous (Tinamidae); *cf.* Parson's nose, recticial bulbs.

pyloric stomach: a chamber between the gizzard and duodenum in cormorants (Phalacrocoracidae), anhingas (Anhingidae), storks (Ciconiidae), and herons (Ardeidae).

pylorus: the opening to the intestine from the gizzard. Also called **pyloric orifice**.

pyrexia: an overly high body temperature.

pyriform: pear-shaped, as, e.g. an egg of a sandpiper (*Calidris* spp.). Also called conical; *cf.* short elliptical, elliptical, oval, subelliptical.

Q

q. e.: Latin *quod est* = which is.

quadrate: one of the paired bones at the base of the skull, through which the lower mandible is attached to the cranium.

quadratojugal: a slender bar on each side of the head, connecting the quadrate with the upper mandible; the terminal end is called the jugal.

quadruped: a four-legged animal, e.g. most reptiles and mammals.

quadrupedal: walking on four legs.

quail disease: 1) a serious viral disease of the avian respiratory tract. 2) a bacterial disease of the gut, also called duck plague.

qualitative: descriptive, as opposed to quantitatively or numerically expressed.

quantitative: numeric, determined through measurement, or counts, etc.

quarantine: enforced isolation, e.g. of newly imported birds to avoid potential spread of disease.

quasi-dispersal: an extended local excursion or exploration, e.g. by colonial birds to other colonies in distant parts of their home range: *cf.* dispersal.

Quaternary: the geologic period of the Cenozoic era, from approx. 1.8 million years BP to the present, divided into the epochs Pleistocene and Holocene.

quill: 1) the main shaft of a feather (i.e. the calamus and rachis). 2) or sometimes only the naked basal part embedded in the skin. 3) also applied to the calamus only. 4) in popular works and literature often used as a synonym of feather, especially flight feathers.

quintocubital: an older name for eutaxic = having secondaries that form an unbroken series, as opposed to diastataxic.

quivering: rapidly repeated wing movements, e.g. performed by females in sexual contexts or by begging juveniles, but also given in some aggressive contexts; also called fluttering.

R

r: a common symbol for intrinsic rate of natural increase.

rabies: viral infection in mammals, rarely infecting birds.

race: 1) a variety of a domestic animal, e.g. a breed of chicken, such as the Rhode Island red. 2) sometimes used synonymously with subspecies. 3) some authors use it as a synonym of gens.

rachis: pl. rachides, the shaft of a feather except for the basal part (called calamus).

racing pigeon: a domesticated homing pigeon (*Columba livia*).

racket: the vaned tip of a central tail feather (rectrix) of which some of the rachis is bare; found in, e.g. motmots (Momotidae) and the Greater Racket-tailed Drongo (*Dicrurus paradiseus*). Also seen spelled **raquet.**

RADAR: abbr. for radio detection and ranging. Radar is often used to study bird migration, and in so doing can detect altitude, orientation, major routes taken, and the timing of migratory movements, but not, unfortunately, species.

radiale: a small bone at the outside of the wrist (carpal joint) at the terminal end of the radius; *cf.* ulnare, carpals.

radiation: 1) in evolution, the often relatively rapid appearance of multiple new forms from a single lineage. 2) geographical dispersal; *cf.* adaptive radiation.

radio-carbon dating: method to determine the age of samples containing organic matter of less than about 50,000 years old; based on measuring the ratio of the radioactive carbon isotope ^{14}C to normal carbon ^{12}C.

radiography: the making of X-ray images, also called X-ray 'photography'.

radio tracking: tracking an animal that has been equipped with a small radio transmitter; the instrument package should not exceed 3-5 percent of the body mass when attached to birds.

radius: pl. radii, 1) one of the two bones of the forearm, the other being the ulna. 2) a barbule in a feather.

raft: 1) a compact flock of birds on water. 2) a floating nest platform. 3) a floating mass of organic material detached from land, and then often used as a verb (e.g. 'rafting') meaning the crossing of a water body by terrestrial organisms that float to sea on organic material, e.g. clinging to a tree washed down a river to sea.

rain-bathing: bathing in rain; *cf.* flight-bathing, in-out bathing, plunge-bathing, stand-in bathing, stand-out bathing, and swim-bathing.

rainforest: a humid evergreen forest receiving more than 254 cm or 100 inches of rain annually. Also spelled rain forest.

Ramsar Convention: a convention on the protection of wetlands of international importance. Formulated in 1971 in Ramsar, Iran, and came into force in 1975.

ramus: pl. rami; 1) the side of a barb fitted with barbules on both the proximal and distal upper sides. 2) generally meaning a branch of something, so also applied to, e.g. one of the two halves of the lower mandible. 3) the base of the lower mandible. 4) or a projection from any bone.

random drift: random changes in gene frequencies within a population, not caused by selection, mutation, or immigration. Also called genetic drift; *cf.* mutation, natural selection, sexual selection.

random walk: an irregular track of movement caused by random directional changes, such as a particle under Brownian movement.

range: 1) the geographical distribution of a species or population. 2) the minimum and maximum values in a statistical data set.

rank: 1) taxonomic rank of a group, meaning its taxonomic category; family, genus, species, and subspecies are examples of different taxonomic ranks. 2) the position of an individual in a social dominance hierarchy or pecking order, the top of which is often termed the dominant or alpha individual and those below subordinate.

rank correlation: in statistics, the degree of concordance between two rankings of the elements of a data set.

rank order: another name for dominance hierarchy or pecking order.

RAOU: abbr. for Royal Australasian Ornithologist Union. Published *Emu* during 1901-2000, thereafter called *Emu Austral Ornithology*.

Raphidae: the family comprising two extinct birds of the Mascarene Islands, the Dodo (*Raphus cucullatus*) of Mauritius and the Solitaire (*Pezo-*

phaps solitaria) of Rodriguez. A third species may have inhabited Réunion.

rapid mate switching: rapid switching of pair-bonded mates during the breeding season, resulting in apparent extra-pair paternity within a female's single clutch, documented in typically monogamous colonial nesters such as swifts (Apodidae); *cf.* extra-pair fertilisation.

Rapoport's Rule: the biogeographic rule according to which the range size of birds tends to increase from the tropics towards higher latitudes.

raptor: a bird of prey, member of the order Falconiformes. Adj. **raptorial**.

Raptor Research Foundation: a society founded in USA in 1966, focusing on the protection of birds of prey.

rarity committee: a committee considering and evaluating records of rare birds; such committees have been established by ornithological societies in many countries and states to review records of the occurrence of rarities within their respective areas of interest.

rassenkreis: a series of populations showing clinal differences, whose overall distribution curves back around on itself such that the populations at the ends meet geographically but are so different that they are essentially two different species that do not interbreed. Also called ring species.

ratio cline: the clinal change in the proportion of different morphs over the geographical range of a polymorphic species.

ratite: 1) any of the ostrich-like flightless birds (the Ostrich, rheas, cassowaries, emus, and kiwis), now usually all placed in the same order Struthioniformes. 2) as a carry-over from the now defunct taxonomic category Ratitae, occasionally seen as indicating possession of a flat breastbone without a keel (carina), as most flightless birds have irrespective of their affinities; as opposed to carinate.

rat run: a method of departing the nest seen in many shorebirds in which the incubating bird runs away ducking low and moving rodent-like; may function as a distraction display and/or as a means to avoid detection until sufficiently far from the nest that a predator has difficulty finding it. Also termed **rat trick** or most widely rodent run.

rattan: a thorny climbing palm.

rattle: a harsh trill.

reactive coping style: characteristic of the properties of a 'slow' explorer, an individual that adapts slowly to new environmental changes, as opposed to proactive coping style.

reafforestation: the re-establishing of forest in a formerly forested area. Also called reforestation; *cf.* afforestation.

recapitulation: the embryological development of an organism passing through stages resembling phylogenetic ancestors, or at least possessing traits from such ancestors, e.g. the gill arches of embryos of land vertebrates.

recency effect: the circumstance that food most recently stored by a hoarding bird is the food it first retrieves.

Recent bird: an extant bird species, or at least a species that survived into the Holocene (i.e. to within the last 10,000 years).

Recent Ornithological Literature: during 1983-1997 a supplement to the journals *Ibis, Auk,* and *Emu*; *cf.* Ornithological Worldwide Literature, Zoological record.

receptacle of the ductus deferens, the: a sperm storage area at the end of the ductus deferens. In most passerines called the seminal glomus.

recessive: of an allele whose expression is fully or partially suppressed by a dominant allele (variant form) of the same gene, usually given as a lower case letter, e.g. 'a' versus the dominant allele 'A' in a heterozygous individual 'Aa', in the same way used of a trait expressed by a recessive allele in the homozygous state (i.e. 'aa'). Because parents pass only one allele for each nuclear gene to their offspring, recessive traits can disappear and reappear across generations through chance; *cf.* dominant.

reciprocal altruism: apparently unselfish behaviour by an animal in the (evolutionary) 'expectation' that it will receive similar assistance in the future, or as a means to obtain such assistance. Also called mutualism.

reclinate: bent backward, as opposed to proclinate.

recognition species concept: species concept based on the idea that individuals of a species recognize only one another as potential mates, i.e. they share a mate recognition system; *cf.* biological species concept, ecological species concept, phenetic species concept.

recovery rate: the proportion of ringed birds that are subsequently encountered, dead or alive.

recruitment rate: a measure of population structure, the percentage of offspring of the year a population contains; *cf.* mortality rate.

recti: prefix from Latin *rectus* meaning straight.

recticial bulbs: bulbs on each side of the pygostyle that form the seat of the 12 tail feathers (rectrices).

rectrix: pl. **rectrices**, tail feathers. Most species have 12; they are counted from the middle outwards as T1, T2, etc.; *cf.* remex.

rectum: the posterior part of the intestine, in most birds from the caecum to the cloaca.

recurved: curved upward, as the bill of an Avocet (*Recurvirostra avocetta*), the opposite of decurved (curved down-ward).

red data species: a red-listed species, a species included in a red data book covering a region's rare and threatened species.

redirected activity: a meaningless behaviour exhibited in the absence of a relevant stimulus, as when a bird tries to copulate with a substitute partner, or when it redirects its attack towards an object other than the animal that elicited the response; *cf.* displacement behaviour, intention movements.

red mites: ectoparasites of the family Dermonyssidae that suck blood, thus causing skin irritation and sometimes causing infections and feather damage.

red queen effect: a sequence of mutual counter-adaptations of two coevolving organisms, e.g. a parasitic cuckoo and its host, or a predator and its prey, in which any advance of one species is detrimental to the other, so both must keep evolving apace or face extinction (creating a so called arms race).

reductionism: the study of ever smaller levels of organization in the belief that understanding them will enable explanations of higher-order phenomena. Although this can be a sensible approach, the existence of emergent phenomena not least in biological systems, limits its utility.

reeling: the producing of a monotonous trill, as by the Grasshopper Warbler (*Locustella naevia*); *cf.* churring.

reeve: the female of the Ruff (*Philomachus pugnax*).

reflectance: a measure of the amount of light reflected back from an object.

reflectance spectrophotometer: an instrument that emits a standard pulse of light and then measures the amount and characteristics of that light reflected from a surface at a standard distance from the light source. Commonly used to quantify variation in bird plumage coloration. Also called spectrophometer or spectrometer.

reflex: an action not dependent on the involvement of the brain but governed by more peripheral parts of the central nervous system.

reforestation: the re-establishing of forest in a formerly forested area. Also called reafforestation; *cf.* afforestation.

refractory period: a postbreeding period during which the reproductive system does not respond to any stimuli (e.g. day length) that earlier in the cycle would initiate reproductive behaviour. Also called photorefractoriness. In late summers of temperate zones birds enter a period in which their hormonal systems cease to respond to longer periods of daylight with renewed production of sex hormones.

refuge: 1) an area set aside for preservation of a more or less wild ecosystem. 2) a refugium.

refugium: pl. refugia, an area in which populations and species survived during a prolonged unfavourable period, for example an ice age (and thus termed a glacial refugium).

regression: in statistics an analytical procedure that determines the relationship between one variable (the dependent) and one or more different variables (the independent) and expresses it as a function, either linear or nonlinear. May be extended to cases with several independent variables (multiple regression). 2) a process in which something is diminished.

regurgitation: the ejecting of food through the mouth, for example to feed nestlings.

rehabilitation: the return of a wounded bird, healed by humans, to the wild.

reinforcement: 1) evolution of any mechanism that prevents two forms from hybridizing prior to fertilisation (prezygotic barriers to gene flow) as a response to selection against hybrids in diverging forms that have come into contact and are hybridizing. Reinforcement is unlikely unless disruptive selection acts directly upon the trait; *cf.* reproductive character displacement. 2) in behaviour, an action such as a reward or punishment that promotes or deters an action.

rejector species: a bird species that refuses parasitic eggs in its nests, as opposed to acceptor species; refusing here meaning removing the parasite's egg or abandoning the clutch entirely, the bird in the latter case is called a deserter species; *cf.* selective rejector, unselective rejector.

relative egg weight: the mass (weight) of an egg relative to the mass of the female.

releaser: a call, a movement, a specific object, or a scent serving as a stimulus that releases a response. Also termed **releasing mechanism, releasing factor** or innate releasing mechanism.

releasing hormones: neurosecretions from the hypothalamus that stimulate the release of specific hormones from the adeno-hypophysis; abbr. RHs.

relict: 1) an isolated remnant population of a once widespread organism. 2) an extant lineage known to have existed in the same form in previous geological ages.

remex: pl. **remiges**, collective name for primaries, secondaries, and tertials, the flight feathers of the wing; *cf.* rectrix.

remicle: the outer, often vestigial, primary.

ren: pl. *renes Latin* = kidney.

renal: pertaining to the kidney.

renal depression: bony recesses deep in the pelvis where the kidneys are situated.

renal portal system: a circulatory arrangement by which venous blood is passed from the intestine and other organs of the abdomen to the kidneys instead of going directly back to the heart.

Rensch's Rule: the biogeographic rule that the more mobile birds, especially migratory species breeding in cooler climates, have narrower and more pointed wings than less mobile birds, especially those found in warmer regions.

replacement clutch: a new clutch laid to replace one that has been lost.

replacement species: 1) two closely related species living in the same region but in different biotopes; *cf.* differential species. 2) species that across geographic space, replace each other, occupying the same or very similar niches (the two forms often being parapatrically distributed, in which cases they are often very closely related).

Report of the Severn Wildfowl Trust: periodical published by *Wildfowl and Wetlands Trust* from 1948-1952, and continued as ***Report of the Wildfowl Trust*** during 1953-1966; *cf.* Wildfowl and Wetlands Trust.

reproduction capacity: the propagation capability of a pair or of a population; in the case of a pair either during one year or throughout a lifetime; *cf.* natality.

reproduction rate: the number of offspring successfully produced by a pair of adults, a species, or a population in a single breeding season.

reproductive character displacement: an enhanced divergence in a character that promotes prezygotic isolating mechanisms (i.e. minimizes hybridization) between closely related forms where their ranges meet. It is a type of character displacement that affects reproductive isolation rather than ecological competition; *cf.* reinforcement, character displacement.

reproductive behaviour systems: see: monogamy, polygamy, polyandry, polygyny, polygynandry, lekking, male deception polygyny, promiscuity, extra-pair copulation.

reproductive isolation: the absence of gene flow between populations, i.e. the absence of interbreeding between them, either because they inhabit different geographical areas, or because intrinsic or external factors make it impossible for them to produce viable offspring together; *cf.* geographic isolation, isolation mechanism.

reproductive skew: a measure of how offspring production is distributed among members of a social group. A high-skew society is a group in which only a small minority of the pairs reproduce.

reproductive system: the gonads (testes, ovary), ducts (vas deferens, oviduct), and genitalia (penis, when present, cloaca) associated with reproduction.

reptile-hipped dinosaurs: one of the major groups of dinosaurs, composed of two groups, the carnivorous theropods and the herbivorous sauropods. Also called Saurischian dinosaurs.

repulsion: the mutual avoidance of conspecifics by individuals of a non-social species; *cf.* individual distance.

resident: nonmigratory, staying in the breeding area year-round. Also called sedentary.

residual reproductive value: future reproduction.

resistence: the ability to cope with detrimental environmental influences, especially infections.

resonance: the effect of exposing a system to vibrations of the same frequency as the system's natural oscillations, leading to oscillations of the system that increase over time in amplitude and energy.

resource-defense polygyny: a mating system in which multiple female's mate with a single male, the females choice being made on the basis of the evaluating the quality of the male's territory.

respiratory system: the system responsible for the exchange of gases in an organism, supplying it with oxygen from the air and clearing it of metabolic carbon dioxide; in tetrapods, the lungs and associated trachea (and in birds, also the air sacs). See: air capillaries, air sacs, bronchi, bulla, larynx, lungs, mesobronchus, pharynx, pneumatic skeleton, syrinx, and trachea.

restocking: the release into formerly occupied habitat of individuals of an animal that has become either very scarce there or extirpated entirely. Also called reintroduction.

rest-phase hypothermia: the state of having a reduced body temperature during sleep (rest), without being in torpor, and with the temperature usually staying within 10° C of normal levels; also called controlled rest-phase hypothermia.

restricted range species: as defined by BirdLife International, a species that in recent history has had an overall range of under 50,000 km²; *cf.* Endemic Bird Areas.

retaliatory copulation: a forced copulation, or rape.

retardation: a decrease in rate, e.g. of development; also a change in ontogenetic development within a lineage across evolutionary time such that a character appears later in the ontogeny of a descendant than it did in the ancestor.

retarded return: a term used of immatures in species that wait until returning to breeding areas because sexual maturity is reached only after several years, and they stay on their resting grounds, e.g. many birds of prey (Falconiformes), storks (Ciconiidae), herons (Ardeidae), etc.; *cf.* graded return.

rete mirabile: pl. *retia mirabilia*, Latin = wonderful net, arrangement in which arteries and veins are split into numerous fine, parallel vessels in close contact, with arterial and venous blood flowing in opposite directions, forming a countercurrent system; found in various places in the vertebrate body where efficient exchange of solutes or heat is needed; *cf.* tibiotarsal rete, sphincter muscles.

reticulate: of a foot covered by a fine patchwork of plates or scales in a net-like fashion. Found, e.g. in falcons (Falconidae); *cf.* scutellate-reticulate, booted, scutellate-booted.

reticulation: the process of reticulate evolution, i.e. intercrossing between formerly genetically isolated lineages without negative fitness consequences, resulting in the uniting of formerly isolated lineages into one. Not restricted to sister lineages.

reticuloendotheliosis: a viral disease causing morbidity and mortality in a number of bird species, including domestic chickens and turkeys, and perhaps also the cause of a recent decline in Lesser Prairie-Chicken (*Tympanuchus pallidicinctus*).

retina: the membrane at the back wall of the eye with light-sensitive cells of two types, rods, and cones; *cf.* sclera, choroid.

retort nest: a globular nest with an entrance tunnel.

retrap: a ringed bird caught again shortly after ringing at the same place; *cf.* control, ringing recovery.

retro-: prefix from Latin *retro* meaning backwards.

retroarticular process: an inner lateral process at the base of the lower mandible that articulates with the quadrate.

retrogressus: Latin = degeneration.

retrorse: pointing backwards, or in a direction opposite to the usual (esp. in botany).

return migration: migration towards the breeding grounds, in contrast to outward migration.

reverberation: the reflecting of sound from the surroundings; in relation to bird song this can have either an amplification or dampening effect, e.g. canyon walls versus dense vegetation.

reversal sexual size dimorphism: females larger than males, common in raptors, shorebirds, and some other groups.

reversed sex: changed sex.

reversed sex role: breeding system in which females compete for access to males, and males provide the majority of the care for the offspring, e.g. as in cassowaries (Casuariidae) and jacanas (Jacanidae).

reverse migration: temporary migration in the opposite direction of that normal for the season, e.g. if birds migrating north in spring meet unusually cold weather en route and retreat southward.

reverse mounting: the female mounting the male.

reverse sexual dimorphism: pattern in which, opposite to the normal, the female is the more colourful sex; usually also involves size, but females are the larger sex in many species with normal or no colour dimorphism. Clarification is often given by using the word dichromatism rather than dimorphism when appropriate.

Rey's eggshell weight index: ab^2/w, in which a is egg length and b egg width (both in mm), and w is eggshell mass (weight) in mg.

rhachis: the part of the tapering, angular shaft of a feather bearing the barbs. Normally spelled rachis; *cf.* calamus.

rhamphotheca: the horny plates covering the bill of a bird. It grows throughout the life of a bird. Also called rhinotheca; *cf.* gnathotheca, premaxilla.

rhamphus: Latin = bill or beak.

Rheiformes: order comprising the two species of rheas (Rheidae).

rhinotheca: the horny part of the upper mandible; *cf.* rhamphotheca, gnathotheca.

rhodoxanthin: a carotenoid pigment found in feathers of some cotingas (*Phoenicircus*) and fruit pigeons (*Ptilinopus*).

rhomboid sinus: an opening in the dorsal lumbosacral enlargement in birds, containing glycogen-rich cells. Its function is still unknown.

rhynchokinesis: the ability to open the tip of a long bill, as seen in some shorebirds such as the Eurasian Woodcock (*Scolopax rusticola*), as an adaptation to feeding on organisms buried in sand, silt, or soil; *cf.* prokinesis.

ribs: long, curved bones that articulate with the vertebrae and the sternum and enclose the thoracic cavity, each of them subdivided in dorsal (vertebral) and ventral (sternal) parts; each dorsal rib usually possesses an uncinate process that overlaps with the dorsal rib posterior to it, providing enhanced rigidity of the thoracic region.

riboflavin: vitamin B_2. An orange-yellow crystalline compound, $C_{17}H_{20}N_4O_6$, the principal growth-promoting factor in the vitamin B complex, naturally occurring in milk, leafy vegetables, fresh meat, and egg yolks. Also called lactoflavin.

rickettsia: any of a multitude of bacterially-induced diseases, many of them caused by members of the bacterial genus *Rickettsia*; the diseases are commonly arthropod-borne and include typhus.

rictal bristles: bare, stiff feather shafts flanking the outside of the gape of certain birds catching insects in flight, such as nightjars (Caprimulgidae), swallows (Hirundinidae), and flycatchers (Tyrannidae and Muscicapidae); *cf.* bristles.

rictal commissure: another term for gape flange or **rictal flanges**.

rictus: skin at the junction of the two mandibles, often referred to as the gape flange or **rictal flanges**.

rigor mortis: stiffening of the body after death.

ring angel: circular pattern seen on a radar screen when birds leave a roosting site in the morning, for example Starlings (*Sturnus vulgaris*).

ringing: Am. banding. Putting a metal ring with a unique number on a bird's leg for identification purposes; *cf.* close ringing.

ringing pliers: an instrument for closing a ring around a bird's leg.

ringing recovery: report of a ringed bird found again, dead or alive.

ring species: a series of populations showing clinal differences whose overall distribution curves back around on itself such that the populations on the ends meet geographically but are so different that they are essentially two different species and do not interbreed. Also called rassenkreis.

ringworm: a fungal disease affecting chickens, turkeys, pigeons, and passerines; produces ring-like pigmented patches of vesicles or scales on the skin; also called favus or honeycomb fungus.

riparian: of or inhabiting a riverbank; *cf.* riverine.

ritualization: evolutionary change that causes a normal behaviour to become ritualized to serve in communication or to enhance its effectiveness in communication; many displays have been evolutionarily developed through this process; *cf.* intension movements.

rivalry: the act of competition, of being a rival or rivals. In avian terms may relate to being rivals for food, nest sites, access to mates, etc., and may rarely result in the death of one rival.

riverine: pertaining to a river or stream; *cf.* riparian.

Robin: part of the vernacular name of many muscicapid species. 1) In Europe the vernacular name of *Erithacus rubecula* (Muscicapidae). 2) in America, uncapitalized, a common name for *Turdus migratorius,* the American Robin (Turdidae). 3) a falconer term for a male Hobby (*Falco subbuteo*).

Roc: a mythical bird from Eastern legends, huge and strong enough to carry off elephants in its claws. Also called Rukh or Rucke.

rocket net: a rocket-propelled net fired to cover and catch flocking birds such as geese, genus *Anser*; *cf.* cannon net.

Rocky Mountain spotted fever: a human disease, often lethal, caused by members of the bacterial genus *Rickettsia,* borne by wood ticks (*Dermacentor*) and often deadly. Also birds can be infested.

rods: light receptors in the retina of the vertebrate eye, containing the pigment rhodopsin; rods are much more sensitive than the other type of light receptors, the colour sensitive cones, and therefore are of most use in dim light. The resolution of rod-based vision is poorer than that of cone-based vision, because several rods are connected to a single retina neuron, an architecture that enchange sensitivity; *cf.* cone, dichromatism, trichromatism, tetrachromatism.

rodent: any member of the mammalian order Rodentia, gnawing mammals with one pair of chisel-like incisors in the upper and lower jaws.

rodent run: a method of departing the nest seen in many shorebirds in which the incubating bird runs away ducking low and moving rodent-like; may function as a distraction display and/or as a means to avoid detection until sufficiently far from the nest that the predator has difficulty finding it. Also termed rat trick or rat run.

roding: the twilight display of male European Woodcock (*Scolopax rusticola*).

roof-prism binoculars: binoculars with the prisms arranged in a single row, in contrast to porro-prism binoculars in which the prismatic arrangement is displaced.

rookery: a bird colony, in the strict sense of Rooks (*Corvus frugilegus*), but often applied to colonies of other species, e.g. penguins (Spheniscidae). In America the term is used for nesting colonies of herons (Ardeidae) or crows (Corvidae). By some authors also applied to roosting sites.

rookooing: the bubbling voice of a lekking Black Grouse (*Tetrao tetrix*).

roost: to rest, or a resting or sleeping place where birds spend the night or congregate at other periods, e.g. shorebirds at a high-tide roost. Some birds fly long distances to roost, e.g. the Starling (*Sturnus vulgaris*).

root: 1) below-ground vegetation of plants that extract water and nutrients from the soil and provide support to the plant. 2) the lineage(s) in a tree or cladogram chosen to be the outgroup taxon (or taxa), usually either the sister to or the most distant from the ingroup or group under study.

rooted cladogram: a cladogram or tree that is rooted, i.e. has a root, the position of the root is determined by including one or more outgroups in the analysis; *cf.* unrooted tree.

rostral: towards the anterior end of the body, more commonly called anterior or cranial, towards the tip of the bill.

rostrum: 1) a pointed process on a bone. 2) the bill. 3) a small forked process on the anterior margin of the breastbone (sternum), between the coracoidal facets. Adj. **rostral**.

round-wing: a falconer's term for an eagle or buzzard; *cf.* short-wing, long-wing.

roundworm: any member of the phylum Nematoda, which includes a number of endoparasitic species. Their form is cylindrical with tapered ends.

route-based navigation: homing based on unspecified information perceived during active or passive displacement; can result in learned, repeatedly used routes.

roving bird: nomadic bird.

Royal Australasian Ornithologist Union: abbr. RAOU. Published *Emu* during 1901-2000, thereafter called *Emu Austral Ornithology*.

Royal Society for the Protection of Birds: abbr. RSPB, formed in 1889 in Great Britain as the second society having conservation as part of its constitution. Has published *RSPB Conservation Review* and the quarterly magazine *Birds* since 1987.

r-selected species: *r*-strategists generally short-lived animals with a high reproductive rate, typically species of small body size and early maturity that occupy variable environments and often experience large fluctuations in population size, as opposed to *K*-selected species.

r-selection: natural selection favouring rapid maturity and high reproductive rates; *cf. K*-selection.

RSPB: abbr. Royal Society for the Protection of Birds, formed 1889 in Great Britain; publishes *RSPB Conservation Review.*

r-strategist: *r*-selected species, typically short-lived and with early maturity, small body size, and a high reproductive rate, as opposed to *K*-selected species.

ruber: Latin = red.

Rucke: a mythical bird from Eastern legends, huge and strong enough to carry off elephants in its claws. Also called Roc or Rukh.

ruderal species: species living in waste places or among rubbish, for example the Crested Lark (*Galerida cristata*) in areas in which it prefers man-modified environments such as urban and industrial wastelands.

ruff: elongated and often erectile feathers on the neck, best known from the male Ruff (*Philomachus pugnax*) in its breeding plumage.

Ruffini endings: receptors in the skin that respond to heat; their main function is thermoreception.

Rukh: a mythical bird from Eastern legends, huge and strong enough to carry off elephants in its claws. Also called Roc or Rucke.

rump: the upperparts between the lower back and upper tail coverts. Also called uropygium.

runaway: a term from Fisher's runaway model, males with special exaggerated traits that have some selective advantage attributable to female choice. Females that mate with such males produce more offspring. The sons inherit the male trait and daughters inherit the female preference for the trait. This process leads to an accelerating enhancement through positive feedback from generation to generation, hence the term "runaway".

runaway [sexual] selection: a hypothetical evolutionary process in which females prefer to mate with males having the most elaborate secondary sexual traits because their sons will thus be so adorned and thereby be themselves successful in obtaining mates. Over time, those traits upon which the females focus will achieve extreme forms that may handicap the males wearing them and thus lower their survival.

runt: an abnormally small chick, most often found in asynchronously hatching birds.

runt egg: a miniature egg less than 75% of the normal size.

rush: 1) a 'fall' of birds during migration. 2) an occasion in which several rare birds are seen at the same period. 3) a general term for tall wetland vegetation such as cattails, bullrushes, reeds, etc.

S

sacculus: a chamber in the inner ear; *cf.* utriculus.

sackeret: a falconry term for a male Saker Falcon (*Falco cherrug*).

sacrum: fused vertebrae to which the pelvic girdle is attached; in birds (where usually called synsacrum) it directly follows the thoracic region, with no intervening vertebrae, and consist of 9-22 fused vertebrae, firmly attached to the elongated ilium of the pelvic girdle; adj. **sacral**.

saddle: pertaining to the centre of the back, a term used when this area has contrasting colour such as, e.g. the Saddleback (*Creadion carunculatus*) from New Zealand or the Greater Black-backed Gull (*Larus marinus*).

sagebrush: 1) a term collectively given to shrubs of the genus *Artemisia,* habitat for Sage Sparrow (*Amphispiza belli*), Sage Thrasher (*Oreoscoptes montanus*), and Sage Grouse (*Centrocercus urophasianus*). 2) a North American biome in the Great Basin between the Rocky Mountains and the Sierra Nevada-Cascade system, dominated by densely foliaged sagebrush with associated rabbit bush, shad scales, greasewood, and other woody plants 0.6 to 2m tall.

sagittal: pertaining to the median longitudinal plane of the body from the head to the tail, dividing the body into left and right halves. Latin *sagittalis.*

sagittal suture: the medial junction of the parietal bones of the skull.

Sahel: the zone of arid savannah immediately south of the Sahara in west and central Africa.

saline: an area with a high concentration of salt, e.g. a lake, salt field, salt marsh, salt pan, or lagoon.

salivary glands: the saliva-producing glands beneath the tongue that secreate saliva and primarily act to moisten food in the mouth, but swifts (Apodidae) also use it for nest building, and the Edible-nest Swift (*Aerodramus fuciphagus*) builds its nest entirely of saliva. Many woodpeckers (Picidae) have sticky saliva that make prey stick to the tongue; *cf.* glandula picorum.

sally-gleaner: an animal that will capture prey both by sallying and by gleaning insects from the foliage.

sallying: flying out from a perch to capture an insect or other prey and then returning to the same or a nearby perch.

salmonellosis: a disease caused by bacteria of the genus *Salmonella*, causing diarrhoea. Both birds and mammals may be infected, including humans. Also called bacillary white diarrhoea, infectious enteritis, paratyphoid infection, and fowl typhoid.

salpingitis: inflammation of the oviduct.

saltational evolution: evolutionary change due to a sudden origin of a new type that gives rise to a new group of organisms.

salt gland: paired, salt-excreting glands found in marine birds, often located in grooves above the orbita of the skull (in that case also called supraorbital glands); in most species the excreted salt solution is conducted to the nostrils from which it runs down the bill as concentrated saline drops; also called nasal salt glands; *cf.* naricorn.

saltmarsh: a biotope of intertidal mud with salt-adapted plants.

salvage: any fresh bird material obtained for scientific use by methods other than direct collecting. Examples include: collisions with tall buildings, wind turbines, windows, cars, airplanes, utility towers, oil rigs, etc.; sport hunting, casualties at rehabilitation centers, nuisance bird control, oil spills, banding casualties, storm kills, disease outbreaks, fishery bycatch, casualties from zoos and private aviaries.

sanctuary: an area from the size of a country garden to many thousand ha in which wildlife has partial or full protection.

Sandgrouse, The: the periodical of the Ornithological Society of the Middle East, named after the 16 sandgrouse species (Pteroclididae).

sapro: prefix meaning rotten, decaying.

saprophagous: feeding on dead and decaying matter, such as a vulture does; **saprophagy**; *cf.* carnivorous.

sap well: a hole made in the bark of a tree by a sapsucker (Picidae), from which sap flows, attracting many insects; the woodpecker feeds on both the resulting sap and insects.

Sarmatic: of (the coastal fauna of) the Sarmatia Sea, an extension of the Mediterranean during late Tertiary and Pleistocene times.

sartorius: 1) a muscle on the anterior part of the thigh bone (femur). 2) the name of a manufacturer of digital balances.

satellite island: a smaller island adjacent to a larger one.

satellite tracking: radio tracking in which the signal from the transmitter is picked up by a satellite and relayed to a ground receiver. This technique makes it possible to track animals over a wide range, for example the entire migratory route of a migratory bird, or the full feeding trip of a chick-rearing albatross (Diomedeidae).

saurischian dinosaurs: one of the major groups of dinosaurs, composed of the carnivorous theropods and the herbivorous sauropods. Also called reptile-hipped dinosaurs.

Sauriurae: the subclass of birds with, e.g. *Archaeopteryx* and its (unknown) relatives; syn. Archaeornithes; *cf.* Ornithurae.

saurognathous: an obsolete, meaningless, term for having a palate like that of woodpeckers.

Sauropods: Sauropodomorpha, a group of herbivorous saurischian dinosaurs.

Sauropsida: a rarely used name for a group consisting of extant lizards and snakes (lepidosaurs) and related fossil forms, one of the two main groups within the Diapsida (the other being Archosauria, comprising birds and other dinosaurs plus relatives such as pterosaurs and crocodiles). In older literature, Sauropsida has occasionally been used as a synonym of Diapsida, or nearly so.

savannah: semi-arid grassland with scattered trees and scrub. Also spelled **savanna**.

sawbill: a rarely used name for a merganser, i.e. any member of the genus *Mergus* of the duck family Anatidae; these are characterized by having serrated cutting edges on the ramphotheca.

saxicoline: Latin, meaning rock-inhabitant.

scalation: something (anything) that has the appearance of overlapping scales, as for example plumage patterns in many birds.

scala naturae: an historic philosophy that all organisms are part of a single linear scale of increasing perfection, culminating with human. 'It received its final death blow when Cuvier (1812) asserted emphatically that there are four distinct phyla of animals, no more and no fewer, and that there was absolutely no connection among them' (Mayr 1982:201). Also called Great Chain of Being.

scaley-leg mite: *Knemidokoptes jamaicensis*, an ectoparasite causing warty lesions on the legs and ribbon-like proliferations on the skin of birds.

Scandinavian Ornithologists' Union: Published *Ornis Scandinavica* 1970-1994, from 1995 continued as *Journal of Avian Biology*.

scansorial: trunk-creeping, such as do woodpeckers (Picidae).

scapula: shoulder blade, the pair of which forms part of the shoulder girdle; *cf.* acromion process.

scapulars: elongated feathers growing from the shoulder that cover the area where the wing joins the body.

scapulohumeral: the feather tract from the shoulder and upper surface of the wing to the elbow. Also called humeral tract; *cf.* pterylography.

scapus: a rare term for the whole feather shaft, i.e. both calamus and rachis.

scavenger: an animal that feeds on dead organic matter that it did not kill itself.

sceletus: Latin = skeleton.

schemochrome: feather colour resulting from microscopic structures that diffract or scatter light rather than absorbing it; responsible for most whites, blues, greens, and purples. Comprises both iridescent and non-iridescent colours, the former rarely occurring on wings because their structural basis weakens the strength of feathers. Also termed structural colours.

schizochroism: abnormal paleness resulting from the absence of one or more dark pigments, usually eumelanin or phaomelanin but sometimes various carotenoid pigments, e.g. xanthophylls, leaving white areas where the missing pigment(s) would normally be present. Also an ash-grey variant and a white variant where red and yellow would occur. Blue forms occur in otherwise green parrots when yellow pigment is missing. Usually only found in females; *cf.* albino, melanin, leucistic.

schizognathous: Greek *schizo* = cleaved; a palate with vomers tapering in front, found in penguins (Sphenisciformes), pheasants (Galliformes), shorebirds (Charadriiformes), and pigeons (Columbiformes); *cf.* desmognathous, dromaeognathous, aegithognathous.

schizorhinal. the state of the bony posterior margin of the nostril when it forms a slit. Found in gulls (Laridae), cranes (Gruidae), and some other groups.

Schweizerische Gesellschaft für Vogelkunde und Vogelschutz: the ornithological society in Switzerland. Has published *Der Ornithologische Beobachter* since 1902.

scientific name: the formal name of a taxon, internationally agreed upon and given according to strict rules so as to avoid ambiguity. Often called Latin name, but may also be of Greek or other origin, usually with a latinized ending. Also called technical name.

sclera: the outer whitish fibrous layer of the eyeball. Also called **scleroid coat**; *cf.* choroid, retina.

scleral ossicles: the elements of the bony sclerotic ring in the eye of birds.

sclerophyll: a plant with leathery or hard evergreen leaves, growing in dry areas, adj. **sclerophyllous**.

sclerotic ring: bony ring around the cornea in the scleroid coat of the eye of birds and many other vertebrate groups, but not mammals. In birds composed of 14-16 overlapping plates (scleral ossicles).

Scopus: the periodical for the Ornithological Sub-committee of the East African Natural History Society, Kenya.

scotopic vision: night vision, vision in light too dim for the cones to detect, so that the only active sensory retina cells are the rods; *cf.* photopic vision, cones, rods.

Scottish Birds: the periodical of the Scottish Ornithological Club.

scrape: a shallow hollow made in the ground as a nest.

scrawled: an egg marked by tortuous streaks.

screamer: 1) a falconry term for a nestling falcon. 2) or a screamer from South America, family Anhimidae.

screw-worm: the larva of a bluebottle fly, e.g. *Protocalliphora avium*, laying eggs in nests of birds in which the larvae suck blood from the nestlings.

scrub: vegetation community of low trees and bushes (mostly < 5 m), e.g. occurring as early-intermediate successive stages during regrowth of forest. In Australia the term is often applied to any rainforest.

Scrub Desert Biome: one of North America's nine ecological divisions or biotic communities from western Texas to southwestern California; *cf.* Tundra, Coniferous Forest (also termed Taiga), Deciduous Forest, Grassland, Southwestern Oak Woodland, Pinyon-Juniper, Chaparral, and Sagebrush. Now rarely used in science; *cf.* life zones.

scute: literally a shield, a scale on the tarsus or toes of a bird.

scutellate: of a bird species bearing scutes (i.e. large scales) on the tarsus; *cf.* reticulate, scutellate-reticulate, booted, scutellate-booted.

scutellate-booted: of a foot being scutellate anteriorly and booted posteriorly (i.e. having one long scale); also called laminiplantar; *cf.* reticulate, scutellate, scutellate-reticulate, booted.

scutellate-reticulate: of a foot being scutellate anteriorly and reticulate posteriorly, as for example in doves (Columbidae); *cf.* scutellate, reticulate, booted, scutellate-booted.

SD: abbr. for standard deviation, a statistic quantifying the dispersion of a set of observations about the mean; the square root of the variance, the latter being the squared deviations.

SE: abbr. for standard error, generally used for standard error of the mean and equivalent in this context to standard deviation of the mean (standard deviation). The difference is that standard error is not an appropriate term for the standard deviation of individuals in a sample or population (perhaps the most common use of SD). Standard error of the mean is instead calculated as the square root of the squared sample deviation divided by the sample size and is thus a population–scale estimate obtained from a single sample.

seagull: an old (inappropriate) word for any gull (family Laridae), not all of which are marine.

secondary: any of the inner flight feathers attached to the forearm (ulna) including the tertials, and varying in number from six in hummingbirds (Trochilidae) to 34 in albatrosses (Diomedeidae). Always counted from the outermost inwards (ascendantly), using the symbols S1, S2, etc (some authors use lower case letters s1 etc.). Also called secondary remiges; *cf.* primary.

secondary bronchi: narrow bronchi branching from the mesobronchi within the avian lung, *cf.* parabronchi.

secondary cavity nester: a bird adopting a nest cavity made by another bird species. Also called cavity adopter.

secondary consumer: a meat eater or carnivore.

secondary contact: the re-establishing of an overlap zone between the ranges of related populations after a period of geographic isolation.

secondary forest: forest regrown after severe, usually human-caused, disturbance or deforestation.

secondary intergradation: the hybridization of two distinct and previously isolated populations along a line or zone of secondary contact.

secondary sex organs: in the male the ductus deferens and, when present, the cloacal penis, in the female the oviduct and in some species a cloacal clitoris. Also termed accessory sex organs.

secondary sex ratio (or sex-ratio): the sex ratio found in young at the end of parental care, as opposed to the primary sex ratio at fertilisation; *cf.* primary sex ratio, tertiary sex ratio.

secondary sexual character: sex-specific external morphological traits (e.g. of plumage, bare parts, wattles, etc.).

second (third, etc.) alternate: Am. term for second (third, etc.) summer or breeding plumage or the moult into this plumage.

second (third, etc.) basic: Am. term for second (third, etc.) winter or non-breeding plumage or the moult into this plumage.

second non-nuptial: older Am. term for second winter plumage or the moult into this plumage.

second nuptial: older Am. term for second summer plumage or the moult into this plumage.

second order superspecies: a group of species derived from the same ances-

tor, which replace each other geographically and that are morphologically too distinct to be regarded as constituting a single species. Also called superspecies or mega superspecies; *cf.* subspecies, species.

second (third, etc.) prebasic molt: Am. term for post-breeding moult.

secundum: abbr. *sec.* Latin = according to.

sedentary: non-migratory, remaining in one general area throughout the year; also called resident.

sedge: any member of family Cyperaceae of grass-like plants (*Carex*, *Scirpus*, *Eriophorum*, and others).

seed disperser: a frugivore that, in not damaging or digesting them, moves and deposits seeds away from the parent plants (in contrast to a seed predator).

seed predator: a seed eater that breaks and digests the seed, such as, e.g. a parrot (Psittacidae), in contrast to a seed disperser.

segmentum: Latin = segment.

sehnenhalter: from German; tendon holder, an articular process on trochlea IV of the tarsometatarsus, found in zygodactylous birds.

selection: often used for natural selection.

selectionism: the theory that adaptive changes in evolution are the result of natural selection.

selective advantage, being of: favoured by natural selection.

selective rejector: a parasitized host species that can remove a brood parasite's egg from the nest without harming its own clutch, as opposed to unselective rejector.

self-maintenance behaviour: life-sustaining activities such as feeding, bathing, and preening.

sematic: serving as a signal of warning or of attraction; *cf.* aposematic.

semelparous: of an organism that only reproduces once during its lifetime; *cf.* monotely.

semi-: prefix from Latin *semi* = half, intermediate, partly.

semi-altricial: of chicks that hatch open-eyed and with downy plumage but are helpless and dependent upon their parent(s) for food and protection, e.g. herons (Ardeidae) and raptors (Falconiformes); *cf.* altricial, precocial.

semibristle: a feather intermediate between a bristle and a contour feather, found on the head and neck of some birds, but in its most typical form on the feet of barn owls (*Tyto* spp.).

semicircular canals: canals in the inner ear region, filled with a fluid called endolymph; forming a sense organ responsible for the 'sense of balance'; *cf.* cochlea.

semilunar membrane: a membrane in the syrinx which, together with the pessulus, is only found in the true songbirds (oscine Passeriformes).

semilunar valves: valves preventing a backflow of blood into the heart ventricles.

semimembranosus: a muscle on the thigh bone (femur).

seminal sac: sperm storage organ situated at the end of the ductus deferens, adjacent to the cloaca. Also called **seminal vesicle** or **seminal glomus**; *cf.* cloacal protuberance.

seminiferous tubules: fibrous epithelium of the dorsal side of the testis that produces sperm and sex hormones.

semipalmate: of a webbed foot in which the webs are curved inwards between the toes, as seen in, e.g. terns (Sterninae).

semiplume: a plumulaceous feather having a shaft longer than the longest barb and therefore slightly more like a contour feather than other types of down. Found at border areas between feather tracts (pterylae) and apteria; *cf.* down, natal down.

semi-precocial: of nestlings that hatch at a fairly advanced state, covered in down and with open eyes, but which, despite being somewhat mobile, usually stay in or near the nest, where they are fed by the parents; as in, e.g. gulls (Laridae).

semispecies: populations at the borderline between being considered a subspecies or species so that, even though hybridization is restricted between them, nevertheless occurs to a fairly substantial extent. One example is the species pair Pied Flycatcher (*Ficedula hypoleuca*) and Collared Flycatcher (*F. albicollis*); *cf.* allospecies, superspecies.

semispinalis: an elongated muscle extending down the length of the posterior side of the neck.

semitendinosus: a muscle on the thigh bone (femur). Also called **semitendinosus flexor**; *cf.* ilio tibialis.

senescence: ageing, accompanied by decreasing vigour, fecundity, and/or survival; *cf.* gerontology.

senior synonym: in nomenclature, the earlier established of two synonyms; the opposite of a junior synonym.

Senmurv: a fabulous creature, half-bird and half-mammal, of Persia.

sensitive phase: the period during which a chick is most sensitive to imprinting. Also called critical period.

sensory neurons: convey nerve impulses to the central nervous system from muscles and sensory organs; *cf.* motor neurons.

sensory receptor: a cell able to detect specific stimulus (temperature, light, vibrations, pressure, etc.) from th surroundings and transform it into a nervous signal, and so responsible for the sensory abilities of an organism; receptors may be found in specialised organs such as eyes, ears, the nasal mucosa, etc., or be more diffusely distributed.

sensu: Latin meaning in the sense of. Most often used by an author to specify that they are using a term precisely in the way another cited source used it.

sensu lato: Latin, meaning in a broad sense as opposed to *sensu stricto*.

sensu stricto: Latin, meaning in the strict sense, as opposed to *sensu lato.*

sentinel: a high-perched, non-foraging bird that actively scans, and warns of predators.

septicaemia: blood poisoning, caused by an infection of bacteria and their toxins in the bloodstream. Also spelled septicemia.

septum: a wall separating, e.g. the nostrils. It can be perforated or not (imperforate).

sequencing: 'reading' the sequence of bases in DNA or RNA.

sequential polyandry: the mating system in which a female has two or more males during the breeding season, but only one at a time, courting the next male after having laid a clutch for the first to tend; *cf.* polyandry, simultaneous polyandry.

seral: of a plant community prior to reaching equilibrium or climax.

serially descendent moult: the situation when a second moult starts before the first has finished, resulting in two active moult centres in a wing. Also called continuous step-wise moult or staffelmauser.

serological characters: the chemical nature of the blood serum.

serratus: Latin = sawed, or made after the manner of a saw, such as the saw-like edge of the bill of a merganser, genus *Mergus.*

Sertoli cells: cells in the testes of vertebrates involved in the maturation of the sperm.

sesamoid bone: skeletal connective tissue and the skeleton of an embryo before calcium is added, largely converted in adults to bone. A 'cartilage bone' can refer to any bone formed from cartilage but tends to be used

in ornithology to denote an ossified tendon or the kneecap or patella; also called 'cartilage'.

sessile: immobile; an organism lacking motility, often attached to a substrate.

sessility: the inability of an organism to move to another habitat, as opposed to vagility.

setose: having bristle-like feathers.

Severn Wildfowl Trust: a society founded 1948 in Britain, now known as the Wildfowl and Wetlands Trust.

sex chromosome: a chromosome or multiple chromosomes determining the sex in eukaryotic organisms, most animals have two, either a homologous pair (in the homogametic sex) or a dissimilar pair, (sometimes an unpaired chromosome), in the other (heterogametic) sex; in animals where the homogametic sex is the female (e.g. mammals), the sex chromosomes are called X and Y (females XX, males XY), in animals where females are heterogametic (e.g. birds), they are called Z and W (females ZW, males ZZ). In birds, a trait determined by a gene on the W chromosome is inherited directly from mother to daughter, with no influence from the father.

sex dimorphism: the condition that the sexes in a species differ in plumage, form, or size; usually termed sexual dimorphism.

sex ratio: the proportion between males and females in a population; also seen spelled with a hyphen *cf.* primary sex ratio, secondary sex ratio.

sex-specific PCR primer: a primer designed to amplify a specific portion of DNA from a sex chromosome, e.g. chromosome W in avian females.

sexual dichromatism: sexual difference in colour.

sexual dimorphism: a morphological difference between the sexes, usually referring to size or form, but also often used (less accurately) for colour as well.

sexual imprinting: imprinting of a bird raised by another species so that it will later attempt to mate with birds of the foster species rather than with birds of its own species; *cf.* filial imprinting.

sexual isolation: the absence of intermixing of gene pools, either because the members of different populations for some reason do not interbreed, or because hybrids are not viable.

sexual monogamy: the mating system in which the sexes associate in pairs (at least for the season) with no apparent sexual intercourse outside the pair; *cf.* social monogamy.

sexual ornaments: ornamental secondary sexual characters presumed to have arisen, and to be maintained, by sexual selection.

sexual reversal: when a female attains the plumage of a male.

sexual selection: the type of natural selection in which traits are selected solely on the basis of the advantage they give in competition for mating; most often the competing sex is the male, the choosing sex the female. Especially in polygamous and lekking bird species, sexual selection has promoted the evolution of peculiar and extravagant traits (plumage and other ornaments, displays, and behaviour); *cf.* founder effect, genetic drift, natural selection, runaway selection, intersexual selection, intrasexual selection.

sexy sons: a term for male offspring with genes that produce traits (e.g. long tails) attractive to females and thus permitting them to produce sons with such advantageous traits.

shaft: the central part of the feather to which the vanes are attached; the calamus and rachis together; *cf.* scapus.

shag: a widespread alternative name for cormorant. In Great Britain, however-

er, Shag is applied to *Phalacrocorax aristotelis* and Cormorant to *P. carbo*.

shank: lower leg, tarsometatarsus (often just 'tarsus' for short); bone consisting of fused tarsals and metatarsals and together with the toes comprising the avian foot.

sharming: the grunts and squeals uttered by the Water Rail (*Rallus aquaticus*).

shearing: the dipping or near dipping of the wing tip into the water by a banking shearwaters, family Procellariidae.

sheathed: applied to growing feathers still encased (at least in part) in a waxy sheath; also termed 'in sheath' when the feather is almost grown but is still sheathed at the base of the shaft (calamus).

shell-gland: synonymous with uterus, the part of the oviduct in which the shell is added.

shell membrane: two membranes on the inside of the shell, called outer and inner membranes.

shield: a naked, shield-like plate on the forehead, as in coots (*Fulica* spp.).

shivering: muscle contractions as a way to produce heat, often occurring simultaneously with heat-conserving behaviour such as fluffing the plumage and tucking the feet and legs against the body.

shock moult: defensive shedding of feathers during an encounter with a predator. Most frequently only the tail and rump feathers are shed to distract a predator. Also called fright moult.

shorebird: Am., collective name for plovers (Charadriidae), sandpipers (Scolopacidae), and other 'wading', charadriiform birds, i.e. syn. with 'wader' of U.K. usage.

short-distance migrant: a bird migrating short distances only, usually staying within a continent, in contrast to long-distance migrant; *cf.* elevational migrant.

short elliptical; the form of an egg that is only slightly more pointed at one end than the other, for example eggs of hawks (*Accipiter*).

short-wing: a falconry term for a hawk (*Accipiter*); *cf.* long-wing, round-wing.

shoulder girdle: the pectoral girdle, the skeletal elements associated with the forelimbs: the coracoids, clavicles, and scapulae; *cf.* pelvic girdle.

shoveler: a common name of some large-billed dabbling ducks, e.g. Northern Shoveler (*Anas clypeata*).

SI: abbr. of International System of Units from the French name *Système International d'Unités*, the modern form of the metric system and the most widely used system of units.

sibe: jargon among European bird ringers for a Siberian subspecies.

Sibley and Ahlquist system: a taxonomic listing of the birds of the world based on systematic relationships determined by DNA hybridisation; *cf.* Wetmore system, Voous system.

siblicide: the killing of a sibling. Not uncommon among nestling birds, best known in some raptors (Accipitridae), in some species/populations of which it is almost invariable that the oldest in the brood kills the other(s); in such cases also called cainism; *cf.* brood reduction, hatching asynchrony, fratricide.

sibling species: two or more species that are morphologically very similar, often sympatric, but not interbreeding; *cf.* sister species.

sic: Latin, meaning in this manner; added in parentheses when an author uses a quotation containing an error, in order to show that he/she is aware of the error.

sickles: the sickle-like elongated central tail feathers of some birds; *cf.* streamers.

sifting: a foraging technique in which a bird sweeps its open bill from side to side in water to sieve small animals and plants; *cf.* sweeping.

sigmoid: s-shaped.

sigmoidal growth curve: the typical growth pattern of a chick, in being slow initially, then more rapid, and finally slow again, so that a graph of size over time will be sigmoid; many other things may grow in a sigmoidal fashion, e.g. the size of a population starting at a very low level.

sign: any indication of the previous presence of a bird; e.g. droppings, food remains, pellets, moulted feathers; *cf.* track.

signal: 1) a call, posture, or plumage display that communicates something to another individual. 2) a quality-indicating trait such as the long tail of many male birds or the black badge of a male House Sparrow (*Passer domesticus*); *cf.* cues.

sign test: a nonparametric statistical test for a trend based on paired samples of 'before' and 'after' scores, respectively. Comparison of these samples gives one sample of ups and downs (plusses and minuses), which is tested for deviation from a random pattern.

signed-ranks test: a statistical test similar to, but more powerful than, the sign test, because it takes the size of the recorded differences into account.

significance: in the statistical sense a statement of our confidence that a difference between samples reflects a real difference between populations, and not merely a sampling accident. The statement is usually accompanied by a 'level' (*P*-value), the probability that the difference was accidental (or an upper limit of this probability).

Silurian: the geological period of approx. 440-400 million years BP in the Palaeozoic era.

simultaneous polyandry: the mating system in which a female mates with more than one male during a single breeding attempt; *cf.* polyandry, sequential polyandry.

Simurg; a fabulous bird that replaced the Senmurv of Persia.

Sindbis virus: a mosquito-transferred alpha virus *Alphavirus* (Togaviridae), occurring in passerine birds, in which it causes self-limiting febrile viral disease; may also infect humans. Sudden onset of fever, rash, arthralgia or arthritis, lassitude, headache, and myalgia; rash may precede or follow joint manifestations by 1-2 days; exanthem on trunk progressing to face, legs, palm, and soles, and lasts on average 10 days; signs of jaundice and myocardial damage are reported but rare; often no recognized clinical disease manifestations.

sine loco: Latin meaning without a place.

single-brooded: having only one clutch each year, as opposed to multi-brooded.

singular breeding: communal breeding, with only one female actually breeding per group.

singularis: Latin = single.

sink habitat: an area in which the death rate exceeds the birth rate, the opposite of a source habitat; *cf.* core area.

sink population: a population that is only maintained through immigration from neighbouring populations; as opposed to an established population called a source population.

sink rate: the downward speed of a glider, e.g. a gliding bird.

sino-atrial node: a group of cells in the heart functioning as a pacemaker.

Sinornis: a sparrow-sized fossil enantiornithine ('opposite') bird from the Early Cretaceous, found in China.

sinuate or **sinuated**: a feather that has one edge appearing as if cut away along a wavy line.

sinus: 1) any of several air-filled cavities in the skull bones around the nasal cavity. 2) any of various irregular venous or lymphatic cavities. 3) an infected tract from a deep-seated infection, discharging pus.

sinusitis: inflammation of the membrane lining of a sinus, causing watery discharges from the eyes and nostrils.

sinusoidal waveform: cyclically varying function, usually of time, in the strictest sence restricted to any functions of the form $y(t) = A\sin(at+b)$.

sinusoids: 1) sinusoidal waveforms. 2) or liver capillaries.

sister lineage: the most closely related lineage to the one under consideration, whatever the taxonomic or evolutionary level.

sister species: e.g. a pair of species that are the closest relatives of each other, having a common ancestor not shared with any other species. Also called **sister taxa** or species pair.

site: a place.

site fidelity: the habit of returning to the same breeding area each year. Also called **site tenacious;** *cf.* philopatric.

Sitta: 1) periodical of the Stazione Italiana per la Ricerca Ornitologica, Italy, since 1987, published in English and Italian. 2) the scientific name for a nuthatch genus.

skein: a flying flock of geese; *cf.* gaggle.

skeletal muscle: any muscle that moves bone. Also called voluntary muscle; *cf.* smooth muscle, cardiac muscle.

skerry: a marine islet or rock.

skin: 1) a stuffed but unmounted specimen of a bird. Also known as study skin. 2) animal hide, consisting of the outer epidermis and the underlying dermis.

skulking behaviour: moving around within dense cover, difficult to get a view of.

skull: all the bones of the head; see: articular, cranium, dentary, ectethmoid, exoccipital, frontals, hinge, interorbital septum, jugal bone, lacrymal bones, lower mandible, maxilla, maxillary bones, nasal, orbit, otic, palate, parasphenoid, parietals, postorbital, premaxilla, pterygoids, quadrate bone, quadratojugal, squamosal bone, supraoccipital, surangular, upper mandible, vomer, and zygomatic process.

skulling: a way to asses the age of live passerines in the autumn using the degree of skull ossification as seen through the skin.

skull ossification: the roof of the skull of a young bird has only one layer of bone, but soon a second layer is grown, the two layers are connected with bone pillars, and the space between them becomes filled with air (pneumatized). While the second layer is growing, the areas with only one layer remaining are transparent and popularly called 'windows', which allow rather accurate age determination in many songbirds (oscine Passeriformes). In a live bird one can see through the translucent skin and the skull looks white on an adult bird and dark pink on a young bird. Also called skull pneumatization (after the second step of the process); *cf.* pneumatic skeleton.

slimness index: a curious index, defined as the wing chord multiplied by the tail length.

slope soaring: soaring in air rising at the windward side of a slope. A special case occurs when petrels (Procellariidae) and other oceanic birds soar along an ocean wave, in which the slope itself is moving. Also called static soaring; *cf.* thermal soaring.

slots: the gaps between flight feathers (e.g. typical of vultures) that enhance lift, and hence reduce the stalling speed. Mainly seen in large, heavy landbirds, facilitating take-off, landing, and soaring in thermals.

slotting: the spreading of flight feathers so that slots are created.

small intestine: the part of the intestine between the gizzard and the large intestine, consisting of the U-shaped duodenum and the long and coiled jejunum and ileum; *cf.* large intestine.

smoke bathing: birds may perch within smoke and perform bathing movements, possibly as a means of displacing external parasites.

smooth muscle: muscle not consciously controlled, as occur in the alimentary, circulatory, respiratory, and urogenital systems; *cf.* skeletal muscle, cardiac muscle.

snarling: close mobbing attacks as performed by flycatchers of the genus *Ficedula* in mobbing a woodpecker (Picidae).

snood: the fleshy appendage that projects from the bill of a Wild Turkey (*Meleagris gallopavo*).

soaring: gliding flight in which a bird stays aloft and gains height by using rising air in thermals or along slopes; *cf.* slope soaring, thermal soaring.

sociability: gregariousness.

social: living together with conspecifics, in contrast to being solitary.

social behaviour: communicative behaviour such as vocalization and courtship, as opposed to self-maintenance behaviour. Much behaviour may, however, be a mixture of both.

social facilitation: enhancement of the behaviour of one individual through the presence and behaviour of others; e.g. the opening of milk bottle tops learned by tits.

social hierarchy: the social order among members of a flock-living species. Also called dominance hierarchy, peck or pecking order, rank order.

social monogamy: the mating system in which the sexes associate in pairs and rear chicks together (at least for the season), but may or may not partake in extra-pair copulations; *cf.* sexual monogamy.

social selection: selection that acts on traits that serve in behavioural interactions between individuals.

Sociedad Española de Ornitologica: abbr. SEO. A Spanish society that has published *Ardeola* since 1954.

Société d'Etudes Ornithologiques: a French society that has published *Alauda* since 1929.

Société Ornithologique de France: published *Oiseaux*, 1920-1928, continued as *L'Oiseau et la Revue Française d'Ornithologie* since 1929.

Societé Romande pour l'Etude et al Protection des Oiseaux: based in Switzerland, has published *Nos Oiseaux* since 1947.

society: a gathering of individuals, a flock or an association.

Society for the Promotion of Nature Conservation: founded in 1912 with headquarters in Nettleham in Lincolnshire, UK. Publishes *Conservation Review*. Formerly called the Society for the Promotion of Nature Reserves.

Society for the Protection of Birds: founded in 1889 in UK, now the Royal Society for the Protection of Birds; has published *RSPB Conservation Review* since 1987.

sociobiology: the systematic study of social behaviour in the context of the biology of an animal.

soft-billed bird: a bird that feeds on fruit and insects, e.g. a thrush or a warbler; *cf.* hard-billed bird.

soft parts: the areas of a bird without feathers, that is the naked areas on the head or neck, bill, eye surroundings, legs, and feet, now more correctly called bare parts.

solar plexus: a aggregation of nerve cells and fibres situated between the stomach and spine near the kidneys; distributes nerves to the abdominal organs.

Solitaire: an extinct bird (*Pezophaps solitaria*) of Rodriguez Island. A related species may have inhabited Réunion Island; *cf.* Dodo, Raphidae.

solitarius: Latin meaning single, alone, by itself.

Solnhofen Lithographic Limestone: upper Jurassic deposit covering an area of 70 by 30km north of Munich in Germany, attaining a thickness of up to 95m. Famous for its extraordinarily well preserved fossils, not least those of the oldest known bird, *Archaeopteryx*.

soma: the body of a plant or animal as a whole except the sex cells.

somatic cell: any cell other than a sex (germ) cell; *cf.* germline.

somatostatin: a growth-inhibiting hormone produced by the hypothalamus; *cf.* somatotropin.

somatotropin: a growth hormone, a protein hormone of about 190 amino acids that is synthesized and secreted by cells called somatotrophs in the anterior pituitary. It is a major participant in control of several complex physiological processes, including growth and metabolism.

sonagraph: a machine that makes sonagrams; also called sonograph, sound spectrograph.

sonagram: a graph depicting vocalizations or other sounds, generally showing time along the horizontal axis and frequency along the vertical axis, with intensity indicated by darkness of shading. Also called sonogram, spectrogram; *cf.* melogram, oscillograph.

sonar orientation: short-distance orientation by use of echolocation as, e.g. swiftlets (Apodidae).

song: species specific, often fairly long and complex vocalization given by a high number of bird species in connection with the establishment and maintenance of a territory, and/or with pair-formation; may be given by both sexes, but in most species by the male alone; *cf.* call.

songbird: any member of the oscines, the true songbirds (Passeres) in the order Passeriformes.

song neighborhood: an area in which neighbours adopt similar songs, so that a distinct local dialect is produced.

sonogram: a graph depicting vocalizations or other sounds, generally showing time along the horizontal axis and frequency along the vertical axis, with intensity indicated by darkness of shading. Also called sonagram, spectrogram; *cf.* melogram, oscillograph.

sound spectrograph: syn. of sonagraph.

source habitat: an area in which the birth rate exceeds the death rate so that the area is a net exporter of individuals; the opposite of a sink habitat; *cf.* core area.

source population: population producing a surplus of offspring, the emigration of which supplies immigrants to other areas and populations; *cf.* sink-population.

sour crop: disease caused by mycotic (fungal) infection of the digestive tract. A life-threatening disorder usually confined to baby birds in which the crop stops emptying and becomes distended with fermenting food and fluids. One of the most common complications of hand rearing. Found in geese, genus *Anser*, pheasants (Phasianidae), pigeons (Columbidae), and parrots (Psittacidae). Also called candidiasis, moniliasis, oidiomycosis, or thrush infection.

South African Ornithological Society: abbr. SAOS, has published *Ostrich* since 1930.

Southeast Asia: the geographical area (sometimes used in a zoogeographical sense) comprising the Andaman Islands, Myanmar, Thailand, Laos, Vietnam, Cambodia, southernmost China including Taiwan and Hainan, Malaysia, Brunei, Indonesia, and the Philippines.

Southern Marine region: a faunal region encompassing all waters south of 35°S, well known for its penguins (Spheniscidae) and albatrosses (Diomedeidae); *cf.* Tropical Marine region, Northern Marine region.

Southern Ocean: the ocean between Antarctica and the southern tips of Africa, Australia, and South America.

southern oscillation: full name El Niño Southern Oscillation (ENSO), phenomenon recurring irregularly at 4-6 year intervals on average, causing widespread disturbance of oceanic surface currents and temperatures, and of weather patterns of adjacent land masses. Mainly known from the South Pacific and Indian Oceans, although effects are probably global; *cf.* La Niña.

Southwestern Oak Woodland: one of nine North American ecological divisions or biotic communities, situated in southwestern USA.

spacing: dispersal behaviour and the dispersion of individuals mediated by intraspecific interactions such as territoriality.

spangles: conspicuous contrasting glossy, typically iridescent spots, formed by fusion of barbs, e.g. found on the plumage of the Scale-feathered Malkoha (*Phaenicophaeus cumingi*) and the Spangled Drongo (*Dicrurus bracteatus*).

spatial learning: the learning of the location of, e.g. food and other objects.

spatulate: shovel- or spoon-shaped.

Spearman's rank correlation: a specific way of quantifying the concordance between two rankings of the objects/individuals of a set. The resulting number, Spearman's rank correlation coefficient, is akin to a normal correlation coefficient, and its statistical significance can be tested by use of a specific test.

specialist feeder: an animal eating only one or a few different sorts of food, in contrast to a generalist feeder.

speciation: the process by which two populations differentiate and become two distinct species, most often as a result of genetic divergence in isolated populations; cf. natural selection.

species: key concept in biology, and at the same time a taxonomic rank. According to the biological species concept (Mayr 1994), a species is 'a group of actually or potentially interbreeding populations or organisms which are reproductively isolated in nature from other such groups'. The species is the primary unit in biological classifications.

species border: the distributional limit of a species; often, although fluctuating back and forth, such borders remain dynamically stable.

species concept: the meaning or definition of the word 'species'; several have been formulated, with differing implications for the science of biology; see biological species concept (emphasising reproductive isolation), phylogenetic species concept (emphasising morphological difference), evolutionary species concept (emphasising evolutionary origins), ecological species concept (emphasising ecology), phenetic species concept (emphasising morphological similarity), and recognition species concept (emphasising behaviour).

species nova: abbr. *sp. nov.* or *sp. n.,* Latin = new species; more rarely encountered as *nov. sp.,* or *nova species.*

species pair: loose term, often meaning a pair of species that are the closest relatives of each other, having a common ancestor not shared with any other species; i.e. a pair of sister species.

species replacement: in ecology, the replacement of one species across geographic space although the apparent realized niche remains the same; in evolution, the change occurring when one species goes extinct and a new one develops and replaces it.

specific name: the second part of the scientific name, referring to the species; cf. generic name, subspecific name.

spectacles: Am. term to describe a combination of a contrasting eye ring and supra-loral stripe and/or postocular line, giving the appearance of a bird wearing spectacles, as, e.g. the Spectacled Duck (*Speculanas specularis*).

spectrogram: a graph depicting vocalizations or other sounds, generally showing time on the horizontal axis and frequency on the vertical axis, with intensity indicated by darkness of shading. Also called sonagram or sonogram; cf. melogram, oscillograph.

spectrometer: an optical instrument used to measure properties of light over a specific portion of the electromagnetic spectrum. The variable measured is most often the light's intensity but could also, for instance, be the polarization state. Also called spectrophotometer.

spectrophotometer: an instrument used to measure colours, also called spectrometer or reflectance spectrophotometer.

speculum: pl. specula, a contrasting, often iridescent, area on a duck's wing; also called mirror.

sperm: male germ cell, in almost all vertebrates motile with a head and a propulsive tail. Also called spermatozoon.

spermatid: haploid germ cell that matures into a spermatozoon without further cell divisions.

spermatocyte: an immature germ cell which, during meiosis, gives rise to spermatids and spermatozoa; during the first meiotic division a diploid, primary spermatocyte, becomes two haploid, secondary spermatocytes, and in the second meiotic division these give rise to four spermatids.

spermatogenesis: the formation of spermatozoa.

spermatogonium: pl. spermatogonia, diploid germ cell which, eventually, gives rise to a primary spermatocyte.

spermatozoon: pl. spermatozoa, male germ cell, in almost all vertebrates motile with a head and a propulsive tail. Also called sperm.

sperm competition: the competition (for fertilising an egg) between sperm from different males having inseminated the same female during a single breeding episode; usually used in a wider sense that includes the entire behavioural repertoires of both sexes that influences the outcome of the competition.

spermiducts: the epididymis and vas deferens together.

spermophagous: seed-eating.

sperm storage tubules: organ in which female birds can store sperm for up to two months after insemination, situated near the junction of the shell gland with the vagina.

Sphenisciformes: order comprising the 17 species of penguins (Spheniscidae).

sphenoid: bone forming part of the cranial floor in birds.

spherical: round like a sphere or ball.

sphincter muscle: 1) a muscle forming a ring around an opening that it closes when contracted. 2) a muscle that can change the direction of the blood stream; *cf.* countercurrent heat exchange system..

spider fly: a member of the family Hippoboscidae, flattened ectoparasitic flies with a leathery surface and well-developed claws, mostly wingless at least after having settled on a host. Also called birdfly, feather-fly, flat-fly, hippoboscid fly, ked-fly, louse-fly, or tick-fly; *cf.* ectoparasites.

spiking: the removal of parasitic eggs by puncturing them with the bill and then removing them from the nest, also called puncture ejection.

spinal column: or vertebral column, the skeletal axis consisting of the vertebrae of the neck, chest, loin, hip, and tail region, in birds 40-60 in total, with most variation in the neck region.

spinal cord: the bundle of nerve fibres running from brain to body in a channel formed by the vertebrae; *cf.* lumbosacral plexus.

spinal nerves: paired nerves from the spinal cord.

spinal tract: the feather tract from the base of the skull dorsally to the base of the tail. Also called dorsal tract; *cf.* pterylography.

spine: 1) ridge formed by the bony projections from the dorsal surface of the vertebrae, particularly well developed in the fused thoracic vertebrae. 2) the backbone or vertebral column. 3) rarely, the shaft of a feather. 4) sometimes a syn. for barbicel.

spinifex: an inland Australian habitat of coarse, tussock-like grasses of the genus *Triodia,* more correctly called porcupine grasses (spinifex is a coastal grass, *Spinifex hirsutus*); *cf.* Spinifex Pigeon (*Geophaps plumifera*).

spinous process: projection from the dorsal surface of a vertebra in birds, particularly well developed in the fused thoracic vertebrae. Also called spine.

spirochaetosis: a bacterial blood infection of vertebrates, in birds transmitted mainly by blood-sucking ticks. Also called **spirochaete infection.**

Spiruroidea: a large group of endoparasitic roundworms in birds, parasitizing different parts of thc body.

spishing: a birdwatcher's term for calling up owls or bringing in birds of any other sort by repeated squeaks made by sucking or blowing air through teeth and/or pursed lips. Also called squeaking, or pishing.

splashed: of an egg with many large, dark spots.

spleen: an organ of the immune system, composed of lymphoid tissue and located between the gizzard and liver. It is the main source of lymphocytes and also removes old erythrocytes and foreign bodies from the blood; *cf.* T-cell.

splitter: a taxonomist who tends to emphasize differences and hence to split populations into many different taxa (genera, species, or subspecies) on the basis of fine distinctions; as opposed to a lumper.

spongy: porous and, sometimes, malleable; also called spongious.

sport: avicultural term for an aberrant or mutant bird.

spot-mapping: plotting the location of birds recorded during repeated counts on a map to obtain detailed information about density, habitat preference, etc.

spotted: of an egg with many pigmented spots evenly distributed over the whole surface.

spotting scope: a compact telescope, usually with magnification power between 15× and 60×.

spring: vernacular name for a flock of Teal (*Anas crecca*) taking flight. May also be applied to other small dabbling ducks with a nearly vertical take-off into flight.

spur: a sharp, bony projection on leg or carpal joint, found, e.g. in pheasants (Phasianidae) and the Spur-winged Plover (*Vanellus spinosus*).

spurius: Latin, meaning false.

squab: a nestling of a pigeon or dove (Columbidae); *cf.* squeaker.

squamate: of a feather looking like a scale.

squamosal bone: paired bone of the skull situated at the posterior end of the orbits.

squared-change parsimony: a statistical method for reconstructing ancestral character states while minimizing the sum of squared changes along the branches of a phylogenetic tree, producing the same estimates as methods used in independent contrasts.

square tail: a tail in which all feathers are of about the same length; *cf.* forked tail, streamers.

squeaker: 1) nestling pigeon or dove (Columbidae); *cf.* squab. 2) alternative name for the Grey Currawong (*Strepera versicolor*) of the family Cracticidae.

squeaking: Am. for spishing, a birdwatcher's term for calling up owls or songbirds by repeated squeaks made by sucking or blowing air through teeth and/or pursed lips.

SSCP techniques: single strand conformation polymorphism (SSCP) techniques represent a method based on gel electrophoresis for the separation of homologous, denatured, amplified DNA fragments by exploiting their differences in secondary structure.

stable isotope analysis: determining the ratios of stable isotopes of common elements in biological materials, often used in vertebrates to ascertain or infer food sources (e.g. marine, terrestrial), geographic points of growth (e.g. feather moult), or of natal or wintering sites in migratory organisms. Commonly used elements include carbon, nitrogen, and hydrogen, and the natural isotopic ratios of these elements, which vary geographically, are incorporated into tissues during growth.

staffelmauser: German term adopted in English for wing moult in which a new cycle starts before the last has finished, resulting in two active moult centres. Also called serially descendent moult, continuous stepwise moult; *cf.* transilient moult and alternating moult.

staging ground: a place for resting and/or feeding during migration. Also termed **staging post,** stopover site.

stalling: the loss of lift experienced by a glider (such as a gliding bird, or a powered or unpowered aircraft) going too slow, i.e. having too low an airspeed.

standard deviation: abbr. SD, a statistic quantifying the dispersion of a set of observations about the mean; equal to the positive square root of the variance, the latter being the mean of squared deviations.

standard error: abbr. SE, generally used for standard error of the mean, in which case the SE resembles the standard deviation (SD); but while the SD is a measure of the variation among sample values - the width of the distribution - the SE is a measure of the accuracy by which the sample mean approximates the unknown population mean.

standard metabolic rate: abbr. SMR, the metabolic rate (energy requirement per time) of a resting organism, measured under standardized conditions; similar to the basal metabolic rate (BMR) of homeotherms, but because no thermoneutral zone exists for a poikilotherm, the choice of temperature is not obvious; instead the temperature is chosen by some convention and must generally be given together with the result.

stand-in bathing: bathing behaviour of a bird, ruffling its feathers, flicking its wings, spreading its tail, and dipping its head into the water and letting the water run over the body; *cf.* flight-bathing, in-out bathing, plunge-bathing, rain-bathing, stand-out bathing, swim-bathing.

stand-out bathing: bathing behaviour of a bird, splashing about at the edge of a pond; *cf.* flight-bathing, in-out bathing, plunge-bathing, rain-bathing, stand-in bathing, and swim-bathing.

stapes: the small bone in the ear, also called columella auris.

staphylococcal infection: a bacterial infection causing swollen joints.

star compass: of birds, the ability to orient by use of stars in the sky. Planetarium experiments have confirmed this ability; *cf.* magnetic, olfactory, sun compass, vector orientation.

star-gazing: in pathology, grotesque attitudes caused by a brain tumour.

starring: the formation of the first cracks in the shell of an egg about to hatch. Also called pipping or chipping.

starvation mark: a narrow, often translucent, transverse band found in individual feathers of birds, e.g. common in crows (Corvidae), as a result of physical stress during the feather's growth, e.g. through handling by humans. It is the result of abnormally formed or missing barbules that weaken feathers, making breakage more likely. Most often called fault bar, but also hunger streak, hunger fault, hunger trace, feather mark, starvation mark, subordinate bar, or by veterinarians stress band. When formed as spots called fault spot or fault hole.

stasis: 1) in evolution, the apparent lack of major evolutionary change over long periods of time, e.g. in fossil records. 2) interruption in growth or development.

static pressure: the inwardly directed force on the surface of any object submerged in a fluid (air or liquid), produced by random motion of the molecules of the fluid; *cf.* dynamic pressure.

statant cup nest: a nest built on top of a hard support.

static soaring: normal soaring without wing flapping, because rising warm air enables the bird to use it to gain height; *cf.* soaring, obstruction currents, dynamic soaring flight.

statistical significance: a concept treating the mathematical probability that an observation or set of observations is not different from another set of observations (or from a random condition, e.g. a null model). This probability is compared against an *a priori* threshold value to determine whether a genuine difference exists. Low probability values (P) indicate an unlikelihood of, e.g. two samples coming from the same population, and under a commonly used threshold value of $\alpha = 0.05$, P-values of < 0.05 are taken to indicate that the null hypothesis of sameness should be rejected, i.e., that there is a > 95% probability that they did not come from the same population and thus that statistically significant differences exist between the two samples being compared.

statistical testing: determining the mathematical probability that a given hypothesis explains a set of data, e.g. determining the probability that two sets of data come from the same population, or that a set of observations comes from a distribution having certain characteristics. The result of the test is given in terms of statistical significance.

statoconia: crystals made of calcium carbonate embedded in a gelatinous-like material in the inner ear.

Stazione Italiana per la Ricerca Ornitologica: an Italian ornithological research station. Has published *Sitta* since 1987.

stem material: distinguished as fine woody plant stems, regardless of species, provided they are less than about 2mm in diameter and are flexible.

steno-: prefix from Greek *stenos*, meaning narrow.

stenoecious: having a narrow habitat preference, the opposite of euryoecious.

stenophagous: having a limited diet with one or few food types, i.e. being a food specialist, **stenophagy**; *cf.* monophagous, euryphagous.

stenotopic: syn. of stenoecious, **stenotopy**.

stenozonal: being restricted to a narrow range of altitudes, as opposed to euryzonal.

steppe: semi-arid grassland without trees, especially common at mid-latitudes in interior parts of continents; mainly applied to Eurasian grassland, the usual term for similar habitats in North America being prairie, in South America pampas, in South Africa veld, etc.

stepwise migration: a term for birds making many stopovers on the migration route.

stepwise moult: moult in which some wing feathers are being moulted during any month of the year. Also called serially descendent moult, continuous stepwise moult; *cf.* transilient moult, alternating moult.

stepwise regression: variant of multiple regression in which the factors are included (step-up) or excluded (step-down) successively, so that they can be ranked from the most to the least important.

stereotyped: of behaviour performed with little variation, irrespective of the specific situation or the releasing stimuli.

sternal: pertaining to the breastbone (sternum).

sternal notch: the vacant spaces or 'windows' at the posterior end of the breastbone (sternum). Also called fenestra; *cf.* metasternum.

sternal rib: the lower segment of the rib, nearest the breastbone. Also called ventral rib segment; *cf.* vertebral rib, false rib.

sternocostal process: where a rib unites with the sternum.

sternotrachealis: muscle complex that controls the vibration of membranes in the syrinx.

sternum: the breastbone. In all flying birds except tinamous (Tinamidae) the breastbone has a keel; *cf.* carina, posterolateral process, metasternum, fenestra, costal facets, rostrum, coracoidal facets.

steroid: any of a large group of lipids, examples include the bile acids, cholesterol, various sex hormones, and adrenal cortical hormones; *cf.* protein, peptide.

stick posture: a cryptic posture that makes a bird looks like an extension of a stub or branch, seen in, e.g. frogmouths (Podargidae).

stigma: 1) a mature egg (ovum). 2) the tip of the pistil in flowers, which receives the pollen.

stimulus: anything that produces a response, such as a sound or a movement, an approaching animal, the sight of food, etc.

stint: a small sandpiper of the genus *Calidris*; synonymous with 'peep' in Am.

stochastic: of anything involving randomness, such as a process the outcome of which to some extent depends on chance; *cf.* environment stochasticity.

stochastic effects: effects of factors outside the control of the experimentalist, or of factors not considered by the observer, and therefore appearing as added, stochastic or random 'noise' in the results or observations; often used synonymously with random effects.

stomach: the proventriculus and the gizzard, together constituting the ventriculus.

stomach oil: oily liquid with which most procellariiform seabirds feed their chicks; also regurgitated in self defence, both by chicks and adults.

stool pigeon: a captive live pigeon used to lure wild ones to where they can be caught.

stoop: 1) a steep aerial dive by a falcon, in a hunting or in courtship. 2) a dive by a bird, e.g. when harassing an intruder.

stopover ecology: study of the ecology of migrants at stopover sites, e.g. feeding, fattening, habitat selection, territoriality, etc.

stopover site: any area used for resting and/or feeding during migration.

storey: Am. **story**, a level of the forest, e.g. understorey; *cf.* canopy.

straggler: 1) a bird species that occurs only rarely in any particular area (i.e. as a vagrant). 2) any individual that is clearly behind its fellows, e.g. behind in a flock or family group, notably late in migration, etc.

strategy: in a biological or evolutionary sense, a life history trait that a species has evolved in maximizing its fitness.

stratification: 1) vertical grouping within a community, social stratification, for example, is the dividing of a society into levels based on hierarchical arrangement. 2) the vertical aggregation of horizontal layers of substrate used in geology, paleontology, and archaeology to denote positions of, e.g. mineral layers, fossils, and objects, respectively.

stratum corneum: the outermost layer of the epidermis.

stratum germinativum: the innermost layer of the epidermis.

stray: a vagrant or straggler. A bird outside its normal range.

Stray Feathers: an ornithological periodical for India and its dependencies, published 1873-1888 with an index 1899, edited by Allan Hume.

streaked: of an egg with many streaks and lines.

streamers: greatly elongated and ribbon-like tail feathers as found in, e.g. in tropicbirds (Phaethontidae), some rollers (Coraciidae) and bee-eaters (Meropidae), and many swallows (Hirundinidae); *cf.* forked tail, square tail.

stress: undue strain upon a bird from external influences; e.g. extreme cold weather, noise, over-population, harassment, etc.

stress band: a veterinarian's term for a narrow, often translucent, transverse band found in individual feathers of birds, e.g. common in crows (Corvidae) as a result of physical stress during the feather's growth, e.g. through handling by humans. It is the result of abnormally formed or missing barbules that weaken feathers, making breakage more likely. Most commonly called fault bar, but also hunger streak, hunger fault, hunger trace, feather mark, starvation mark, and subordinate bar. When formed as spots called fault spot or fault hole.

stressors: stress factors.

striated: streaked.

Stricklandian Code, The: the first Code (named after Hugh E. Strickland), adopted in 1842 by the British Association for the Advancement of Science, and soon thereafter by similar bodies in other countries; *cf.* Code.

Strigiformes: order comprising 15 species of barn owls (Tytonidae) and 180 species of owls (Strigidae).

strip census: counting birds along lines of fixed width (transects); also called line transect, **strip transect**.

Strongyloidea: endoparasitic group of roundworms, for example those living under the horny coat of the gizzard in geese, the gapeworms of poultry, and a strongyle living in grouse (Tetraoninae) and other birds.

structural colours: colours resulting from microscopic feather structure that cause diffraction and scattering rather than absorption and reflection of light; responsible for most white, blues, and purples in bird plumage. The two main types of structural colour are iridescent and non-iridescent, the former being caused by structures compromising the mechanical strength of feathers and therefore rarely found in wing feathers. In contrast to iridescent colours, non-iridescent colours do not change with the angle of light. Also termed schemochromes.

Struthioniformes: order comprising the Ostrich (Struthionidae), two rhea species (Rheidae), three emu species (Dromaiidae), three cassowary species (Casuariidae), and three kiwi species (Apterygidae), and in addition two extinct families, the Elephant Bird (Aepyornithidae), and the moas (Dinornithidae). Some authorities place most of these families in separate orders, leaving the Ostrich (*Struthio camelus*) as the order's sole member.

strutting ground: the display area of the Sage Grouse (*Centrocercus urophasianus*).

stuck-in-the-moult: an aviculturist's term for a prolonged moult.

studbook: in captive breeding, book containing all data of the relevant individuals, e.g. date of birth, parents, siblings, date of last moult, disease, etc.

Studies in Avian Biology: an occasional publication of the Cooper Ornithological Society since 1978.

study skin: unmounted bird or mammal skin stuffed for scientific use, prepared in a position like a dead animal and without glass eyes but with an attached label for associated data. Also called museum skin or cabinet skin.

stupefying bait: a chemical that stupefies birds, used in the control of bird pests.

Stymphalian Bird: a fabulous man-eating bird with arrow-like feathers.

sub-: prefix from Latin *sub* meaning under, beneath, lesser.

subadult: 1) the last distinctive plumage before the full adult, or an immature bird actively moulting into adult plumage. 2) a synonym of immature (which may itself have different meanings).

subantarctic: of oceans and islands in the cooler parts of the southern hemisphere, roughly between the Subtropical Convergence and the Antarctic Convergence.

subbasal: toward or near the base (e.g. a subbasal band on the tail).

subcanopy: the midstorey level of the canopy of a forest.

subclass: the taxonomic level between class and infraclass. All recent birds belong to the subclass Neornithes.

subclinical: of infection, when no clinical symptoms are yet manifested.

subcutaneous: being or happening under the skin, e.g. subcutaneous fat, subcutaneous injection.

subcutaneous emphysema: air trapped under the skin.

sub-eclipse plumage: a third annual plumage worn by a few birds, e.g. ptarmigans (*Lagopus*) in the family Phasianidae, in addition to the normal two. Also called supplemental (supplementary) plumage.

subelliptical: applied to an ovoid shape, e.g. an egg, that has one end slightlymore pointed than the other end; *cf*. elliptical, oval, and pyriform.

subfamily: the taxonomic level between family and genus with the name ending in -inae.

subfossil: skeletons that have not been mineralised; *cf*. fossil.

subgenus: pl. subgenera, the taxonomic level between genus and species.

subhumerals: under wing coverts covering the bases of the humerals; also called axilaries.

sub-lingual pouch: a small area of expandable skin under the tongue in some birds, distendable into a pouch and used to carry food; found, for example, in nutcrackers (*Nucifraga* spp.) and some finches (Fringillidae).

submarginal: situated near the edge or margin.

sub-moustachial stripe: a streak from the base of the bill backwards or downwards, between the moustachial and malar stripes.

suborbital patch: a patch of contrasting colour located immediately below the eye.

suborder: taxonomic level between order and infraorder.

subordinate: an individual other than the dominant one in a group or the less dominant of two contesting individuals.

subordinate bar: a narrow, often translucent, transverse band found in individual feathers of birds, e.g. common in crows (Corvidae) as a result of physical stress during the feather's growth, e.g. through handling by humans. It is the result of abnormally formed or missing barbules that weaken feathers, making breakage more likely. Most commonly called fault bar, but also hunger streak, hunger fault, hunger trace, feather mark, starvation mark, and by veterinarians stress bands. When formed as spots called fault spot or fault holes.

suboscine (sub-oscine) bird: any passeriform bird not belonging to the Oscines (songbirds). The 'group' is comprised of many Neotropical families: Furnariidae, Dendrocolaptidae, Thamnophilidae, Formicariidae, Rhinocryptidae, Cotingidae, Pipridae, and Tyrannidae, the Old World families Eurylaimidae (including Philepittidae), and Pittidae and the Australasian families Acanthisittidae, Atrichornithidae, and Menuridae. Sometimes considered the suborder Tyranni.

sub-precocial: of downy chicks able to move about, but fed by the parents; e.g. as in grebes (Podicipedidae), rails (Rallidae), and cranes (Gruidae); *cf.* super-precocial.

subsong: a loose, often rambling, softly-delivered song that is audible within only a few meters; also the first, helpless and unstructured song of a young bird.

subspecies (sub-species): abbr. ssp., pl. sspp., one or more populations being morphologically distinct from other populations considered to belong to the same species, for example because interbreeding is possible (and perhaps occurs) between the individuals; such subspecies of a given species are distributed over largely separate distributional ranges. One proposed standard for defining a subspecies is the '75% rule', stating that 75% of the specimens of a valid subspecies must be identifiable. Scientifically, a subspecies is named by adding a third name (the trinomial) to the scientific genus and species name. Subspecies should not be confused with morphs, which generally are variants of sympatric animals in a single trait only (often colour), governed by one or very few genes. Also called race and, historically, varieties; *cf.* cline, trinominal nomenclature.

subspecific name: the third scientific name, if existing (e.g. if we are looking at a trinomen); *cf.* generic name, specific name.

substrate: 1) a surface, e.g. one to which prey clings and on which a bird forages. 2) the substance transformed by an enzyme.

subterminal: near the end, e.g. near the tip of the tail.

subtribe: the taxonomic level between tribe and genus.

succession: the change of a habitat over time, especially after a radical disturbance (e.g. earth slide, fire, or clearcutting of forest).

succulent: of a water-storing plant adapted to dry conditions.

sucrase: an enzyme breaking down sucrose into two monosaccharides.

sucrose: a disaccharide sugar.

suffix: pl. suffixes, terminal addition to the stem of a word, such as -idae in a family name.

suffused: tinged, tinted, or washed with a colour, e.g. the common rose suffusion of the otherwise white underparts of a Black-headed Gull (*Larus ridibundus*).

sulcus: groove, furrow, e.g. along the bill of albatrosses (Diomedeidae) and some petrels (Procellariidae).

sun compass: figuratively, the adaptations making it possible for diurnal migrants to navigate by the sun, also called azimuth compass; *cf.* magnetic, olfactory, or star compass, vector navigation.

Sundas: the Indonesian islands that are part of the Oriental faunal region. May be divided into Greater Sundas (Borneo, Sumatra, Java, Sulawesi) and Lesser Sundas (Bali, Lombok, Sumbawa, Sumba, Flores, Timor, and many small islands).

Sundiac region: the zoogeographical region comprising the Malay Peninsula, the Greater Sundas, and Palawan.

sunning: behaviour associated with feather care, in which a bird spreads its wings and tail and exposes them to sunlight; may have an antiparasitic function; also called sun exposure, sun-bathing; *cf.* anting, dusting.

super-: prefix from Latin *super* meaning above, greater than.

superciliary stripe: a line from above the lores back over the eye, the eyebrow; *cf.* eye stripe.

superfamily: the taxonomic level between infraorder and family with the name ending in -oidea.

superior: Latin = upper.

superorder: the taxonomic level between class and order.

super-precocial: of hatchlings that are totally independent of their parents such as those of the megapodes (Megapodiidae) and the brood-parasitic Black-headed Duck (*Heteronetta atricapilla*); *cf.* sub-precocial.

superspecies: a closely related group of largely allopatric species, too distinct to be considered subspecies but more closely related mutually than to other species of the same genus or subgenus; *cf.* semispecies, allospecies, paraspecies, sympatric species.

supination: backward rotation; *cf.* pronation.

supplanting: a form of attack in which one bird approaches and displaces another.

supplemental (supplementary) plumage: a third annual plumage worn by a few birds, e.g. ptarmigan (*Lagopus*) in the family Phasianidae, in addition to the normal two. Also called sub-eclipse plumage.

supra-: prefix from Latin *supra* meaning above.

supracoracoideus: the inner breast muscle (under the pectoralis muscle), responsible for raising the wing; *cf.* pectoralis muscle. Also called **supracoracoid muscle**.

supracoracoid foramen: the opening between the three bones, the clavicle, scapula, and coracoid, through which the tendon from the major elevator of the wing (the supracoracoideus) passes to the humerus. Also called foramen triosseum or triosseal canal.

supra-loral: situated over the lores; also spelled **supraloral**.

supraoccipital bone: a paired bone located above the eye orbits.

supraorbital glands: salt-excreting glands situated in grooves above the orbits of the skull in many saltwater birds; other marine birds also have salt glands, located elsewhere in the head.

supraorbital ridge: a fold over the eye in many birds of prey (Accipitridae).

suprarenal glands: paired, composite glands located at the anterior end of the kidney, the cortex producing steroid hormones (including various androgens and oestrogens), and the medulla producing catecholamines (epinephrine, norepinephrine). Also called adrenal glands.

supraspecies: a group of species derived from the same ancestor that replace each other geographically and are too distinct morphologically to be regarded as forming a single species. Also called mega-superspecies or second order superspecies; *cf.* subspecies, species.

surangular: a paired bone of the lower jaw.

surface diving: diving from a swimming position as seen in divers (Gaviidae), grebes (Podicipedidae), cormorants (Phalacrocoracidae), and some ducks (Anatidae).

surface-to-volume ratio: the surface area of the body divided by its volume. Smaller birds have higher metabolic rates than larger birds, partly because they lose relatively more heat due to their higher surface-to-volume ratios.

surreptitious behaviour: behaviour carried out surreptitiously, such as using indirect routes when returning to the nest, sneaking back, or pretending to look for food.

survival: the process of staying alive.

survival rate: the proportion of individuals in a population that survive for a particular length of time.

suspended moult: moult that is temporarily interrupted due to food shortage or during migration; *cf.* arrested moult.

sustainable development: development using natural resources and ecosystems in a way that meets present needs without compromising future ones.

suture: 1) connection of two bones so that they cannot move relative to one another, in contrast to articulation; *cf.* symphysis. 2) the stitching of a wound.

suture zone: a band of geographical overlap between major biotic assemblages.

Sveriges Ornitologiska Förening: abbr. SOF. The Swedish Ornithological Society. Has published *Vår Fågelvärld* since 1942.

sweating: an aviculturist's term for a chick born with salmonellosis and therefore small and weak.

sweeping: a foraging technique in which avocets (*Recurvirostra*) and some other birds sweep their bills through water.

swim-bathing: bathing when swimming on the water surface, as seen in ducks; *cf.* flight-bathing, in-out bathing, plunge-bathing, rain-bathing, stand-in bathing, stand-out bathing.

Sylvia: periodical of the Czech Society for Ornithology, founded in 1936; publishes papers in Czech and English. Name taken from the genus name of some sylviid warblers.

sym-: prefix from Greek *syn* meaning with.

symbiosis: close association between two species, both of which are profiting from the relationship, as for example the African oxpeckers (*Buphagus* spp.) and the large mammals from which they remove ectoparasites; *cf.* cleaning symbiosis, mutualism, obligatory mutualism.

sympathetic neuron: one of two main types of neurons in the autonomic nervous system; *cf.* parasympathetic nervous system.

sympathetic nerves: one of two categories of autonomic nerves (nerves originating in ganglia outside the central nervous system); sympathetic ganglia are arranged in two regular chains, one on each side of the vertebral column in the thoracic and lumbar regions; *cf.* parasympathetic nerves.

sympatric speciation: speciation into two reproductively isolated species between populations with overlapping geographic distributions.

sympatry: the condition that different populations or species share the same geographical area, or have overlapping ranges (although they may not necessarily occur in the same type of habitat), adj. **sympatric**; *cf.* allopatric, parapatric.

symphysis: union of bones by fusion, cartilage, or ligament; *cf.* suture.

symplesiomorphy: a 'primitive' (plesiomorphic) character shared by two or more taxa and understood to have been possessed by an ancestor; *cf.* apomorphy, homoplasy, plesiomorphy, synapomorphy, adj. **symplesiomorphic**.

syn.: abbr. Latin *synonymon* = synonym.

syn-: prefix from Greek *syn* meaning joined (in space of time) or with.

synanthropic: living close to human habitations, also called eusynanthropous, the opposite of exanthropic.

synapomorphy: apomorphy (specialized or derived character) shared by two or more taxa and therefore likely to have been present in their most recent common ancestor; *cf.* apomorphy, homoplasy, plesiomorphy, and symplesiomorphy.

synaposematic: of aposematic (warning) patterns or colours shared with other species, also called aposematic.

synapse: point at which the axon of an upstream nerve cell makes contact with a downstream nerve cell and communicates with it by releasing chemical mediators (neurotransmitters).

synchronic: simultaneous, living or happening at the same period, the opposite of allochronic.

synchronous hatching: simultaneous hatching of all eggs of a clutch, in practice within a 24-hour period; as opposed to asynchronous hatching. Synchronous hatching occurs when incubation is delayed until the last egg is laid.

syndactyl: a bird's foot in which two or all three of the forward-directed toes are fused for part of their length, as in kingfishers (Alcedinidae) and hornbills (Bucerotidae), adj. **syndactylous**.

syndrome: a complex of symptoms characteristic of a particular disease.

synecology: the ecology of animal communities.

synonym: an alternative taxonomic name for a taxon that is not valid for technical reasons, often because another name has priority; adj. **synonymous**; *cf.* homonym.

synonymy: the list of scientific names considered by an author to have been used historically to represent a given taxon, but which are subsumed by the name by which it is now recognised.

synonymum novum: abbr. syn. nov., from Latin = a new synonym.

synovial joint: a freely movable joint between two bones, enclosed by a membrane of connective tissue so that a closed cavity is formed, this being filled with a viscous fluid.

synsacrum: pl. synsacra, a bone in the dorsal pelvis, formed by the fusion of thoracic, lumbar, sacral, and caudal vertebrae, the number of vertebrae varying (9-22) in birds. Also called lumbosacrum.

synspecies: a morphologically differentiated taxon that is genetically and reproductively isolated.

synthetic theory of evolution: synthesis of Darwin's theory of evolution by natural selection with knowledge later acquired, especially from the field of genetics.

syntopic: of two or more populations or species occurring in the same habitat and in the same area, allowing the opportunity for interbreeding; *cf.* sympatric.

syntype: in taxonomy, if the first description and naming of a taxon was based on a series of specimens, these are all called syntypes, unless a particular one has expressly been designated as the type specimen (holotype); *cf.* lectotype, neotype, paratype, protype, pseudotype, topotype.

syringeal: of the syrinx.

syringeal muscles: the muscles of the syrinx that enable it to produce and modulate sounds.

syringitis: inflammation of the syrinx.

syrinx: pl. syringes, the vocal organ of a bird, situated where the trachea bifurcates into the bronchi; *cf.* bulla, labia, pessulus, tympaniform membrane.

Systema Naturae Regnum Animale: by Linnaeus; the 10th edition (1758) is chosen as the starting point for modern zoological nomenclature.

systematics: the study of evolutionary relationships; according to Ernst Mayr, systematics is the scientific study of the diversity of organisms and their relationships, and taxonomy is the theory and practice of classifying organisms into taxa; *cf.* phylogeny.

systemic circulation: the major part of the circulatory system, which carries blood from the heart to the body and back again (the lungs and heart have their own, separate systems, the pulmonary and cardiac circulations).

T

T$_a$: ambient temperature.

tactile: pertaining to the sense of touch.

taiga: northern coniferous forest from arctic tundra to more temperate forest types across North America and Eurasia, often referred to as the boreal zone or northern boreal forest.

tail feather: one of the large feathers on the tail; most birds have 12, also called rectrix, pl. rectrices.

tail coverts: the feathers covering the base of the tail on both upper- and undersides. In the adult male Indian Peafowl (*Pavo cristatus*) the upper tail coverts are extremely elongated and are most often erroneously referred to as the 'tail'.

tail-index: tail length multiplied by 100 and divided by wing length.

talon: a strongly curved claw used by many predatory birds to seize and to kill prey.

talon-grappling: (two flying birds) interlocking feet, a common behaviour in display or contest of many accipitriform raptors.

Tapestry, the: common name of the results of Sibley and Ahlquist's DNA-DNA hybridization experiments to reconstruct the phylogenetic relationships among the birds of the world as they were displayed at the 1986 International Ornithological Congress in a 10m long poster.

tapetum: a layer of light-reflecting lipid droplets behind the retina in some nocturnal animals, giving the reflected light a second chance to trigger a receptor; makes eyes shine when externally lit, e.g. by vehicle headlights. Present in many families of most vertebrate classes, but among birds unique to nightjars (Caprimulgiformes) and allies.

tapeworm: an endoparasitic segmented flatworm of the class Cestoda; many species parasitize birds.

taphonomy; the study of environmental changes to organic remains after death, e.g. scavenging, weathering, and fossilization.

tarsometatarsal: pertaining to the tarsometatarsus or 'tarsus' for short.

tarsometatarsus: 'tarsus' for short, the bone consisting of fused tarsals and metatarsals and together with the toes comprising the avian foot. Sometimes called the lower leg or shank.

tarsus: pl. tarsi, shortened form of tarsometatarsus.

tassel foot: a pathological condition of the foot showing enlarged scales that can be broken off in flattened flakes; *cf.* knemidocoptic mange.

taste receptors: sensory cells (chemoreceptors), mainly in the roof of the mouth; four types are together responsible for the experience of sweet, salt, sour, and bitter taste impressions; together with supporting cells grouped in organs called **taste buds**.

tautonymy: when the scientific genus and species name are identical, as in *Grus grus* (Common Crane).

taxaspidean: of a tarsus that anteriorly is covered by large scales, posteriorly by small scales, also called pycnaspidean; *cf.* endaspidean, exaspidean, holaspidean, ocreate.

taxidermy: the stuffing or skinning of vertebrates, usually used in terms of mounting animals for exhibit; the person doing the work is a **taxidermist**.

taxis: 1) an organism's movement towards or away from a source of stimulation. 2) an orient behaviour related to a directional stimulus.

taxon: pl. taxa, any group of organisms and irrespective of taxonomic rank. Often used when discussing multiple taxonomic ranks or when there is doubt as to whether some populations are species or subspecies, in the latter context also termed a form.

taxon cycle: the different stages a taxon may pass through during its evolution, such as range expansion, local adaptation (anagenesis), and range contraction.

taxonomist: one who practises the classification and naming of animals (taxonomy).

taxonomy: 'the theory and practice of classifying organisms into taxa'. Often, inaccurately, considered synonymous with systematics, which is better defined as 'the scientific study of the diversity of organisms and their relationship' (Mayr 1969); *cf.* phylogeny.

T_b: minimum body temperature.

T-cell: type of white blood cell also called T-lymphocyte, part of the immune system; two main subtypes exist, helper and killer T-cells; while produced in the bone marrow like other blood cells, T-cells differentiate in the spleen; *cf.* B-cell, memory cell, spleen.

technical name: the same as scientific name, an internationally agreed upon name given according to strict rules so as to avoid any ambiguity. Often called Latin name, but may also be of Greek or other origin, usually with a latinised ending.

tectorial membrane: a membrane in the inner ear, with sensory hair cells, *cf.* utriculus.

tectrix: pl. tectrices, flight feather covert, each supporting the base of a specific primary (greater primary coverts or, simply, primary coverts) or secondary (greater secondary coverts). Also includes tail coverts.

telencephalon: the anterior part of the forebrain with the olfactory lobes.

teleoptile: feather in the plumage of an adult bird; *cf.* neossoptile, protoptile.

temporal canthus: the posterior corner of the eye in which the eyelids come together; *cf.* nasal canthus.

temporal region: the sides of the forehead.

temporal separation: separation in time, e.g. of different species occupying the same or similar ecological niches but breeding at different periods of the year, or of species that use the same resource at different times.

temporary parasites: parasites that briefly visit hosts; e.g. mosquitoes and leeches, to suck blood; *cf.* facultative parasites, obligate parasites.

tendon: band or sheet of connective tissue joining a muscle to a bone, in bird limbs sometimes ossified, Latin *tendo*; *cf.* ligament.

Tengmalm's Owl: Eur. name for Am. Boreal Owl (*Aegolius funereus*).

Tengus: a fabulous bird of Japan.

Teratornis: an extinct genus of bird from the last ice age; a species in Argentina had a wingspan of 8m.

terminal: at the end, e.g. a terminal band on the tail.

termitarium: a nest structure of termites.

terra firma: Latin = firm land.

terra incognita: Latin meaning unknown land.

terrestrial bird: a land bird, in contrast to an aquatic bird.

territory: an area defended against conspecific intruders (or other species) by means of display, advertisement, or overt aggression, used for breeding and/or feeding; some species also have a winter or a roosting territory; *cf.* home range, feeding territory.

tertials: the innermost secondaries (three in passerines), often differing in colour from the other secondaries. True **tertiaries**, with their bases on the distal end of the humerus (upper arm), are found only in long-winged birds such as albatrosses (Diomedeidae).

Tertiary: a geological period from approx. 65 million to 1.6 million years ago, comprising five epochs: the Palaeocene, Eocene, Oligocene, Miocene, and Pliocene. Most of the major divisions of modern birds apparently arose during this period.

tertiary sex ratio (sex-ratio): the sex ratio at adulthood; *cf.* sex ratio, primary sex ratio, secondary sex ratio.

testa: 1) the mainly chalky part of an egg shell upon which colour is laid down. 2) the coat of a seed; *cf.* cuticle.

testis: pl. testes, the male paired gonads, in birds situated in front of the anterior lobe of the kidney; testicles is largely a mammalian term; *cf.* seminiferous tubules, sertoli cells.

testosterone the male sex hormone secreted mainly by the testes; *cf.* oestrogen.

tetrachromatic: a four-cone colour vision; *cf.* dichromatic, trichromatic.

Tetrapoda: all four-legged vertebrates (inclusive of other vertebrates having four-legged ancestors).

thalamus: pl. thalami, part of the forebrain, functions in the transmission of sensory information; *cf.* epithalamus, hypothalamus, diencephalon.

thecodonts: assemblage of early archosaurs, mainly from the Triassic.

thelytoky: obligate parthenogenesis in which females produce female progeny without fertilization.

theory: a set of ideas generally accepted by the scientific community because of it is supported by substantial evidence and has withstood numerous critical tests; e.g. Darwin's theory of evolution by natural selection; *cf.* hypothesis.

thermal conductivity: the property of a material in conducting heat; feather down has very low thermal conductivity, while metals have high thermal conductivity.

thermal soaring: gliding flight that exploits thermal columns of warm air that rise at places where the earth is heated by the sun, thermals are usually of limited size, so to keep within them the rising birds will circle around their center until they leave them and continue in normal gliding flight, loosing height to keep up a steady speed. Many birds may soar, but the behaviour is especially common in large, heavy species, often with emarginated primaries and slotted wingtips, such as vultures, buzzards, and eagles (Cathartidae & Accipitridae), and storks (Ciconiidae), etc.; *cf.* slope soaring.

thermogenic homeostasis: an animal maintaining the same body temperature.

thermoneutral zone: temperature interval within which a given homeothermic animal does not need to generate heat to keep its body temperature at the normal level, heat produced by general metabolism being sufficient; the metabolism of the animal therefore does not change with temperature, as long as this is kept within the thermoneutral zone.

thermoreceptor: a sense organ (Ruffini ending) that responds to temperature stimuli.

thermoregulation: the maintenance of normal body temperature in a warm blooded (homeothermic) animal; cf. homeothermic, poikilothermic.

theropod: any member of Theropoda, the generally bipedal carnivorous dinosaurs that, together with Sauropodomorpha, constitute the Saurischia, one of two major lineages of dinosaurs (the other being Ornithischia). Birds were the only theropods, and dinosaurs, to survive the transition from the Cretaceous to the Tertiary period.

threatened: a conservation term for a species that is declining, but not so much that it is endangered.

thick-knee: another name for stone-curlews (family Burhinidae).

thigh: typically refers to the feathered part of the tibia or femur.

thoracic: pertaining to the breast (thorax) region of the body.

thoracic air sacs: paired thin-walled sacs in the thoracic part of the body, part of the avian respiratory system; cf. air sacs.

thoracic rib: a rib fastened to one of the synsacrum vertebra (on the pelvis), instead of the dorsal vertebrae, and often lacking a sternum segment.

thoracic vertebra: any vertebra in the rib cage with their facets for rib articulation.

thorax: the part of the body between the neck and belly containing, e.g. the lungs and the heart; adj. thoracic.

thorny-headed worm: any member of the phylum Acanthocephala, endoparasitic worms in the digestive tract of vertebrates, anchored to the gut wall by recurved hooks in the head region.

threadworm: a roundworm of the genus *Capillaria*, all members of which are endoparasites in the alimentary canal of vertebrates; length 10-80 mm.

threshold: the minimum level of a stimulus necessary to trigger a response.

throat: the area between chin and breast; cf. gular pouch, jugulum.

thrombocytes: tiny blood cells found in vertebrates other than mammals, in which they are represented by the blood platelets. Involved in blood clotting.

thrush infection: a mycotic infection of the digestive tract of geese, pheasants, pigeons, and parrots. If resulting in disease, this is called candidiasis, moniliasis, oidiomycosis, or sour crop.

thrust: the forward force created by flapping flight, as opposed to drag.

thymus gland: one or more endocrine glands on each side of the neck, often formed as a long row of fat-coloured lobes or pearls along the neck. Working in the immune system of young birds but can occur in adult birds.

thyroid gland: a paired endocrine gland situated close to the syrinx and producing thyroxin, responsible for heat production in adults and thought to control moult and to affect the reproductive system; also interacts with the hypothalamus; cf. goitre, parathyroid glands.

thyroxin: a hormone containing iodine produced in the thyroid glands; increases the metabolic rate of most tissues and also appears to play a role in moult and reproduction.

tibia: pl. tibiae, the lower part of the leg between the knee and the foot (tarsometatarsus and toes); also called tibiotarsus or drumstick; cf. fibula, thigh

tibial cartilage: cartilage at the joint between the tibiotarsus and tarsus.

tibialis anticus: a leg muscle on the tibiotarsus. Also called **tibialis anterior**.

tibiotarsal rete: a heat exchange system in the tibiotarsus; *cf.* rete mirabile, sphincter muscles.

tibiotarsus: the lower part of the leg between the knee and the foot (tarsus), often abbreviated tibia, also called drumstick; *cf.* fibula, thigh.

tick: ectoparasitic mite, the word being used exclusively of the family Ixodidae, whose members may cause eye diseases and blindness and are vectors for pathogens causing, e.g. Lyme disease; *cf.* mites, lice, louseflies.

tickbirds: another name for oxpeckers (Buphaginae).

ticker: a person that seeks to see and record as many bird species as possible and at least figuratively ticks them off in list, also called **tick-hunter**; twitcher.

tick fly: a member of the family Hippoboscidae, flattened ectoparasitic flies with a leathery surface and well-developed claws, mostly wingless at least after having settled on a host. Also called birdfly, feather-fly, flat-fly, hippoboscid fly, ked-fly, louse-fly, and spider-fly; *cf.* ectoparasites.

tidbitting: 1) a form of courtship feeding in the domestic fowl (*Gallus domesticus),* in which a male scratches up soil for a female. 2) parental behaviour toward precocial chicks, in which parents tempt chicks to feed by pecking the earth or by calling.

tidal flat: a flat area exposed at low tide and covered by water at high tide, usually being a muddy or sandy substrate commonly used by birds for feeding.

tidal marsh: a coastal marsh strongly affected by tidal flows, typically muddy, dominated by grassy vegetation, and usually a highly productive ecosystem.

tide pool: a depression in the intertidal zone that retains water at low tide.

tiercel: a falconry term for a male Peregrine Falcon (*Falco peregrinus).*

time budget: how a bird allocates its time to different activities.

time-synchroniser: 1) environmental stimulus for periodic biological activity, e.g. rain in Australia that stimulates breeding. Also called proximate factor or zeitgeber; *cf.* ultimate factor. 2) or a biological clock that causes migration to cease when the migrating bird has arrived upon the winter or breeding ground.

Tinamiformes: order comprising 47 species of tinamous (Tinamidae).

tinged: suffused with a particular colour or shade. Also called washed.

tippet: a structure formed by elongated head feathers, e.g. of some grebes (Podicipedidae).

tipping of balance: the enhancement of a water body with nutrients such as nitrates, phosphates, and other fertilizers resulting in an overproduction of algae, the decomposition of which uses so much oxygen that all aerobic life below the surface dies out, also called eutrophication, overthrow, or capsizing.

T-lymphocyte: a type of white blood cell also called T-cell, part of the immune system with two main subtypes, helper and killer T-cells; they are produced in the bone marrow and differentiate in the spleen; *cf.* B-cell, memory cell, spleen.

tobogganing: a method of propelling the body across ice and snow, used by penguins when they lie on their bellies and push with their feet.

tomium: pl. tomia, the cutting edges of the bill. Also called upper or lower mandibular tomia.

tomial tooth: a notch in the cutting edge of the upper mandible of a falcon or a shrike, used to kill prey.

tongue: the appendage in the mouth used to manipulate food; see: basibranchial, basihyal, ceratobranchial, entoglossal, epibranchial, glossohyal, glossa.

tonus fibres: slowly contracting muscle fibres, in contrast to twitch fibres.

topography: 1) in ornithology, the various parts of a bird's exterior, its 'geography'. 2) land forms or the study of them.

topotype: a specimen collected later than the type specimen but at the same locality.

top predator: the last link in the food chain.

Tori: the periodical of the Ornithological Society of Japican.

torpor: an energy-conserving state of a homeotherm animal, with radically reduced but regulated body temperature; the torpid animal can easily be roused to normal activity; widespread in hummingbirds (Trochilidae). Also called **torpidity**. Distinction of this term remains controversial, but a pronounced decrease in body temperature for less than 24 hrs. seem adequate; *cf.* hypothermia, hibernation, rest-phase hypothermia, controlled rest-phase hyperthermia.

Torresian Fauna: the tropical and subtropical fauna of northern Australia; *cf.* Bassian Fauna, Eyrean Fauna.

totipalmate foot: a foot with all four toes connected by a web, e.g. in cormorants, gannets, and pelicans (Pelicaniformes); *cf.* palmate, semipalmate, lobate.

toxication: poisoning.

toxic chemicals: poisons, including chemicals spread by man in the environment.

trabecula: pl. trabeculae, a bar or bundle of fibers serving as connective tissue, e.g. within organs, or microscopic columnar structures in the core of bone such as upper mandibles.

trace element: an element necessary for normal activity and growth of an organism, but in small quantities only.

trachea: the wind-pipe of cartilaginous rings; originates behind the mouth (larynx) and ends near the lungs, where it divides into the primary bronchi.

tracheal bulla: a bony enlargement of the trachea just where it divides into the two primary bronchi; modifies the sounds produced by the syrinx. Also called bulla ossea or, simply, bulla. Found in some ducks (Anatidae).

tracheal pit: a hollow area between the two clavicle bones forming the furcula, often examined to determine overall fat deposits in live birds, because fat here correlates with total body mass and with fat depositions in other body parts; in ringing literature often termed furculum.

tracheal syrinx: a syrinx in which the membranes and intrinsic muscles are located anterior to the tracheo-bronchial junction. Found in antbirds Thamnophilidae and ovenbirds Formicariidae; *cf.* bronchial syrinx, tracheobronchial syrinx.

tracheobronchial syrinx: a syrinx in which the membranes and intrinsic muscles are located at both sides of the tracheo-bronchial junction, the most common arrangement; *cf.* tracheal syrinx, bronchial syrinx.

track(s): 1) marks left by birds, e.g. foot marks in a substrate. 2) the path of a flying bird over the surface of Earth; *cf.* sign.

tracts: bundles of axons in the central nervous system; *cf.* white matter.

tradeoff: a compromise between two strategies, the value of which depends on cost-benefit considerations, e.g. the tradeoff between rapid early growth, to avoid predation, and slower growth to avoid premature death because growing quickly is costly since tissues may not be developed at full strength, or the tradeoff between feeding, which causes increased exposure to predation, and remaining hidden from predators, which causes hunger.

traffic accident: an animal killed by a vehicle. Also called a road kill.

trailing edge: 1) the posterior or hind edge of the wing (and thus of the flight feathers), as opposed to the leading edge. 2) or the inner and wider part of the web of a single flightfeather.

train: 1) the upper tail coverts of an adult peafowl male (*Pavo*). 2) a falconry term for a raptor's tail.

transect: a line along which birds are counted using the transect method; *cf.* line transect, belt transect, strip transect.

transequatorial: crossing the equator, e.g. in annual migration.

transformational evolution: a gradual change in an organism over time from one condition into another, usually combined with invariable change from 'lower' to 'higher', or from less perfect to more perfect; *cf.* Lamarckism, saltational evolution, variational evolution.

transient: a passage migrant, a migrating bird that neither breeds nor winters in the area in question.

transilient moult: flight feather replacement that proceeds by forward or backward leaps across one or more adjoining quills. A feather is only moulted if there is a full-grown feather, new or old, on each side of it. The centres of moult activity are identical in most individuals of a species, and the distance of leaps is genetically controlled. Only known in some cuckoo species (Cuculidae).

transitional migrants: birds that occur in a geographical area on migration (i.e. do not breed or over-winter). Also called passage migrant.

Transition Zone: one of the six life zones in North America that is transcontinental and is divided between the eastern humid divison, Alleghanian, and western arid and humid zone called Arid- and Humid Transition.

translocation: moving individuals to a new area, e.g. to renew populations where they have declined or been extirpated, or to conduct oriented experiments (e.g. homing pigeons).

transponder: an electronic device placed, e.g. under the skin of an animal and coded to give a specific answer when prompted by a powered sensor placed close by. Also called passive integrated transponder, abbr. PIT.

transverse plane: a vertical plane dividing the body into a cranial (anterior) and a caudal (posterior) part.

transverse processes: pairs of lateral processes on vertebrae in birds near the vertebrarterial canal.

transversus: Latin = lying across, crosswise, transverse.

traplining: a method of foraging used by some hummingbirds (Trochilidae) that feed along a regularly repeated route.

tread: a verb used when a male mounts and then copulates with, or treads, a female.

tread feather: syn. of filoplume.

treadworm: any member of the phylum Nematomorpha, which are long, thin worms parasitic in arthropods while young but free-living as adults; more commonly called hairworm.

tree: 1) a perennial plant with a woody stem that grows to a substantial height. 2) a cladogram or phylogram depicting the branching sequence in a phylogeny.

treeline: the latitude or elevation above which trees cannot grow.

Trematoda: flukes, a class of endoparasitic flatworms; primary hosts (hosts of the adult parasites) are vertebrates, including birds, whereas the intermediate hosts are invertebrates, often snails. Formerly, a group of ectoparasites on fish were treated as a subclass within Trematoda ('monogeneid trematods'), but the two groups are now believed to be unrelated.

trespass: a bird entering or passing through an established territory occupied by a conspecific that is not its mate is a trespasser; *cf.* floater.

Triassic: the geologic period of approx. 245-208 million years BP, the first period of the Mesozoic era. Climatologically one of the hottest periods in the world's history.

tribe: the taxonomic category between subfamily and genus with the name ending in -ini.

triceps brachii: a wing muscle that extends the forearm, situated atop the humerus.

Trichinella: a genus of endoparasitic nematods (roundworms).

trichomonad: a flagellated parasitic protozoon of the genus *Trichomonas*, for example *T. gallinae*, transmitted by adult pigeons in their crop milk. Also transmitted to raptors through their prey.

trichomoniasis: a protozoan infection causing creamy white necrotic material in the mouth, pharynx, inner nares, and oesophagus. Young pigeons may die from the infection. Also called diphtheria, frounce, or dove disease.

Trichoptera: caddisflies, an order of insects with two pairs of hairy wings. The aquatic larvae build a protective case of various materials.

trichoptile: a hair-like feather found on newly hatched nestlings.

trichromatic: of three-cone colour vision; *cf.* dichromatic, tetrachromatic.

tridactylous: having only three toes as, e.g. the Sanderling (*Calidris alba*).

trigeminal nerve: a cranial nerve with both motor and sensory components.

trill: a vocalization formed as a fast repetition of similar notes; e.g. as uttered by the Little Grebe (*Tachybaptus ruficollis*).

trinomial (trinominal) nomenclature: scientific naming using three names; each subspecies of any species having recognized subspecies receives a third name, appended to the binomial name of the species; *cf.* binomial nomenclature, scientific name.

triosseal canal: a canal formed where the coracoid, clavicle, and scapula meet, and through which the tendon from the supracoracoideus muscle (wing raiser) passes before becoming attached to the dorsal side of the humerus. Also called supracoracoid foramen or foramen triosseum.

trip: a flock of Dotterels (*Charadrius morinellus*).

trituration: the grinding of food in the gizzard.

triumph ceremony: a pair-bonding display that is typically performed by a mated pair following the successful displacement of an intruder (the display often including raised wings and neck and simultaneously loud calls); seen e.g. by swans, genus *Cygnus*.

trivial name: a vernacular or common name.

trochanter: a process on the proximal end of the thigh bone (femur).

trochlea: a process on the distal end of the tarsometatarsus.

trochlear nerve: a nerve that controls one eye muscle; *cf.* oculomotor muscles.

Trogoniformes: the order comprising 39 species of trogons and quetzals, family Trogonidae.

trophic: pertaining to feeding.

trophic level: ecological generalisation of the step-wise progression from primary producer (e.g. algae, plants) to higher levels in the food chain (e.g. primary, secondary, etc. consumers), roughly enumerating the links of the energy stored in the biomass of an organism through chemical bonds in the process of photosynthesis. Meat eaters thus reside at higher trophic levels than plant eaters.

tropics: the geographical region between the tropic of Cancer and the tropic of Capricorn.

Tropical Marine region: a faunal region encompassing all waters between 35°N and 35°S. A nutrient-poor body of water, among ornithologists known for its tropicbirds (Phaethontidae), frigatebirds (Fregatidae), and boobies (Sulidae); *cf.* Northern Marine region, Southern Marine region.

tropic of Cancer: the parallel of latitude at 23º26′ N, the northernmost latitude where the sun will ever culminate at zenith.

tropic of Capricorn: the parallel of latitude at 23º26′ S, the southernmost latitude where the sun will ever culminate at zenith.

troposphere: the stratum of the atmosphere appr. 6-10 km above sea level.

trousers: the elongated feathers on the thighs, e.g. of a raptor.

truncated: abruptly terminated or cut off.

trunk: the body.

trypanosomes: parasitic, flagellate protozoans, some species infecting the blood of birds where they may cause symptoms; if so the disease is called **trypanosomiasis**.

tsunami: long, low wave (or series of waves) caused by an earthquake; may build up to considerable height when reaching shelf and coastal waters and cause enormous destruction when hitting a coast.

***t*-test**: in statistics, a commonly used test that compares the means of two samples assumed to come from normally distributed populations. Based on Student's *t*-distribution, which also appears in several other tests.

tubenoses: collective name for all members of the order Procellariiformes, referring to the tubular nostrils found in this group.

tuberculosis, avian: a common bacterial disease (*Mycobacterium*), in birds causing lesions of the spleen, liver, and gut; *cf.* pseudo-tuberculosis

Tubinares: an outdated syn. of Procellariiformes.

tumbunum: the subtropical rainforest of eastern Australia and montane New Guinea; *cf.* Bassian, Eyrean, Irian, and Torresian.

tuft: a group of elongated feathers on the crown of a bird's head, which in some species may be raised or lowered, more often called a crest.

tumour: Am. **tumor**, a swelling caused by abnormal cell proliferation; *cf.* benign tumour, malignant tumour.

tundra: the low, treeless vegetation found atop permafrost at high latitudes and elevations, e.g. an ecotone in the Arctic north of the coniferous forest biomes; a habitat dominated by small shrubs, forbs, mosses, and lichens, and lacking trees. Also one of North America's nine ecological divisions or biotic communities.

tunica vasculosa bulbi: a vascular layer inside the eyeball made up of three parts, the choroidea, corpus ciliare, and iris.

turacin: a complex red, copper-bearing pigment known only in feathers of turacos (Musophagidae). Also called uroporphyrin III.

turacoverdin: a complex green copper-bearing pigment known in Crested Wood Partridge (*Rollulus roulroul*), Blood Pheasant (*Ithaginis cruentus*), and turacos (Musophagidae).

turbinates: turbinal cartilage, concha; three scroll- or spiral-shaped cartilaginous lamellae (bony in mammals) in the nasal cavity, covered by mucous membranes that trap dust and warm inflowing air.

turbulence: a disorderly flow of air or water.

turdid: a member of, or belonging to, the thrush family (Turdidae).

turlough: an Irish term for a temporary limestone lake that contains water only during wet periods.

Turnagridae: an historically extinct family comprising a single species, the New Zealand Thrush or Piopio (*Turnagra capensis*).

turnover: the rate of replacement.

tussock grassland: grassland dominated by tussock-forming grasses, e.g. found in New Zealand, Australia and many subantarctic islands.

twitcher: a person who seeks to see and record many bird species; adj. **twitching**. Also called lister, ticker, tickhunter, or birder.

twitch fibres: muscle fibres that contract rapidly, opposite tonus fibres.

tympanic membrane: a membrane in a hearing organ, for example the eardrum of tetrapods.

tympaniform membrane: a sound-producing membrane in the syrinx.

Tyndall scattering: scattering of light caused by microscopic particles suspended in a fluid, or microscopic air bubbles in a matrix such as the keratin of a feather. The sky is blue because of this phenomenon.

typ.: abbr. of Latin *typus* = type. The individual bird (usually a specimen) upon which a species description and formal name are based; *cf.* type specimen.

typ. cons.: abbr. of Latin *typus conservandus* = conserved type of taxonomic nomenclatural usage.

type I error: in statistics, when the null hypothesis is rejected when it is in fact true.

type II error: in statistics, when the null hypothesis is not rejected when it is in fact false.

type locality: the place where the type specimen was collected.

type species: the species that is chosen to represent and define a genus or subgenus.

type specimen: the specimen on which the original description of the species (subspecies) was based, also called holotype; *cf.* lectotype, paratype, neotype, syntype, and topotype.

typhoid: another name for salmonellosis.

typological species concept: the concept of a species as a group of individuals that conforms to a type, or common morphology, considering these groups as essentially static and invariable; a non-evolutionary concept prevalent among pre-Darwinian taxonomists that recognised natural units as created entities without subsequent change; *cf.* biological species concept.

tyrosinase: an enzyme that helps to produce melanin.

U

ulcer: open, infected area on skin or mucous membrane with underlying tissue exposed.

ulna: the posterior and thicker forearm bone to which the secondaries are attached; *cf.* radius.

ulnare: bone of the wrist (carpal joint) at the terminal end of the ulna; *cf.* radiale, carpal.

ulnimetacarpalis ventralis: a muscle between the ulna and radius of the wing.

ultimate factor: the basal factor (selective or environmental), such as peak of food availability, to which a trait (such as timing of breeding) is adapted in the evolutionary sense, although the actual releaser may be something else (such as day length). Also called **ultimate cause**; *cf.* proximate factor.

ultimobranchial bodies: a pair of endorcine glands situated below the thyroid glands, secreting calcitonin (which is supposed to be involved in the regulation of calcium metabolism).

ultra-: prefix meaning beyond.

ultrasonic: of sound with frequency too high to be audible to humans (i.e. above 15-20 kHz); such sound is called **ultrasound**; *cf.* infrasound.

ultraviolet colour vision: vision able to detect ultraviolet (UV) light (light with wavelengths below 400 nanometers); birds can see wavelengths down to 300 nanometers; *cf.* carotenoids.

ultraviolet plumage colours: plumage patches reflecting ultraviolet (UV) wavelengths, especially found in regions of the plumage shown during display; *cf.* fluorescent plumage colour.

umbilical cord: in the egg of a bird, a tube between the embryo's gut and the yolk sac.

umbilicus: pl. umbilici, either of the two openings at the basal end of a feather shaft, called inferior and superior umbilicus.

umbrella taxon: in conservation literature, a species or subspecies for which the requirements needed to sustain a viable population are so demanding that if these requirements are met, sufficient habitat is conserved to safeguard a high number of other taxa; *cf.* keystone species.

uncinate: 1) hooked or bent downwards at the tip, such as an uncinate bill. 2) also used for the process midrib that projects to overlap with the next-dorsal rib to increase the rigidity of the ribcage, missing in some taxa. Last-mentioned called **uncinate process**. Latin *uncinatus*.

underbrush: the lowest stratum of the forest above the forest floor.

undergrowth: living ground cover in forest, including bushes and saplings.

underparts: the entire under surface of the body, including chin, throat, breast, belly, flanks, and under tail coverts. Always written in plural; *cf.* upperparts.

understorey: the part of a forest just below the canopy consisting of

shrubs and small trees; *cf.* underbrush.

underwing scratching: performed by a
bird raising its foot directly (i.e. not
over the wing) to scratch its head or
neck. Also called direct scratching; *cf.*
overwing scratching.

undirected song: song produced by a
lone bird in a variety of social contents in which the song is not intended for any particular individual; *cf.*
directed song, subsong.

undulating flight: flight in which flapping phases alternate with gliding; a
type of intermittent flight.

ungual: the terminal phalanx of a digit.

unguis: the nail at the tip of the upper
mandible of ducks, geese, and swans
(Anatidae).

UNDP: abbr. of United Nations Development Programme.

UNEP: abbr. of United Nations Environment Programme.

ungulate: a hoofed, grazing mammal.

uni-: prefix from Latin *unus* meaning
one or single.

uniparental care: care provided by only
one of the parents, as opposed to biparental care.

uniparental reproduction: asexual reproduction or self-fertilization; does
not occur in birds.

uniparous: having only one young in
each brood.

**United Nations Development Pro-
gramme**: abbr.: UNDP, programme
that through a network of 134 country offices, works toward poverty
elimination and environmental re-
generation.

**United States Fish and Wildlife Serv-
ice**: abbr.: USFWS or FWS, a unit
of the United States Department of
the Interior dedicated to management and preservation of wildlife. It
began as the U.S. Commission on
Fish and Fisheries under the Department of Commerce and the Division

of Economic Ornithology and Mam-
malogy under the Department of
Agriculture and took its present form
in 1939.

univariate analysis: an examination or
analysis of just one variable; *cf.* multivariate

univorous: feeding on just one food
source.

unrooted tree: a tree or cladogram
showing relationships among lineages presented without the inclusion or
designation of an outgroup.

unselective rejector: a parasitized host
species that risks removing one of its
own eggs when trying to remove a
brood parasite's egg from its nest,
because it cannot tell the eggs apart;
the opposite of a selective rejector.

upending: dipping the head and fore-
parts in water so that only the hind
part of the body is visible, a common
feeding behaviour in some ducks and
swans.

upland: habitats at some elevation and
so above the lowlands.

Upper Austral Zone: one of six North
American life zones: Arctic, Hudsonian, Canadian, Transition, and
Lower Austral Zone. An older concept than that of biotic communities.

upper beak: the **upper bill**, also called
maxilla or upper jaw.

upper critical temperature: abbr. UCT,
the temperature at which homeotherms start to increase evaporative
cooling by, e.g. panting, usually in
combination with other behaviours
serving to cool the body or avoid
heating it: reducing activity, seeking
shade, bathing, etc.; *cf.* lower critical
temperature, hyperthermia.

upper jaw: the upper bill, also called
upper beak, mandible, or maxilla.

upper mandible: the upper part of the
bill, also called maxilla; *cf.* lower
mandible.

upperparts: the dorsal surface of the body, mantle, back, scapulars, rump, and upper tail coverts, often also including forehead, crown, nape, hind neck, and sometimes also the wing coverts. Always written in plural.

upper umbilicus: the hole at the upper end of the calamus of a feather; *cf.* lower umbilicus.

upwelling: mainly applied to the upwelling of cold oceanic water, resulting in high productivity when water rich in nutrients ascends to the surface where light occurs (photic zone) and photosynthesis takes place.

ureter: paired ducts from the kidney to the cloaca carrying nitrogenous waste.

uricotelic: of animals excreting nitrogen as uric acid such as birds, whereas mammals excrete nitrogen as urea.

uric acid: an organic compound, the nitrogen-containing excretory product of birds.

urina: Latin = urine.

urinary bladder: a sac storing urine, among birds only found in the Ostrich (*Struthio camelus*) and rheas (Rheidae).

urinary system: the paired kidneys and the ureters. Also called the excretory system.

urodeum: part of the cloaca where the ureters and genital ducts empty and the urine is mixed with the feces; *cf.* coprodeum, proctodeum. Also spelled **urodaeum.**

urogenital system: the urinary (excretory) and genital systems combined (they are closely associated in vertebrates, anatomically and embryologically). See: kidney, nephron, ureter, cloaca, coprodeum, urodeum, proctodeum, anus, vent, testis, vas deferens, cloacal protuberance, ovary, oviduct, infundibulum, magnum, isthmus, uterus, vagina.

urohydrosis: the excretion of urinary liquids (and simultaneously defeca-tiong) onto the legs (giving the legs a whitish appearance), used by new world vultures (Cathartidae) and the Marabou Stork (*Leptoptilos crumeniferus*) as a cooling mechanism. Also spelled urohidrosis.

urohyal: a tongue bone posterior to the basihyal bone between the two long and slender united bones. Also called basibranchial; *cf.* hyoid apparatus, basihyal, ceratonranchial, epibranchial.

uroporphyrin III: a complex red, copper-bearing pigment known only in turacos (Musophagidae). Also called turacin.

uropygial glands: the paired glands at the dorsal base of the tail of most birds; lacking in the Ostrich (*Struthio camelus*), emus (Dromaiidae), cassowaries (Casuariidae), and some pigeons (Columbidae), parrots (Psittacidae), and woodpeckers (Picidae); the secretions of these glands have antifungal and antibacterial properties and may also have other functions in connection with feather maintenance; possibly containing an ingredient converted to vitamin D when exposed to sunlight. Also called oil glands, preen glands; *cf.* powder down.

uropygium: the tail bone of birds, formed by the fused terminal caudal vertebrae. Also called pygostyle.

urvogel: from German meaning a very old bird, such as *Archaeopteryx.*

U.S. Biological Survey: the Biological Survey, founded in 1898 as a Division and in 1905 as a Bureau, was the first USA government agency responsible for the biological diversity of the United States; later (1940) became the nucleus of the U.S. Fish and Wildlife Service (USFWS), but the research component was later (1990s) transferred to the U.S. Geological Survey (USGS).

USFWS: abbr. of United States Fish and Wildlife Service;. founded 1939-

40 by the merging of the Bureau of Fisheries and the Bureau of Biological Survey.

uterovaginal junction: the junction of the uterus and vagina where, in some species, sperm storage tubules are situated. Also spelled utero-vaginal junction.

uterus: the part of the oviduct where the egg shell is produced. Also called shell gland; *cf.* infundibulum, magnum, isthmus.

utriculus: a chamber in the inner ear containing sensory follicles; *cf* sacculus.

UV light: ultraviolet light, invisible to the human eye.

V

vacuole: a 'pocket', e.g. a minute air cavity in a feather.

vacuum activity: irrelevant behaviour, for example collecting imaginary nest material where no material is found, owing to a lowered threshold for the release of that particular activity; may happen if, e.g. environmental circumstances have hindered the animal in performing that particular activity for some time. Also termed overflow activity or displacement behaviour.

vagabond: a species in which it is difficult to predict migratory behaviour.

vagility: the ability to actively move from one area to the other, as opposed to sessility; adj. vagile.

vagina: the muscular end of the oviduct that opens into the cloaca.

vagrant: a rare visitor found far beyond its normal geographical range, typically recorded only once or twice in any area in question. Also called stray or accidental.

validity: of a scientific name when it accords with rules given in the International Code of Zoological Nomenclature.

valid name: the correct scientific name for a taxon.

vane: web, the two flat sides of a feather, formed by interlocking barbs attached to the shaft. All flying birds have the outer primary vane narrower than the inner vane.

Vår Fågelvärld: the periodical published by Sveriges Ornitologiska Förening (SOF) in Sweden since 1942.

variable: 1) something that is not static or constant. 2) in mathematics, a term in a formula that is not constant. 3) a statistical term indicating a property measured by individual observations (measurements) of a character. 4) may also be applied to any taxon exhibiting morphological variation.

variance: the square of the standard deviation.

variant: a more or less distinct phenotype occurring in a population, deviating from other such phenotypes (or from the norm in the population).

variation, coefficient of: the standard deviation s divided by the sample mean m, often given as a percentage ($100s/m$ %).

varicocele: an abnormality of spermatic chord veins reducing spermatogenesis, the condition being caused by prior overheating of tissue.

variety: the lowest taxonomic category in the Linnean system. Now only used in botanical works.

vascular system: the circulatory system of arteries, veins, heart, and blood, also including the lymph vessels and nodes plus associated organs (spleen).

vas deferens: pl. vasa deferentia, the spermatic chord or sperm-carrying duct from the testes to the cloaca; also called ductus deferens or deferent ducts; *cf.* cloacal protuberance.

vasectomize: to cut the spermatic chord (vas deferens).

vector: an organism (usually an invertebrate animal) carrying pathogens (e.g. viruses or bacteria) from one host to another.

vector navigation: navigation based on a combination of direction and distance, i.e. the ability to orient in a certain direction and to keep track of the distance travelled in that direction; may involve several stages of different directions and distances; *cf.* magnetic, olfactory, star, and sun compass.

vein: blood vessel that, except in portal systems, conveys blood towards the heart, deoxygenated in the general circulation and oxygenated in the lung circulation, wider than arteries; adj. **venous**; *cf.* artery, capillary.

vena cava: one of the two major (anterior and posterior) veins carrying blood from the body to the right atrium of the heart; also called caval vein.

vent: the external opening of the cloaca.

venter: belly or abdomen, or the whole ventral surface.

ventral: referring to the underparts of the body, as opposed to dorsal. Latin *ventralis*; *cf.* lateral, dorsal.

ventral rib segment: the lower part of a rib nearest the breastbone. Also called sternal rib; *cf.* vertebral rib.

ventral tract: the feather tract on the underside of the neck and body; *cf.* pterylography.

ventricle: 1) either of the two muscular chambers of the heart from which blood is pumped, respectively, to the body in general (the left ventricle) or to the lungs (the right ventricle). 2) a hollow space within an organ; *cf.* atrium.

ventriculus: the gizzard; *cf.* proventriculus.

ventrum: underparts, as opposed to dorsum.

venules: tiny veins.

vermis: pl. vermes, Latin = worm.

vermiculated: of eggs or plumage marked by fine wavy lines, those on feathers often being visible at close range only.

vermivorous: eating worms.

vernacular name: name of an organism in daily use in the local language, in contrast to the scientific name. Also called common name.

vertebra: pl. vertebrae, any of the individual elements of the spinal column; *cf.* cervical, thoracic, lumbar, sacral, and caudal vertebrae, centrum, neural spine, neural canal, neural arch, transverse process, prezygapophyses, and postzygapophyses.

vertebral column: the axis of the skeleton of a vertebrate animal, consisting of stacked vertebrae with some differentiation (cervical, thoracic, lumbar, sacral, and caudal vertebrae).

vertebral rib: the upper segment of a rib nearest the dorsal vertebral column. Also called dorsal segment of rib; *cf.* sternal rib.

vertebrarterial canal: paired lateral holes in the vertebrae of birds, forming a pair of canals along the vertebral column in which the vertebral arteries run.

Vertebrata: subphylum comprising all animals with a spinal column; i.e. fish, amphibians, reptiles, birds, and mammals; *cf.* Chordata.

vertical classification: a classification in which ancestral and descendant stages of a phyletic line are grouped into a single taxon; *cf.* horizontal classification.

vertical (dimension of) evolution: the temporal element in evolution; *cf.* horizontal classification.

vertical migration: movements on mountains from higher elevations in summer to lower elevations in winter.

vertically transmitted parasites: parasites transmitted from parents to offspring; *cf.* horizontally transmitted parasites.

vestibular window: in the inner ear, a soft point on the cochlea to which the columella is attached, thus being capable of transmitting sound waves from the tympanum to the cochlea.

vestibule: a tiny chamber in the central inner ear, being an organ affecting balance.

vestigial: of an organ or appendage that has almost disappeared in the course of evolution.

vexillum: the feather vane; the more or less coherent series of barbs on each side of the feather shaft or rachis. Also called the web or vein.

vibrissa: a bristle-like feather, from Latin = something looking like a bristle.

vicariance: a situation in which closely related taxa or population are separated by natural barriers, e.g. mountains or rivers.

vicariants: closely related taxa or populations separated by natural barriers, e.g. mountains or rivers, also called vicariant populations.

vice versa: Latin = conversely, the other way round.

villi structures: minute outgrowths confined to the proximal plumulaceous barbules of barbs of the main feathers; *cf.* node.

villus: pl. villi, finger-like projection from the internal wall (mucous membrane) of the small intestine, 0.5 to 1 mm long, which absorbs nutrients.

vinculum: pl. vincula, a slender band of tendon that 1) e.g. holds flight feathers in place. 2) unites the anterior and posterior tendons in a bird's foot (present in almost all orders except passerines).

viral enteritis: a viral disease of ducks, geese, and swans (Anatidae), particularly prevalent where birds gather in high densities; cannot be transferred to humans. Accidentally introduced to America from Europe in 1967. Also called duck plague.

viral hepatitis: a disease of the liver caused by viral infection.

viral hepatosplenitis: a viral infection found rarely in owls.

virology: the study of virus.

virus: pl. virus, viruses, or vira; particle composed of protein and nucleic acid, possessing some genes of its own but needing the enzymatic machinery of a living cell to reproduce. Usually, the host cell is killed in the process, so viruses are generally pathogenic. Hosts include all kinds of organisms, including bacteria. Whether viruses should be considered organisms or not is debatable.

viscera: collective word for the organs of the chest and abdomen; singular is viscus, and is rarely used.

visitor: a bird occurring in a certain geographical area only at certain periods of the year.

visual orientation: the use of visual landmarks to orient during migration, also called parallactic or piloting orientation; *cf.* goal, compass, and directional orientation, vector navigation.

visual receptors: sensoric cells sensitive to light: in vertebrates there are two types called, respectively, rod-cells and cone-cells (sometimes rods and cones for short, although these terms should properly be reserved for the outer segments of these cells). Rods are responsible for vision in dim light, especially at night, while cones, which need fairly high light intensities, are responsible for colour vision.

vitamins: chemical compounds not produced by an organism but necessary in small quantities and so required as a regular intake with food. Vitamins necessary to humans are named with letters: A, B, C, D, E, K, although some of these letters actually represent more than one compound; *cf.* carbohydrate, fat or lipid, protein.

vitellogenin: a yolk precursor, abbr. VTG.

vitellus: the yolk of an egg; adj. **vitelline**.

vitelline membrane: a membrane surrounding the yolk in an egg; *cf.* chalazae.

vitreous body: a transparent gelatinous substance (vitreous humor) that fills the eye between the lens and the retina, giving rigidity to the eye.

vitreous chamber: the posterior volume inside the eyeball and behind the lens that is filled with the vitreous body.

viviparous: giving birth to live young, as opposed to laying eggs (oviparous).

vivo: Latin = alive.

viz.: abbr. from Latin *videlicet* = namely.

vocal appropriation: synonymous with vocal mimicry.

vocalization: production of sound by use of a specialized organ, in birds the syrinx, as opposed to mechanical sounds; *cf.* duetting, vocal mimicry.

vocal mimicry: imitation of sounds from other species and incorporating them into the imitator's own song. Occurs in many bird species, but really skilfull imitators are rather few; examples are the Marsh Warbler (*Acrocephalus palustris*), the Starling (*Sturnus vulgaris*), most species of mockingbirds (Mimidae), and bowerbirds (Ptilonorhynchidae).

voluntary muscles: skeletal muscles whose action is under conscious con-

trol as opposed to involuntary muscles. Also called skeletal muscles.

vomer: paired bones in the middle of the palate. Also called prevomer or ploughshare bone.

vomiting: regurgitating in selfdefence against potential predators; widespread in birds, for example in young vultures (Accipitridae), gulls (Laridae), herons (Ardeidae), and many others. The 'spitting' habit of young and adult petrels (Procellariidae) can be viewed as a special (and specialized) case.

Voous system: taxonomic order of Holarctic birds proposed by K. H. Voous, published in 1977 and adapted from the older Wetmore system.

vortex ring: or **vortice**, swirling fluid, for example in the wake of a flying bird.

voucher specimen: a reference specimen enabling the identification of accompanying material. This may be a skin, skeleton or fluid preparation that is associated with a non-specimen such as vocalizations, associated data, tissue sample etc. Thus if questions about the identity of a singer or tissue arise the voucher specimen provides confirmation.

vs.: abbr. versus

vulnerable: a status category in conservation,; according to the criterion used by BirdLife International, the status of a species having declined by more than 20% during the preceding ten years, or three generations, and not placed in a more critical category.

W

wader: any member of the suborder Charadrii within the Charadriiformes; in Am. usually called shorebirds, whereas 'waders' usually there refers to families such as herons (Ardeidae) or ibises (Threskiornithidae).

wadi: Arabic for stream bed in which water flows only intermittently.

Waldsterben: from German, for the death of a forest (predominantly of pines) due to acid rain.

Wallacea: the biogeographical area or region comprising Sulawesi and the Moluccas and Lesser Sundas, situated between the Oriental and Australasian regions and showing relations to both.

Wallace's Line: the biogeographical demarcation line between the Oriental and Australasian regions, according to A.R. Wallace. Runs between the Philippines and Moluccas, between Borneo and Sulawesi, and between Bali and Lombok; *cf.* Weber's Line.

warble: a bird vocalization that sounds musical to the human ear.

wash: an extensive area of alluvial material deposited by water; e.g. at a river delta.

washed: suffused with a particular colour or shade. Also called tinged.

Washington Convention, The: abbr.: CITES. An international convention regulating the import and export of rare and endangered plants and animals. Came into force in 1975. Also known as Convention on International Trade in Endangered Species.

watching back: describes the finding of a bird's nest by watching its behaviour and movements.

waterfowl: swans, geese, and ducks (Anatidae), the term occasionally including other waterbirds such as divers (Gaviidae) and grebes (Podicipedidae).

water meadow: a low-lying and often flooded riverside grassland.

watt: the SI unit of power; one watt equals one joule per second (1 W = 1 J/s).

wattle: a brightly-coloured fleshy lobe on the head or neck, occurring, e.g. in domestic fowl (*Gallus domesticus*), Double-wattled Cassowary (*Casuarius casuarius*), Red Wattle Bird (*Anthochaera carunculata*), and some plovers.

wattled crows: common name for the three New Zealand species Saddlebird, Huia, and Kokako in the family Callaeidae, with a fleshy and colorful wattle at the base of their bills.

WBDB: abbr. of World Bird Database, an extensive database information system about all birds of the world, containing over 2 million records on c.10,000 species and 22,000 subspecies of birds, including distribution information, taxonomy, synonyms in several languages, and much more.

Maintained by BirdLife International-al. Web site: http://www.bsc-eoc.org/avibase/avibase.jsp

W chromosome: sex chromosome in some groups, for example birds and butterflies, in which females are the heterogametic sex (ZW), and males are the homogametic sex (ZZ); *cf.* X chromosome, Y chromosome, Z chromosome.

weather bird: a species whose migratory timing is strongly influenced by external factors, particularly the weather; contrary to a calendar or instinct bird.

web: 1) the skin between the toes of, e.g. a duck. 2) the vane of a feather (inner web, outer web).

Weber's Line: a line within Wallacea in the Oriental zoogeographical region demarcating the point where the Oriental and Australasian faunal contributions are equal. The line runs south between Sulawesi and the northern Moluccas, between Sula and Obi islands, then west of Buro and southeast to pass between Babar and Tanimbar; *cf.* Wallace's Line.

weed dancing: a pair-bonding ceremony in which, e.g. two Western Grebes (*Aechmophorus occidentalis*) rise up vertically in the water with plant material in their bills and dance often in bodily contact.

weight regression: weight loss, when a growing chick overshoots the normal adult body mass and subsequently loses mass (weight) shortly before or after fledging.

West Nile Virus: an often fatal arthropod-borne virus that primarily affects horses and crows, but it has also been isolated from many other bird and mammal species. Mosquitoes are believed to be the primary means of transmission. Originally found in the Middle East and subsequently discovered in Europe and Africa, where it is relatively harmless. First reported from the Western Hemisphere in the fall of 1999 in New York City and from there spread to all contiguous 48 states, Canada, and Mexico. The virus in America is a particularly virulent form that already has been deadly to more that 600 humans (2005) and many mammals and birds. Also called **West Nile Encephalitis**.

western duck sickness: a severe food poisoning caused by a bacterium, *Clostridium botulinum*, that lives in soil and is anaerobic, i.e. able to exist only in the absence of oxygen. Ducks (Anatidae) and pheasants (Phasianidae) are most often affected and show high mortality. Most commonly called botulism.

Western Foundation of Vertebrate Zoology: a nonprofit foundation in Camarillo, California that has one of the world's largest collections of bird eggs and nests.

Western Hemisphere: the half of the Earth's surface lying west of 0° (the Greenwich meridian) and east of the 180° meridian in the Pacific, although often used synonymously with the New World, or the Americas.

Western Palearctic: the western part of the Palearctic, the biogeographical region encompassing the arctic, boreal, temperate, and subtropical parts of the Old World; includes Europe, the Near and Middle East to the Caspian Sea and Persian Gulf, and North Africa south to the middle of the Sahara.

wetland: a water-logged area, a marsh, fen, or bog. Globally one of the most widely threatened habitats due to drainage and cultivation.

Wetlands International: a global organisation dedicated to the conservation and wise use of Wetlands Founded 1954.

Wetmore system: a taxonomic listing of the birds of the world, devised by A. Wetmore c. 1930.

whalebird: a vernacular name for a prion, petrels in the family Procellariidae.

whiffling: used to describe flying geese rapidly descending by side-slipping one way and then the other. From whiffle, meaning to be blown in gusts.

whisker: describes a contrasting plumage stripe extending back from the bill such as in, e.g. the Bearded Tit (*Panurus biarmicus*). May also extend to the malar region. Also called moustachial stripe; *cf.* malar stripe, sub-moustachial stripe.

whisper song: a loose, often rambling, softly-delivered song that is audible within only a few metres; also the first helpless and unstructured song of a young bird; *cf.* subsong.

white blood cells: also called leukocytes; *cf.* T-cells.

white matter: the myelin sheaths that enclose the axons in the central nervous system; *cf.* grey matter.

white muscle: muscle with fewer capillaries and therefore less oxygen transport. Found in short-burst fliers such as pheasants and grouse (Phasianidae).

WHSRN: abbr. for the Western Hemisphere Shorebird Reserve Network. Formed in 1985 to protect habitats critical for shorebirds. Protects 21 of the most important stopover sites in North and South America, comprising four million acres of wetlands where millions of birds stop to fuel for migration.

wick: vegetable matter dipped in mud and transported to the nest for use in nest construction.

Wilcoxon test: a nonparametric statistical test that ranks differences between observations in two populations and assesses whether the samples were drawn from populations having the same distribution.

wildfowl: a common term loosely applied to ducks, but can also mean other edible birds; *cf.* waterfowl.

Wildfowl: a journal published by the Wildfowl and Wetlands Trust since 1968.

Wildfowl and Wetlands Trust: a society founded in 1947 by Peter Scott for conservation and wildlife management. Has published the journal *Wildfowl* since 1968, formerly *Report of the Severn Wildfowl Trust,* 1948-1952, and *Report of the Wildfowl Trust*, 1953-1966.

Wilson Ornithological Society: an American society publishing *The Wilson Bulletin* from 1902-2005, and *The Wilson Journal of Ornithology* since 2006.

wind-hovering: a rarely used term for flying against the wind at the speed of the wind, for example a hunting Osprey (*Pandion haliaetus*) or Kestrel (*Falco tinnunculus*); *cf.* hovering.

wind tunnel: a closed tunnel through which air is blown at variable speeds, used, e.g. for controlled studies of bird flight. It is a powerful means of analysing the biophysics as well as the physiology of flight.

window: 1) the translucent, still not-quite ossified areas of the skull of a young bird; *cf.* skull ossification. 2) the translucent area of the wing formed by the pale bases of the primaries in some birds, such as the Black-breasted Buzzard (*Hamirostra melanosternon*).

windpipe: or wind-pipe, the trachea. Conveys air from the larynx to the lungs.

wing-arch: used as a verb meaning to raise the wings over the back with carpal joints pushed toward each other, head lowered, and body bent forward; *cf.* comfort behaviour.

wing-bar: a conspicuously contrasting diagonal bar on the upper wing coverts that, if broad, is called a **wing stripe** (e.g. as in the Black-tailed Godwit, *Limosa limosa*).

wing chord: wing length measured on the unflattened wing from the carpal joint to the tip of the longest primary.

wing clapping: clappering wings together over the back in flight as many pigeons do in display.

wing claw: a claw temporarily present on the first or second digit of some young birds, best known in the chick of the Hoatzin (*Opisthocomus hoazin*); *cf.* wing spur.

wing clip: a wing marking, fastened by a stainless steel pin through the patagium or elsewhere in the wing. Also called wing tag or patagial tag.

wing coverts: feathers covering the wings; three groups on each side of the wing: greater, median, and lesser wing coverts, the first covering the bases of the flight feathers. Also spelled witht an hyphen. Also called tectrices.

winged: of a bird that is wounded, typically by gunshot, and unable to escape by flying.

wing-flicking: a short fluttering of the wings, often performed as a bird prepares to fly or to change perch, and often followed by a pumping of the tail, sometimes described as a nervous or 'intention' behaviour.

wing formula: the configuration of primary tips relative to each other, expressed as the distance from each primary tip to the tip of the longest. Some species can be very difficult to identify in the hand by other characters than their wing formula, e.g. Willow Warbler (*Phylloscopus trochilus*) and Chiff-chaff (*P. collybita*), and some *Empidonax* flycatchers (Tyrannidae).

wing-leg stretch: simultaneous stretch of a wing and a leg.

wing-lining: the small feathers on both upper- and underside of the front edge of the wing.

wing loading: important parameter in biophysics, the weight (body mass multiplied by the gravitational acceleration) divided by the total wing area, often expressed in grams per square centimetres (g/cm^2).

wing plexus: a term for the nervous system of the wing; *cf.* hind limb plexus.

wing pouch: a skin pocket under each wing in which the male Sungrebe (*Heliornis fulica*) is able to transport the chicks, even in flight.

wingspan: the distance between the tips of the fully extended wings.

wing spur: a bony outgrowth on the carpal joint of some birds, e.g. the Spurwinged Plover (*Vanellus spinosus*). Also called carpal spur; *cf.* wing claws.

wing stretch: in comfort behaviour, stretch of wing, or, usually, both of them simultaneously.

wing-stripe: a conspicuously broad contrasting diagonal bar on the upper wing coverts (e.g. as in the Black-tailed Godwit, *Limosa limosa*).

wing tagging: marking birds with tags fastened to their wings with a stainless steel pin passed through the patagium.

wing-tail ratio: the relative length of wing to tail, or vice versa.

winnowing: a term for various mechanical (non-vocal) sounds produced by birds, such as the sound made by the vibration of the outer tail feathers during aerial displays of snipe, genus *Gallinago*, The sound is also called bleating; *cf.* drumming or instrumental song.

wishbone: the bone consisting of the fused clavicles in the shoulder girdle, making a flexible structure that acts as a spring during flight; also called furcula or merrythought. Latin *furculum*.

woodland: habitat or biotic community of relatively widely-spaced trees, such as is often found in transitional zones between forest and grassland.

working hypothesis: an hypothesis postulated to explain some observation and subject to future testing and research.

World Bird Database: abbr.: WBDB, an extensive database information system about all birds of the world, containing over 2 million records on c. 10,000 species and 22,000 subspecies of birds, including distribution information, taxonomy, synonyms in several languages, and much more. Maintained by BirdLife International. Web site: http://www.bsc-eoc.org/avibase/avibase.jsp

World Heritage Convention: convention formulated by UNESCO in 1972 and coming into force in 1975. Its objective is the protection of natural and cultural areas of 'outstanding universal value'.

World Wide Fund for Nature: abbr.: WWF, founded in 1961 with its headquarter in Morges, Switzerland. A fund-raising organisation for the conservation of globally threatened animals. Formerly **World Wildlife Fund**.

wounded-bird act: a distraction behaviour, feigning injury in the presence of potential egg- or chick-predators, as seen for example in shorebirds; also called broken-wing display or trick, crippled-bird act, injury feigning.

wreathed: of an egg with many pigmented spots, especially near the thick end.

wreck: an episode of heavy mortality of seabirds within a limited area; may be caused by a shortage of food, often combined with strong winds over a prolonged period but sometimes also used of oiling or poisoning.

wrist: the carpal joint, the bend of the wing.

wrist bone: in birds, two fused bones, the radiale and ulnare, forming the wrist.

WWF: abbr. for World Wide Fund for Nature (formerly World Wildlife Fund).

X

xanthochroism: an abnormal plumage coloration with a surplus of yellow, also called flavism; *cf.* erythrism.

xanthophylls: yellow or brown carotenoid pigments.

x-axis: common name for the horizontal axis (abscissa) of a coordinate system, even though the variable shown along this axis is usually termed something other than x; *cf.* y-axis.

X chromosome: a sex chromosome in animals (such as mammals) in which females are the homogametic sex (XX), and males the heterogametic sex (XY); *cf.* W chromosome, Y chromosome, Z chromosome.

Xenicidae: syn. of Acanthisittidae, the family of New Zealand wrens.

xenobiotics: foreign to a living organism; often used of organic chemical pollutants in the environment.

xeric: dry, or adapted to dry conditions.

xero-: prefix from Greek *xeros* meaning dry.

xerophilous: adapted to a dry climate.

xerophyte: a plant adapted to arid conditions.

X-ray examination: examination of the internal body by radiography.

Y

yaw: rotation of the body, e.g. a flying bird or aircraft, about a vertical axis.

Y chromosome: a sex chromosome in animals (such as mammals) in which females are the homogametic sex (XX) and males the heterogametic sex (XY); *cf*. W chromosome, X chromosome, Z chromosome.

yearling: a one year old animal, or an animal in its second year; in ornithology often used of a bird hatched in the previous calendar year, the same that in Am. ringing or banding terminology is called a second year (SY) bird.

yersinia: the disease caused by the bacteria of the genus *Yersinia* often affecting birds stressed for other reasons and causing yellow-white, 1-2 mm spots on liver and spleen. Found in pigeons (Columbidae), sparrows, (genus *Passer*), and captive passerines. Also called pseudotuberculosis, or pasteurella pseudotuberculosis; *cf*. tuberculosis.

yolk: in bird eggs a central yellow part rich in fats and proteins that nourishes the developing embryo.

yolk sac: the membrane surrounding the yolk.

younger synonym: in taxonomy a name published subsequent to that first applied to a taxon. Also called a junior synonym.

Z

Zar test: a multiple comparison analysis of ranked data.

Z chromosome: a sex chromosome in animals (such as birds) in which females are the heterogametic sex (ZW) and males the homogametic sex (ZZ); *cf.* W chromosome, X chromosome, Y chromosome.

Z-DNA: a left-handed double helix proposed on the basis of the crystal structure of the duplex trinuncleotide d(CG)$_3$, and containing 12 residues per turn; *cf.* deoxyribonucleic acid, A-DNA, B-DNA, E-DNA.

zeaxanthin: a carotenoid found in the feathers of cotingas of the genus *Rubecula*.

zeitgeber: from German 'time-giver', an environmental stimulus that triggers biological activity such as breeding or migration in a species. May or may not in itself be relevant for the triggered activity but if not it generally signals that conditions are becoming favourable, e.g. increasing day length reliably indicating that food conditions are, or soon will be, sufficient for raising a brood of young. Also called proximate factor, time-synchroniser; *cf.* ultimate factor.

zonation: in biology, the naturally occurring arrangement of local or regional communities of organisms across contiguous biotopes.

zoogeographic region: major geographical area with a relatively uniform fauna, i.e., within which different subareas have faunas of similar taxonomic composition. There are six such regions: the Australasian, Ethiopian (or Afrotropical), Nearctic, Neotropical, Oriental, and Palearctic (Palaearctic) regions. Antarctica and the oceans are additional regions. Also called faunal regions. See also Indo-Malayan and Malagasy Subregions.

zoogeographical rules: faunistic and biological generalizations associated with climate and supposedly reflecting adaptations to climatic conditions; well-known examples are Allen's Rule (proportion rule), Bergmann's Rule (size rule), and Gloger's Rule (colour rule).

zoogeography: the science of studying patterns of geographical distribution of animals, both past and present, adj. **zoogeographical**; *cf.* biogeography.

Zoological Record: an annual bibliographical publication listing a major proportion of the world's scientific zoological literature issued during the year. Produces an alphabetical listing of authors with full citation of titles, a list of subjects, and a systematic part.

Zoological Society of London: founded in 1826 for promoting the study of animals worldwide.

zoology: the scientific study of animals.

zoonosis: pl. zoonoses, any disease naturally transmitted to humans from other vertebrates, or sometimes any animal disease transmitted to humans; adj. zoonotic.

zoophagous: of animals eating other animals; *cf.* carnivorous.

zooplankton: small marine or freshwater animals living in the water column and moving passively with water currents; important food for many animals; *cf.* phytoplankton.

zootope: the living space of an animal community within a biotope.

zugdisposition: the large increase in food consumption before migration, which leads to large deposits of fat; from German Zug = migration.

zugscheide: German term adopted into English for the border between the breeding areas of two populations wintering in different areas, or at least following different routes, such as between the east and west European White Storks (*Ciconia ciconia*).

zugstimmung: from German, meaning the behavioural changes in daily activity rhythm that a bird must undergo before it starts its migration.

zugunruhe: German word adopted into English for the restlessness exhibited by captive migratory birds during the period when their free conspecifics are migrating; the phenomenon is exploited in orientation experiments. Also called migratory restlessness.

zwischenzug: a German term, adopted into English, for interim movements.

zygapophysis: one of the articulation processes of a vertebra.

zygodactylous: of a bird foot in which digits 1 and 4 are directed backwards and digits 2 and 3 forwards; found, e.g. in woodpeckers (Picidae), cuckoos (Cuculidae), and parrots (Psittacidae); *cf.* anisodactylous, heterodactylous, pamprodactylous.

zygomatic arch: bony arch beneath the eye socket in the skull in vertebrates, formed by the zygomatic bone and the zygomatic process of the temporal bone.

zygomatic process: a projection of skull bone below the temporal fossa; typically protrudes into the lower rear orbital cavity.

zygote: fertilized egg cell.

APPENDIX

This review listing all of the bird families of the world is based upon that of Dickinson, E. C. (ed.) 2003: *The Howard & Moore Complete Checklist of the Birds of the World*, 3rd Edition. Christopher Helm, London.

Incertae sedis = taxonomic position uncertain. The number in the right hand column is the number of species in the family. Included are species that went extinct within historic times.

NON PASSERIFORMES

Tinamidae, TINAMOUS	47
Struthionidae, OSTRICHES	1
Rheidae, RHEAS	2
Casuariidae, CASSOWARIES	3
Dromaiidae, EMUS	3
Apterygidae, KIWIS	3
Megapodiidae, MEGAPODES	22
Cracidae, CHACHALACAS, CURASSOWS, GUANS	50
Numididae, GUINEAFOWL	6
Odontophoridae, NEW WORLD QUAILS	32
Phasianidae, TURKEYS, GROUSE, PHEASANTS, PARTRIDGES	180
Anhimidae, SCREAMERS	3
Anseranatidae, MAGPIE-GOOSE	1
Anatidae, DUCKS, GEESE, SWANS	158
Spheniscidae, PENGUINS	17
Gaviidae, DIVERS OR LOONS	5
Diomedeidae, ALBATROSSES	13
Procellariidae, PETRELS, SHEARWATERS	74
Hydrobatidae, STORM PETRELS	21
Pelecanoididae, DIVING PETRELS	4
Podicipedidae, GREBES	22
Phoenicopteridae, FLAMINGOS	5
Ciconiidae, STORKS	19
Threskiornithidae, IBISES, SPOONBILLS	32
Ardeidae, HERONS, BITTERNS, EGRETS	65
Phaethontidae, TROPICBIRDS	3

Fregatidae, FRIGATEBIRDS 5
Scopidae, HAMMERKOP 1
Balaenicipitidae, SHOEBILL 1
Pelecanidae, PELICANS 7
Sulidae, GANNETS, BOOBIES 10
Phalacrocoracidae, CORMORANTS 36
Anhingidae, ANHINGAS 2
Cathartidae, NEW WORLD VULTURES 7
Falconidae, FALCONS, CARACARAS 64
Accipitridae, SECRETARY BIRD, OSPREY, KITES, HAWKS, EAGLES 233
*Otidae, BUSTARDS 26
Mesitornithidae, MESITES 3
Cariamidae, SERIEMAS 2
Rhynochetidae, KAGU 1
Eurypygidae, SUNBITTERN 1
Rallidae, RAILS, WATERHENS, COOTS 141
Heliornithidae, FINFOOTS 3
Psophiidae, TRUMPETERS 3
Gruidae, CRANES 15
Aramidae, LIMPKIN 1
Turnicidae, BUTTONQUAILS 16
Burhinidae, THICK-KNEES 9
**Chionidae, SHEATHBILLS AND ALLIES 2
Haematopodidae, OYSTERCATCHERS 11
Dromadidae, CRAB PLOVER 1
Ibidorhynchidae, IBISBILL 1
Recurvirostridae, STILTS, AVOCETS 7
Charadriidae, PLOVERS 66
Rostratulidae, PAINTED SNIPE 2
Jacanidae, JACANAS 8
Pedionomidae, PLAINS WANDERER 1
Thinocoridae, SEEDSNIPES 4
Scolopacidae, SANDPIPERS, SNIPE 92
Glareolidae, COURSERS, PRATINCOLES 18
Laridae, GULLS, TERNS, SKIMMERS 97
Stercorariidae, SKUAS OR JAEGERS 7
Alcidae, AUKS, PUFFINS, AUKLETS 24
Pteroclididae, SANDGROUSE 16
Raphidae, DODO, SOLITAIRES 3
Columbidae, DOVES, PIGEONS 308
Psittacidae, COCKATOOS, PARROTS 364
Opisthocomidae, HOATZIN 1
Musophagidae, TURACOS 23
Cuculidae, CUCKOOS 138
Tytonidae, BARN OWLS 15
Strigidae, OWLS 180
Podargidae, FROGMOUTHS 12
Steatornithidae, OILBIRD 1

Nyctibiidae, POTOOS   7
Caprimulgidae, NIGHTJARS   89
Aegothelidae, OWLET-NIGHTJARS   9
Apodidae, SWIFTS   94
Hemiprocnidae, TREE WIFTS   4
Trochilidae, HUMMINGBIRDS   331
Coliidae, MOUSEBIRDS   6
Trogonidae, TROGONS   39
Coraciidae, ROLLERS   12
Brachypteraciidae, GROUND ROLLERS   5
Leptosomatidae, CUCKOO-ROLLERS   1
Alcedinidae, KINGFISHERS   91
Todidae, TODIES   5
Momotidae, MOTMOTS   10
Meropidae, BEE-EATERS   25
Upupidae, HOOPOES   1
Phoeniculidae, WOOD HOOPOES   8
Bucerotidae, HORNBILLS   49
Bucorvidae, GROUND HORNBILLS   2
Ramphastidae, TOUCANS, BARBETS   120
Indicatoridae, HONEYGUIDES   17
Picidae, WOODPECKERS   210
Galbulidae, JACAMARS   18
Bucconidae, PUFFBIRDS   33

PASSERIFORMES

Acanthisittidae, NEW ZEALAND WRENS   4
Eurylaimidae, BROADBILLS   14
Philepittidae, ASITIES   4
Sapayoaidae, SAPAYOA   1
Pittidae, PITTAS   30
Pipridae, MANAKINS   48
Cotingidae, COTINGAS   96
Piprites, PIPRITES; genus *incertae sedis*   3
Calyptura, KINGLET CALYPTURA; genus *incertae sedis*   1
Tyrannidae, TYRANT-FLYCATCHERS   400
Thamnophilidae, ANTBIRDS   206
Conopophagidae, GNATEATERS   8
Rhinocryptidae, TAPACULOS   55
Formicariidae, ANT-THRUSHES, ANTPITTAS   62
Furnariidae, OVENBIRDS   236
Dendrocolaptidae, WOODCREEPERS   50
Menuridae, LYREBIRDS   2
Atrichornithidae, SCRUBBIRDS   2
Ptilonorhynchidae, BOWERBIRDS   18
Climacteridae, AUSTRALIAN TREECREEPERS   7
Maluridae, AUSTRALASIAN WRENS   28

Neomixis, JERY *genus incertae sedis* — 3
Orthotomus, TAILORBIRDS; genus *incertae sedis* — 11
Artisornis, TAILORBIRDS; genus *incertae sedis* — 2
Poliolais ,WHITE-TAILED WARBLER; genus *incertae sedis* — 1
Pycnonotidae, BULBULS — 118
Neolestes, BLACK-COLLARED BULBUL; genus *incertae sedis* — 1
Nicator, NICATOR; genus *incertae sedis* — 3
Elminia, CRESTED FLYCATCHER; genus *incertae sedis* — 5
Erythrocercus, FLYCATCHER; genus *incertae sedis* — 3
Sylviidae, OLD WORLD WARBLERS — 265
Timaliidae, BABBLERS, PARROTBILLS — 273
Myzornis, FIRE-TAILED MYZORNIS; genus *incertae sedis* — 1
Malia, MALIA; genus *incertae sedis* — 1
Horizorhinus, DOHRN'S TRUSH-BABBLER; genus *incertae sedis* — 1
Chaetops, ROCKRUNNER & ROCKJUMPER; genus *incertae sedis* — 2
Modulatrix, SPOT-THROAT & DAPPLED MOUNTAIN ROBIN;
genus *incertae sedis* — 2
Zosteropidae, WHITE EYES — 95
Irenidae, FAIRY-BLUEBIRDS — 2
***Reguliidae, GOLDCRESTS, KINGLETS — 5
Troglodytidae, WRENS — 76
Donacobius, BLACK-CAPPED DONACOBIUS; genus *incertae sedis* — 1
Polioptilidae, GNATCATCHERS — 14
Sittidae, NUTHATCHES, WALLCREEPER — 25
Certhiidae, TREECREEPERS — 8
Mimidae, MOCKINGBIRDS, THRASHERS — 34
Rhabdornithidae, PHILIPPINE CREEPERS — 2
Sturnidae, STARLINGS — 115
Turdidae, THRUSHES — 165
Muscicapidae, CHATS, OLD WORLD FLYCATCHERS — 275
Cinclidae, DIPPERS — 5
Chloropseidae, LEAFBIRDS — 8
Dicaeidae, FLOWERPECKERS — 44
Nectariniidae, SUNBIRDS — 127
Promeropidae, SUGARBIRDS — 2
Passeridae, SPARROWS, SNOWFINCHES, AND ALLIES — 40
Ploceidae, WEAVERS, SPARROWS — 108
Estrildidae, WAXBILLS, GRASS FINCHES, MUNIAS, AND ALLIES — 130
Viduidae, INDIGOBIRDS AND ALLIES — 20
Prunellidae, ACCENTORS — 13
Peucedramidae, OLIVE WARBLER — 1
Motacillidae, WAGTAILS, PIPITS — 64
Fringillidae, FINCHES, HAWAIIAN HONEYCREEPERS — 168
Parulidae, NEW WORLD WARBLERS — 112
Granatellus, CHATS; genus *incertae sedis* — 3
Xenoligea, WHITE-WINGED WARBLER; genus *incertae sedis* — 1
Icteridae, NEW WORLD BLACKBIRDS — 98
Coerebidae, BANANAQUIT — 1

* Also seen spelled Otididae
** Also seen spelles Chionididae
*** In most chechklists spelled Regulidae

QUOTED AUTHORS

Cuvier, G. L. C. F. D. 1812: Sur la composition de la tête osseuse dans les animaux vertébrés. *Ann. Mus. Hist. Nat. Paris* 19: 123-128.

Humphrey, P. S. & K. C. Parkes. 1959: An approach to the study of molts and plumages. *Auk* 76: 1-31.

Mayr, E. 1963: *Animal Speciel and Evolution*. Belknap Press and Harvard University Press, Cambridge, Mass.

Mayr, E. 1969: *Principles of Systematic Zoology*. McGraw-Hill, New York.

Mayr, E. 1982: *The Growth of Biological Thought: Diversity, Evolution, and Inheritance*. Belknap Press and Harvard University Press, Cambridge, Mass.

May, E. 1994: *Review of Species, Species Concepts and Primate Evolution*. Plenum Press, New York.

LIST OF ILLUSTRATIONS

Other titles available:

- *The Spanish Imperial Eagle* (M. Ferrer)
- *Where to watch birds in Spain. The best 100 sites* (J. A. Montero)
- *A Birdwatcher's Guide to Italy* (L. Ruggieri & I. Festari)
- *Birding in Venezuela* (M. L. Goodwin)
- *A Field Guide to the Birds of Peru* (J. F. Clements & N. Shany)
- *Birds of South Asia: the Ripley Guide* (P. C. Rasmussen & J. C. Anderton)
- *Annotated Checklist of the Birds of Argentina* (J. Mazar Barnett & M. Pearman)
- *Annotated Checklist of the Birds of Belize* (H. Lee Jones & A. C. Vallely)
- *Annotated Checklist of the Birds of Chile* (M. Marín)
- *Annotated Checklist of the Birds of Guatemala* (K. Eisermann & C. Avendaño)
- *Arte de pájaros / Art of Birds* (P. Neruda)
- *Threatened Birds of the World* (BirdLife International)
- *Curassows and Related Birds. Second Edition* (J. Delacour & D. Amadon)
- *Handbook of the Birds of the World* (J. del Hoyo, A. Elliott, D. Christie & J. Sargatal)
   - Vol. 1: Ostrich to Ducks
   - Vol. 2: New World Vultures to Guineafowl
   - Vol. 3: Hoatzin to Auks
   - Vol. 4: Sandgrouse to Cuckoos
   - Vol. 5: Barn-owls to Hummingbirds
   - Vol. 6: Mousebirds to Hornbills
   - Vol. 7: Jacamars to Woodpeckers
   - Vol. 8: Broadbills to Tapaculos
   - Vol. 9: Cotingas to Pipits and Wagtails
   - Vol. 10: Cuckoo-shrikes to Thrushes
   - Vol. 11: Old World Flycatchers to Old World Warblers
   - Vol. 12: Picathartes to Tits and Chickadees
- Wildlife Travel Maps of Spain. Catalonia (1/300,000)
- Wildlife Travel Maps of Spain. Balearic Islands (1/150,000)
- Wildlife Travel Maps of Spain. Extremadura (1/300,000)

For more information, please visit our website:
www.hbw.com

Montseny, 8, 08193 - Bellaterra, Barcelona (Spain)
Tel: (+34) 93 594 77 10 / Fax: (+34) 93 592 09 69
E-mail: lynx@hbw.com